Alabama Stories

Alabama Stories

John Isaac Jones

A * JIJ * Book
2005

Alabama Stories

CONTENTS

LOOKING HOMEWARD....

I always knew I would write this book. I didn't know at exactly what point in my life it would actually occur, but, in my heart, I always knew it was waiting in the wings.

I left Alabama in 1975 after having spent my childhood and young adult years in the Cotton State.

At the time I left, I was glad to be gone. While one part of me loved my native state, another part of me felt that Alabama was too narrow and unprogressive for my personal tastes.

Over the next 25 years, I journeyed to all the places I dreamed of visiting when I lived in Alabama. I lived in Florida, California, Montana, Washington, D.C., Texas, and Colorado. I traveled to Hong Kong, Paris, Istanbul, Nairobi, Caracas, and Bora Bora .

One day after I turned 50, I decided to review my life's journey. Of all the places I had traveled during my lifetime, the single locale that I longed for the most was the pine-studded hills of North Alabama. I had this sudden undeniable need to smell black-eyed peas cooking, to hear a whippoorwill call, to taste chicken dumplings and see a "See Rock City" sign. The hard-core southern boy that had been hiding inside me all those years had suddenly roared to the forefront.

In my heart, I knew I could never REALLY go home again but a special part of me desperately wanted to give it the old college try.

These short stories represent my best efforts to accomplish that singular feat.

John Isaac Jones

For
Darlene *and* **Christopher,**
The two constant joys in my life
and
Shirley J,
My very special friend

PREJUDICE

Jim Crow Tips His Hat

As a small child growing up in the hills of North Alabama, I didn't actually meet a Negro face-to-face until I was five years old. Of course, I was aware of their existence from a distance. While shopping in the nearby town of Hamilton, Alabama, with my parents, I had seen black families browsing in the stores, walking the streets and riding around in cars. I had seen black men working in the chain gangs along the county roadways and I had heard my mother speak to my father about "colored town."

Also, I was keenly aware of Etta Mae Jackson, the young, talkative black woman who would sometimes come to help my mother in the fall when she was canning fruit. When Etta Mae came to our house, she and my mother always stayed on the back porch and in the kitchen, peeling and paring and packing, so I never actually spoke to the Negro woman on a personal basis. That's why, when I did meet a Negro on a one-to-one, up-close social basis for the first time, it would be an experience I would always remember.

One Saturday morning in late May of 1946, I was playing in the front yard at our home when I heard a vehicle on the road and turned to see an old rickety pickup truck pull into our driveway.

A Negro man, lanky, muscular, blue-black in color and maybe 28 or 29, got out of the truck and walked toward me. I could see the man had black skin like the other "Negroes" I had seen, but this single characteristic held no special significance for my young eyes. In every other way, he seemed to fit the same general specifications of most whites I had known.

He stopped about ten feet from me.

"Hi," I said. "My name is Billy."

He examined me for a moment.

"Are you Mister Robert Johnson's son?" he asked finally.

"Yes, sir," I answered. My father had taught me to always address older men as 'sir.'

For a moment, he looked at me inquisitively, almost amused. Then he asked: "Will you go tell yo' daddy that Calvin Washington is here?"

I studied him for a moment, then quickly turned and ran into the house.

In the kitchen, my mother was cleaning up the breakfast dishes while my father was having his last few sips of morning coffee. My father looked up when I burst into the kitchen.

"There's a man outside, daddy," I said. "His name is Calvin."

My father got up from the table, coffee cup in hand, and peered out the window. Then he tossed down the last swallow of coffee, sat the cup on the table and turned to go outside. I ran after him.

Outside, the black man was still standing in the same spot where he had talked to me. I noticed that my father didn't shake hands with the man.

"You Calvin Washington?" my father asked.

"Yes sir."

"Mr. Wiley Gilbert over at the crossroads says you know how to dig a ditch."

"Yes sir."

"A straight one?"

The Negro nodded.

"And I got my own pick and shovels," he added.

My father peered over at the pickup. Then he looked at the black man again.

"See that corner over there," my father said, pointing toward the corner of the house.

The black man peered toward the point my father was indicating.

"I need a ditch for a water line from that corner," my father said, indicating with his index finger, "to the barn over there. It's about fifty feet."

Interested, the black man walked over and peered along the imaginary line between the corner of the house and the barn.

"What about the rose bushes?" he asked.

"Just dig 'em up and put them off to the side," my father said.

The black man studied the project for a moment.

"Looks like about three hours work," the Negro man said.

"That's about right," my father said. "How much you charge?"

"I usually get seventy-five cents a hour," the black man said, almost embarrassed.

My father looked at the man.

"I'll pay fifty," my father said finally.

There was a long pause.

"That the best you can do?" the black man asked. "About everybody I know gets at least sixty cents an hour."

"Fifty is the most I'll pay," my father reiterated.

The black man, emotionless, stepped over and sighted the line between the barn and the house again.

"I'll replant them rose bushes for you for sixty cents a hour," the black man offered.

My father shook his head slowly.

"I'll replant 'em wherever you want 'em," the black man added, almost as an afterthought.

"I'll replant the rose bushes," my father said emphatically. "All I need from you is to dig the ditch. Fifty cents an hour is my best offer."

The black man studied for another moment, looked at me, then back at my father. After a long pause, he inhaled resignedly.

"All right, sir. I'll get my tools," he said, turning back to the truck.

"Have you eat?" my father asked.

The Negro stopped.

"No sir."

"I'll get you some breakfast," my father said.

"Thank you, Mister Johnson."

My father turned to go back into the house. I watched as the Negro man walked back to the truck, then I ran into the house after my father.

Inside, my mother was still washing dishes.

"Virginia," my father called as he walked back into the kitchen. "You got some sausage biscuits and eggs left?"

"I got some sausage and biscuits, but I'll have to cook eggs," she said.

"Fix something for that boy out here," my father ordered.

My mother, wiping her wet hands on her apron, stepped away from the sink and peered out the window at the Negro man.

"It'll take a few minutes," she said.

My father went into the back room to put on his work clothes. I took a seat at the cleared table and watched as my mother put the cold sausage biscuits into the oven.

"Mama, that man's got black skin," I said.

"He's a Negro, Billy," my mother said matter-of-factly, breaking an egg into the skillet. "Way back yonder, his people were slaves on the old plantations."

"Why is he black like that?" I asked.

"'Cause God made him that way back in Africa. Just like He give you white skin, He give Negroes black skin."

"Oh," I said, acting as if I understood.

On the top shelf of the kitchen cabinet, my mother always kept several chipped plates and some old fruit jars for outsiders to eat out of when they came to our house. There was a drifter named Mr. Robertson who passed through our little community from time to time. My mother said he was a 'no-count', but my father gave him odd jobs, let him sleep in the barn and fed him from our table. My mother always served Mr. Robertson's food and drink in the eating utensils on the top shelf.

I watched as my mother reached down one of the chipped plates and a fruit jar for the Negro's food and drink. Then I watched as she dumped the eggs into the plate, neatly placed the warm sausage biscuits beside them and filled the fruit jar with steaming, hot coffee.

Seeing the food was prepared, I wanted to help.

"I'll tell him to come in and eat," I said and started out.

"William Vernon Johnson!" my mother yelled, raising her voice. "Get back here!"

I stopped at the back door, not understanding.

"I'm going to tell him his breakfast is ready," I ventured.

"You stay right where you are, young man," she said firmly. "Yo' daddy will handle this."

"He's got to come in to eat," I said.

"No, he don't," my mother said firmly. "Black folks don't eat at white folks' table."

"Why?!"

For a moment, my mother stared at me long and hard, not knowing quite what to say. Then she regained herself.

"You just hush up," she said angrily. "Yo' daddy will take care of this."

I knew better than to talk back to that tone of voice.

"Robert!" my mother called toward the back room. "Robert! Come out here!"

My father reappeared in the kitchen.

"That boy's food's ready," she said, calmer now.

I watched as my father picked up the plate of food and the fruit jar from the table and started back outside. I followed.

The black man was standing at the back porch steps. My father offered him the plate of food and the hot coffee.

"Thanky, Mr. Johnson," the black man said politely, eyeing the eggs eagerly.

"You're welcome, Calvin," my father replied. "Just give me a good straight ditch."

"I will, Mister Johnson."

With that, my father turned and headed toward the barn. At first I started after him, then I suddenly stopped and turned to the black man.

He had seated himself on the back porch steps, the plate perched firmly on his closed knees and the fruit jar of coffee planted on a higher step within easy reach.

I watched as he ate the eggs and sausage biscuits and I wondered why he was not allowed to sit at our table. Even with his black coloring, I wondered what was so radically different about this man that my parents seemed to view him as a species separate from themselves. Even "no-count" Mr. Robertson ate at our table. But he was white.

As I watched this black man eat, I was somehow filled with a mysterious sadness. Finally, I walked over and took a seat on the steps below him hoping that I could somehow make him feel better after having been treated so differently. I asked him where he lived and if he had any kids and where his mother and father were. I asked him if he liked to dig ditches and how many shovels he had.

The black man listened patiently and politely to my childish attempts to make conversation, eating all the while. I know he heard my every question, but he didn't reply to a single one. When he had finished the food, he handed the empty plate and fruit jar to me and politely said I should take it back inside.

"I gotta work now," he said, getting up from the porch steps.

I watched as he picked up the shovel and broke open the fresh, black earth to start the ditch to the barn. After he had thrown aside several shovelfuls, I went back inside with the empty plate and fruit jar.

In the years that followed, my father tried in every way to school me in the ways of prejudice. He said I should never defer to blacks and they should always call me "sir." My father said blacks had their own way of life, their own set of values and were destined to forever remain separate from the white man. When my father was around his farmer friends, there was a tacit understanding among them that blacks were lazy, illiterate and inferior to the white man. They had their crude jokes and clichéd stories to support their beliefs.

During the early sixties, when the civil rights leaders marched through our little town with signs proclaiming "We want our freedom!" my father, who was almost 70, asked me, "What do they mean they want their freedom? They have their freedom. Nobody has them in chains."

"It's economic and social freedom they want," I said cautiously.

"What does that mean?"

"It means they want the same economic and social opportunities as white people. They want to get a good education, earn a decent wage and have a sense of social pride."

"They're Negroes," my father said, indignantly. "They have their own place in the world just like the white man."

I tried to explain the meaning of social justice and the equality of all men but my father countered that the Negro is not equal to the white man and that Negroes were destined by God to fulfill a subservient role.

From there, the discussion would continue—as it had so many times before—from one impasse to the next until I would finally drop the subject. Then my father would very accusingly say I had learned all "that equality stuff" in college. Then, he would bitterly shake his head and say college had turned me against everything he had tried to teach me. I didn't have the heart to tell him that, throughout all those years, I had always had my own ideas about Negroes and the way they should be treated. I couldn't bring myself to tell him that his so-called "teachings" had all been in vain.

Somehow, I've been sitting on those back porch steps with that Negro man all my life. On one hand, knowing that at some level within the human spirit there is a universal frequency at which all men recognize one another's sameness. Yet, on the other hand, also knowing that human reason always manages to find perceived differences which most men will use to set themselves apart from their fellow man. This is the essential human trait that leads to prejudice. In my heart, I knew that trait would never totally die during my father's lifetime. Many times, I have wondered if it ever would in mine.

BOONE

Psychotic Love

For as long as I can remember, my mother was a practicing registered nurse. Throughout my childhood, when I was near my mother, I
was constantly surrounded by hypodermic syringes, penicillin tablets, skin
ointments, potions for the eyes, mercurochrome swabs, adhesive tape, an-
tiseptics, bandages, cotton balls and a whole host of other nursing-related
articles too numerous to mention.

Although she was licensed to work in a hospital, a doctor's office or a
nursing home, my mother specialized in at-home, private care for the ter-
minally ill. Caring for people who were awaiting their final, inevitable end
held a special fascination for my mother. She felt it was somehow her personal destiny to be with the dying in their final days. She was very proud of
those cases in which she had helped care for, counsel and prepare patients
to meet their deaths as calmly and as resignedly as possible.

In the late spring of 1949, when I was eight years old, my mother
undertook the care of an invalid woman named "Miss Mary" McDaniel,
a gray-haired, bedridden woman in her late sixties who had become paralyzed after a stroke several years earlier. Initially, her husband, Boone, had
hired a neighbor woman named Crick to come live in the home and care
for his wife. For several years, Crick ran the household, cooked and cleaned
and took care of Miss Mary's medical needs as best she could. In the winter of 1948, however, Miss Mary had a second stroke and the doctor told
her husband that she needed full-time, professional nursing care.

With that, Boone asked Miss Mary's physician, a Dr. James Fordham, if he knew of a good private-duty nurse he would recommend. Dr.
Fordham said, as a matter of fact, he did and explained that my mother
had just finished a case with an elderly man near Attalla who had died
after a terrible bout with pancreatic cancer. Dr. Fordham explained how
my mother had provided expert care to the dying man and made his final
meeting with his maker as comfortable and peaceful as possible. The doctor recommended my mother highly.

Three days later, my mother, my father and I drove the 45 miles from our home near Hamilton to the backwoods farming country of Thompson's Bend, Alabama, so that my mother could be interviewed as a possible private duty nurse for Miss Mary McDaniel.

When my mother sat down for the interview, Boone and Mary began asking questions about her background. After only ten minutes, they discovered that my grandmother, Gladys Georgia McKinney, and Miss Mary were long-lost third cousins. That made my mother and Miss Mary fourth cousins. In fact, my grandmother, who had grown up with Miss Mary in Thompson's Bend some forty years earlier, had been a bridesmaid at Boone and Mary's wedding in 1912. That clinched it. A family acquaintance was all the reference that Boone and Mary needed. My mother was hired on the spot.

In mid-May of 1949, I was near the end of the second grade in grammar school. One Friday afternoon when I got in from school, my mother called me into the bedroom where she was packing a suitcase. Once I was seated on the bed, my mother explained that she was going to live with the McDaniels. She said that Hilda, a neighbor woman who did our housekeeping, would be helping me get ready for school each day. She reminded me that, as usual, I was responsible for helping my father with the chores, doing my homework and making sure that my ears were clean each morning before I went to school. She said, when school was out for the summer, I would come to live with her at the McDaniel farm.

So three weeks later, I was sent off to the deep backwoods of North Alabama to live with my mother at the McDaniel homestead. For the trip, Hilda had packed up everything my mother had instructed—toys, clothes, toiletries, books, etc…all the personal items and other gear I would need for my great adventure. Once I was packed, Hilda pecked me on the cheek, reminded me to put on clean underwear every day and warned me to "watch out for rattlesnakes in them woods." With that, my father and I climbed into our black 1947 Oldsmobile and he delivered me to the McDaniel farm.

The farm was a shadowy, foreboding underworld where real time had ceased to exist many, many years before. Standing darkly within a grove of giant oak trees, the McDaniel farmhouse was a weathered, unpainted, clapboard structure with a tin roof and six gables, a single lightning rod at each gable. Originally constructed in the late 1880s, the farmhouse was built in the time-honored shotgun design with a hallway down the middle and rooms branching off to either side. Over the years, however, new rooms—a pantry, a storage room and an enlarged kitchen—had been added and the original shotgun design had been lost to the progress of the years.

The interior of the farmhouse was an eerie place. All the rooms had a musty, decaying smell like old clothes that have hung in the closet too long. Most of the furniture had been ordered out of a Sears and Roebuck catalog from the early 1900s. All of the nightstands and bedside tables had knobbed legs and inlaid mirrors like something out of an English late, late movie. All the bedrooms had fireplaces and the mantle over each featured a hand-carved etching of winged, angelic-faced cherubs playfully holding a burning torch. According to the style standards of 1910, the home was considered elegant. Since there was no electricity in the home, all the fires—whether in the cookstove or the fireplaces—were wood-fed. At night, the only source of light was kerosene lamps.

My bedroom was a musty-smelling front room with tall Victorian windows and a well-used, stone fireplace with fading, sepia photos of Boone and Mary's ancestors on the mantle. The mattress on my bed was filled with pine straw and, when you lay on it or turned over in your sleep, there was the sharp, snapping sound of dried pine needles being crushed. The pillows were made with real down-home goose feathers and sometimes a large, stiff one would punch through the pillowcase and stab you in the neck when you changed positions in your sleep.

Later that summer, I would catch lightning bugs outside, then release them within the musty bedroom so that I could marvel at the warm, translucent flashes of yellow light in the darkness. One night, I chased an errant lightning bug into the closet. Following the insect's brilliant glow to a stack of clothing, I found a huge boxful of pint and quart fruit jars hidden underneath. I knew that canned fruit and vegetables were kept in the pantry near the kitchen, so I wondered why the fruit jars had been hidden in the closet. Curious, I retrieved a flashlight and inspected further. The fruit jars were crammed full of cash money in rolled-up wads. There were huge double handfuls of five, ten and twenty dollar notes crammed into the fruit jars. There had to be thousands and thousands of dollars hidden in the closet.

Frightened at my discovery, I closed the box and returned the clothes atop them. The next morning I told my mother what I had found. She admonished me to never go near the closet again and to not breathe a word of what I had discovered. She said Boone didn't trust banks after what happened in 1929. I promised to do as she had ordered.

One morning, my mother sat me down in my bedroom with an album of old family photos. Boone had had a brother who fought for Admiral Dewey when the Americans routed the Spanish at Manila Bay during the Spanish-American War. Included in the album were fifty to sixty old sepia photos of American soldiers and sailors posing triumphantly in front of the gallows where they had hanged thousands of Spanish soldiers. In photo after photo, I gazed in awe at the dead soldiers hanging lifelessly from the gallows as the Americans—weapons held victoriously aloft—posed like mighty hunters infinitely proud of their kills. To my young mind, I remember thinking how horrible war and death must be.

Miss Mary's room was located directly across the hallway from my room. Her bed, a cast-iron, turn-of-the-century model, faced the fireplace where Boone always kept a fire going. When Boone was in the room, he sat in a rocking chair facing the fireplace while his dog, Nero, lazed on the warm hearth at his feet. Beside Miss Mary's bed was a window that looked out on the front porch and the dirt road that passed in front of the house. Many days, in her bedridden loneliness, Miss Mary would look out the window and up the road to see an occasional car or wagon passing.

During the first few weeks of my stay, I spent all my time near my mother. To occupy myself, she would give me chores and I would gather eggs, bring in wood for the cookstove or feed the dogs. The housewoman, Crick, was a muscular, raw-boned country woman in her late thirties who had never been married and never stopped working. Uneducated and unattractive, Crick was deeply religious and had no understanding of personal hygiene. On hot days, her body odor would be so foul it would pervade the whole house. If I had to go into the kitchen and Crick was cooking over the stove, I would rush right past her as quickly as possible because the heat from the cookstove intensified her odor to a truly overwhelming degree. On several occasions, my mother threatened to buy deodorant and force Crick to use it, but somehow she could never bring herself to actually do it.

When I wasn't doing chores, I would play under the oak trees in the front yard with my toys. I had a set of little plastic circus characters I would arrange in the top of a shoe box. There were three horsemen, several clowns, some ballerinas, a high-wire act with plastic acrobats and a mustachioed magician in a black cape. I would pretend I was the master of a three-ring circus and, in my child's mind, I could set them performing at a moment's notice.

Boone McDaniel was a small, hunch-backed man in his late seventies who had a drawn face and a constant stubble of beard. He always dipped Bruton snuff and never wore anything but bib overalls, brogans and a long-sleeved khaki shirt buttoned at the top. Boone was the epitome of the backwoods Alabama farmer whose entire life had been spent near the earth, farm animals and crops.

The thing I remember most about Boone was his hat. He had a black felt hat that he had been wearing probably 10–15 years...maybe even longer. The hat was so old—Boone had grasped it so many times to place it, then remove it from his head—that the felt at the front of the crown where he grasped it actually had holes worn in it. When Boone took his hat off to eat or sit by the fire, there was a bald, shiny spot right on the very top of his head.

At first, Boone wouldn't have anything to do with me. Either he didn't know what to make of me or he could see no reason to befriend me. After all, I was 8 years old and he was 78. Boone had never had any children of his own and I wasn't sure if he was capable of relating to anyone as young as me.

In the mornings when he went to the fields, he would see me playing with my circus toys and make some brief, off-handed comment. Then, together with his dog Nero, he would trudge off to the cotton fields. At lunch, he would return to the farmhouse and go directly into Miss Mary's room. There he would restoke the fire and talk to Miss Mary about the crops and business and share his day with her. Once he had eaten, Boone would check the fire again, ask Miss Mary about her health, then return to the fields.

After I'd been there for about three weeks, however, something caused Boone to change his mind. For some reason, he decided he wanted to get to know me. I don't believe it was due to loneliness because Boone McDaniel was too hard a man to allow himself such a vulnerable trait. I think I was more of a curiosity than anything else. The old man probably wanted a closer look at this young, modern boy from the nearby town.

So, one morning as I was playing under the oak trees, Boone came out of the house. As usual, his dog Nero was waiting at the back porch steps and, when Boone's foot hit the ground, Nero fell into lockstep behind his Lord and Master. As he rounded the corner of the house, he saw me playing. At first, Boone said nothing, walked past me and started toward the fields as usual. On that particular morning, however, after he had taken several steps toward the fields, he suddenly stopped and turned to me.

"Hey, little turd-knocker...," he said tentatively in a low, uncertain tone.

I looked up from my circus toys.

"Yes, sir," I answered.

"You wanna go to the fields with me today?"

"I have to ask my mother," I replied.

"It's okay," he said. "Come on."

If Boone approved, I knew it would be okay with my mother so I joined him and his dog Nero that day for the first of our many walks during the summer of 1949.

For hours on end, Boone, who walked with a labored, begrudging limp, would lead me and the dog down the cotton rows that were sometimes a full quarter-mile long. We must have been a strange sight, this wizened, hunched-over creature, his aging dog Nero and myself, a slight, skinny kid, walking through a green sea of knee-high cotton plants that seemed to stretch forever and ever to the horizon.

We would walk for what seemed like endless miles, gathering the sandy soil on our shoes. Intermittently, Boone would stop and inspect the cotton plants. Then he would mutter something to the dog about the state of the crop...not enough rain, too much fertilizer, seeds planted too deep or whatever. Then, after his pronouncement, we would start walking again. Further on, Boone would stop to talk to one of the Negro hired hands who was plowing. Boone would ask the hired hand if he thought the ground was too wet or too dry or too something. The black man would offer a reply and Boone would bend down over the plow and take some of the fresh earth from one of the blades. He would rub it between his fingers, then he would tell the hired hand to adjust the blade angle on the plow or pull the mules a little closer to the furrow. Finally, having delivered his input as farm owner, Boone would start limping back down the cotton rows again and the dog and I would follow.

At the end of the fields, Boone, Nero and I would arrive at the river and have a seat under a tree within the sound of the raging water. Boone warned me to never go near the river at that point. There were water moccasins "bigger'n yo' arm down there." he'd say, referring to the heavy undergrowth along the riverbank. He recalled that, during the spring plowing of 1931, a Negro hired hand had stopped at the end of the cotton rows and went down to the river to get a drink. Boone said the man had been bitten seven times. The luckless plowman had made his way back up the river bank to the plow and the mules, but had collapsed and died before he could go any further.

I had a crazy uncle named Milford who liked to brag that he was a big-time farmer. Uncle Milford had ten acres with five in cultivation, two mules, a small tractor, a milk cow, several calves and about thirty chickens. Boone, on the other hand, was a real farmer with over 600 acres and almost 400 in cultivation. Boone had nine mules, five hired hands, 83 head of cattle including thirteen bulls and seventeen cows nursing calves, 53 head of hogs including nine brood sows, and literally hundreds of chickens. On my Uncle Milford's farm, I would go with my cousin Albert to gather eggs and, if we found twenty, it was a big deal. At Boone's, it was nothing for me to gather 200 eggs in one afternoon. Boone also had five horses, not counting a prize palomino he hired out as a stud, three wagons, one of which had rubber tires, and four riding saddles. Boone never owned a car or a tractor. He said they were "too expensive" and he "just didn't believe in 'em." If Boone McDaniel needed transportation, he would either walk or hitch up a two-horse wagon.

Some of my happiest hours that summer were spent riding a cowboy rig that Boone had built for me with an old saddle. Boone had seen me cutting Tom Mix and Lash LaRue posters from the back of cereal boxes and he knew I was caught up in the cowboy craze that swept the late forties. So Boone strapped an old saddle across a piece of lumber under the tool shed and tied it down so I could play like I was riding a horse. When I wasn't in the fields with Boone, I would spend endless hours bouncing in the saddle pretending I was a host of glorious cowboy heroes…The Lone Ranger, Roy Rogers, Gene Autry, Tim Holt, Lash LaRue and Kid Colt.

Boone knew my name was Billy, but he always called me "little turd-knocker." I guess the only way a 78-year-old could see an 8-year-old like me was as a miniature human being whose only purpose in life was to leave behind little pods of excrement like a horse-drawn spreader rhythmically leaves fertilizer in the furrow during planting time. In agricultural parlance, these fertilizing machines were called "knockers" because they make a thick, clunking sound as the mule pulled them down the furrow.

On the other hand, Boone's life was so closely intertwined with the lives of animals that he may have seen human beings—me included—in the same light in which he saw his cows, pigs, chickens and horses...creatures whose only visible legacy to the earth was the daily digestive waste they left in their paths.

After he got to know me, Boone would give me money to buy candy from the peddler. Since Boone didn't have a car and never went to the grocery, he bought all of his household goods from the local peddler. The peddler, a fat, jolly red-faced man named Howard, drove a converted school bus around the countryside and either sold or bartered his store-bought goods to the farmers for their produce.

"Now I'm going to give little turd-knocker a twenty-five-cent piece," Boone would say, taking a time-worn change purse from the bib of his overalls, "so little turd-knocker can go see the peddler and buy him some sweetnin'."

So, with the quarter in hand, I would race down the cotton rows to meet the peddler. When I would arrive, Crick would always be there counting eggs that would be swapped for goods. She would count a dozen eggs and the peddler would make a pencil mark on a small pad. Finally, after she had counted 20 or 30 dozen, the peddler would tell her how much credit she had for the eggs. Then he'd turn to me.

"How much money you got today?" he'd ask.

I'd hold up the quarter.

"Well, start picking," he'd say.

Twenty-five cents was a lot of money when you're eight years old. And it's 1949. First I would get red jawbreakers and some Tootsie rolls. Then I'd choose two or three of those little banana-flavored candies shaped like cricket bats, some peppermint sticks, a cherry-flavored all-day sucker and some licorice. Finally, I'd round out my treasure trove with some bubble gum, a handful of Kit-Kat chewies, some chocolate kisses and three or four grape-flavored sour balls. Finally the peddler would tell me I had twenty-five cents worth and I'd stop picking.

Then, with my pants pockets bulging with candy, I would race back across the cotton field. Breathlessly, I would rush up and Boone would be standing alone, gazing across the cotton rows and talking to his dog Nero. He'd turn to me and I'd show him the pocketful of candy.

"That's lots of sweetnin' little turd-knocker's got there," he'd say.

"Wanna piece?" I would ask.

He'd shake his head.

"No sweets for me," he'd say, "Not after my accident." His intonation emphasized the word "accident" and, when he said that, he would reach down and rub his crooked right leg. I didn't figure the candy would go too well with his dipping snuff anyway, so I didn't press the issue.

Other than Miss Mary, the only creature Boone had any true affection for was his dog Nero. Nero was an aging black and white-spotted feist that was Boone's alter ego and constant companion. Boone said he couldn't remember for sure, but Nero was either 13 or 14 years old.

Nero was one of eight pups that had been born in a hay shed behind the barn, Boone said. When the pups were only a few days old, the hay shed caught fire during a lightning storm and the frantic mother dog started carrying the pups out of the burning shed. She succeeded in bringing out one pup. When she returned for the others, the fire had spread so rapidly that she and the other puppies were trapped and perished in the smoke and flames. Boone said he named the surviving puppy Nero because the emperor Nero had played the fiddle while Rome burned.

There were three other dogs on the farm, but Nero was top dog and all the others knew it. Another dog, a chow-collie mix named George, would sometimes join us on our walks but he always had to defer to Nero. If Nero approved, George could accompany us to the fields. If Nero didn't approve, and somehow Boone could tell when Nero disapproved, George couldn't come along. If George tried to go with us when Nero was in a bad mood, Nero would growl and chase him away. If George persisted, Boone would curse the dog and chase it back to the farmhouse.

Sometimes, during our walks, Boone would ask me what I thought about God and the Bible. Boone said that preachers claimed if you were a good person on earth, you would go to heaven where harps played, angels sang, the streets were paved with gold and you would eat honey and drink milk all day.

"Do you believe that?" he'd ask me, earnestly.

"That's what the Bible says," I would reply, recalling my teachings from the Baptist Church Sunday School my mother and I had attended in the town.

Boone would look at me and say nothing, then we would start walking across the cotton fields again. After we had walked a little ways, he would stop to inspect the cotton plants.

"I don't see much use for preachers," he would say absently, looking closely at a wilted cotton boll. "'Bout all they're good for is to marry you and to bury you."

One day I walked with Boone and Nero through the woods to the nearby Isaiah Dismukes farm where several men were gathered around a hog pen trying to breed an old brood sow. The sow was in heat, but each time the boar would try to mount her, the sow would run away leaving the hapless boar to chase her and futilely try to mount again.

Six or seven men were lined up along the fence trying to figure out some way to get the sow to stand still for the boar. Somebody had suggested that, if you could get close enough to pee on the sow, she would stand still for the boar. As Boone and I watched, Isaiah Dismukes unzipped his pants and went running around the hog pen with his member at ready to urinate on the errant sow. When Boone saw that, he started laughing and, once he started, he cackled like I had never heard before. Boone laughed so hard and so loud that I swear I thought I could hear his dog Nero laughing with him. Never had I seen such an outright, public display of joy in Boone McDaniel.

Finally, Isaiah Dismukes, out of breath from running and irritated at Boone's cackling, told Boone if he had any better ideas, to let him know. Boone looked at the sow, then at Isaiah Dismukes.

"Go to the house and bring some warm dishwater," Boone said.

"Dishwater?" Isaiah said in disbelief.

"Yeah. Dishwater," Boone said authoritatively. "And throw in a good handful of table salt."

Fifteen minutes later, Isaiah returned from the house, lugging the bucket of dishwater. Boone took the bucket and held it over the fence.

"Sooieee! Piggie! Sooie! Sooie! Sooie! Piggie," Boone called to the sow. The timbre of his voice told you immediately that he was somehow communicating with the brood sow.

Instinctively, the sow stopped and looked at Boone. Then she glanced back at the boar who was panting for dear life, his limp, corkscrew penis dragging the ground. Knowing he had the advantage, Boone sharply rapped the side of the tin bucket with his knuckle.

"Piggie! Piggie!" Boone called expertly in a low voice. "Here, piggy, piggy...Piggie! Piggie!"

The sow looked at Boone again. Then she took another look at the boar and, for no apparent reason, walked straight over to Boone and the bucket of dishwater.

The sow came within two feet. Boone tapped the side of the bucket again, then put his hand in the warm dishwater and sprinkled it in the sow's face.

The sow, feeling the wetness, licked her tongue around her mouth and tasted the warm, salty dishwater. Then, as if it were an act of destiny, the brood sow stepped up and started drinking the dishwater. As the sow stood still to drink, the boar came up behind her, mounted her and successfully penetrated and impregnated her.

As Isaiah Dismukes watched the mounted boar impregnating the sow, he smiled triumphantly at Boone.

"You the best, Boone," he said happily, smiling from ear to ear. "I mean the God-damn best."

Boone didn't even acknowledge Isaiah's compliment. As if he didn't hear, Boone continued to hold the bucket of dishwater for the sow as if it was nothing.

Isaiah Dismukes was right; Boone was the best. If any of the other farmers had a problem breeding a horse, a cow, or a pig, they would consult Boone who was the known expert in such matters. Early one morning, Boone and I walked across the mountain to another farmer's house where a calf that was being born had somehow turned inside the cow. The farmer had grabbed the calf and tried to pull the calf out, but the cow, in terrible pain, collapsed. When Boone arrived, the cow was on the ground near death and the calf was half-in and half-out.

Like some sort of mysterious birthing wizard, Boone gently pushed the calf back inside the cow. Then, while the farmer held the cow's head, Boone put his whole arm inside the cow and repositioned the calf in the birth canal. Once positioned properly, Boone gently pulled the newborn calf out of the cow as smoothly and surely as if the birth had been perfectly natural.

The mastery Boone showed when he hired out his prize stud, a giant palomino stallion, to service a mare always held a certain fascination for my eight-year-old eyes.

When a farmer would bring a mare to be bred, Boone would inspect her first. Sometimes Boone wouldn't bring out the stud if he felt the mare hadn't been in heat long enough and the farmer would plead and argue with Boone to go ahead and put the stud on her.

"It won't take," Boone would say. "She's got to have more heat before it will take. Let nature work on her a few more days, then bring her back."

Usually, they would take Boone's advice.

One farmer, a stocky, red-faced Irishman named James Mullins had brought a dappled filly across the river on the ferry, and talked Boone into putting the stallion on her before, in Boone's judgement, she had been in heat long enough.

"I'll put him to her," Boone said finally, "but you have to pay for the service. And if it don't take and you have to bring her back, then I'm charging you again."

"Okay. Okay." the Irishman agreed reluctantly, wanting to breed his mare and get back across the river as soon as possible.

Boone put the stallion on the mare and the stud did his thing. Sure enough, the mare wasn't impregnated and three weeks later, the Irishman was back to have the stud put on her again. The Irishman paid Boone the stud fee a second time and never questioned Boone's judgement again.

During the breeding sessions, Boone could somehow tell when the stud had had an orgasm sufficient to impregnate the mare because he would signal to the hired hand and say, "That's enough. He's got her." With that, the hired hand would return the stallion to the barn. Once Boone announced that a mare had been impregnated, the farmers paid their money and took his word as gospel.

The only relief for the cold, brazen hardness that lived inside Boone McDaniel was Miss Mary. Everything he did, he did for Miss Mary and the only time he ever seemed to be truly happy was when he was with her in her room with a good fire going and his dog Nero lazing on the hearth. During those times, he felt secure and at peace with himself and the world around him.

My grandmother said it had always been that way and the day he finally married Miss Mary in the spring of 1912, Boone was the happiest man in North Alabama. For more than two years, Boone had courted

Mary, trying to get her to marry him, my grandmother said. Mary, a beautiful young woman, told Boone she liked him and wanted to marry him, but she couldn't leave her father to live alone.

When she was five, Miss Mary's mother died of fever and left her and her younger brother Benjamin to be raised by their father. Then, after Benjamin was killed in a hunting accident in 1910, all the family that Mary had left was her father.

As fate would have it, my grandmother said, Mary's father fell ill with the flu the following winter and had to close the hardware store he operated at Moody's Chapel. While he was sick, he raved on and on about how he was losing business by being closed. After several days, he started improving and, although weak and pale, he left the sickbed and reopened the hardware store despite Miss Mary's protests. Three nights later, he closed his business again and came home with severe chills and a high fever. He died in Mary's arms the following morning.

When Boone heard about the death, he rushed to Mary's side to comfort her and help clean up the family business. Then, two days after her father's funeral, Boone proposed again that she marry him. This time, Mary accepted. After the marriage, Boone bought a small farm on the north side of the Tallapoosa River and planted cotton and corn and started breeding animals. Miss Mary wanted to help with the farm work, but Boone wouldn't have it. He said he didn't want her "out there tusslin' in the fields with the hired hands." He wanted her to stay at home, cook for him, keep house and mother his children.

But Miss Mary would never become a mother, my grandmother said, because Boone's "accident" occurred three months after the marriage. Boone decided he wanted to build a herd of riding horses to sell to the local farmers, so he bought a stud, an aging Appaloosa stallion, to start the herd. During the first spring, my grandmother said, the old stud performed well and successfully impregnated all four of Boone's mares. Then Boone decided to hire out the stud to service the mares of nearby farmers. That's when the problems started. For some reason, the old stud suddenly lost the ability to maintain an erection. When the stud was brought out to a mare, he would mount her, but he couldn't maintain a sufficient erection to penetrate successfully.

In one of the breeding sessions, the stud, with his flaccid member, failed again and again to penetrate the mare. After numerous unsuccessful attempts, Boone became frustrated and grabbed the horse's member and tried to force it inside the mare. With that, the old stud, angered at the interference, kicked Boone in the testicles. The blow slammed Boone against the side of a hayrack and knocked him unconscious.

For over seven months, Boone was immobilized, my grandmother said. At first, the doctors said he would never walk again. When the horse had kicked him, the powerful blow had not only ruptured Boone's testicles, it had also cracked several small bones at the base of his spine. This meant there was nerve damage and possible paralysis. When Boone finally decided he was well enough to get out of bed and walk, he simply fell on the floor. His right leg was permanently paralyzed and crooked at the knee. The doctor said Boone would have to learn to walk with the crooked leg.

With that, Miss Mary sent off to Sears and Roebuck, my grandmother said, and bought Boone an apparatus that would help him learn to walk again. For several weeks, he hobbled around the house on the device until he regained enough strength in the good leg to take some halting steps. Finally, Boone learned to walk again, but he had to hunch his back over to do it, my grandmother said.

Once Boone was mobile again, the doctor said he was lucky to regain his ability to walk, but explained it would be asking too much to expect to regain his ability to produce children. As a result, Boone and Mary spent the rest of their lives childless. At one point, Mary had talked about adopting a child, my grandmother said. They had even hired a lawyer and talked to the state adoption people in Birmingham, but nothing ever came of it. Finally, they decided to spend their lives together without children.

This singular piece of happenstance bound Boone to Miss Mary in the most incredible way imaginable, my grandmother said. By being unable to have children, Boone knew that the only person his heart would ever be completely open to was Miss Mary. As a result, the depth of the love and devotion Boone had for Miss Mary was frightening, my grandmother said.

One hot morning in late August, I was with Boone in the cotton fields when I heard my mother calling from somewhere in the distance. I scanned the cotton rows until I located the sound of her voice. A quarter-mile away, I could see my mother waving. I ran down the cotton rows as fast as I could and finally, breathlessly, I was within earshot of my mother.

"Tell Boone that Mary is getting worse and he should come right in," she said.

I raced back down the cotton rows and told Boone. He turned immediately and started trudging back down the cotton rows as fast as his awkward walk would allow.

When Boone went into Mary's room, the old woman was gasping for breath. Miss Mary had always looked pale and weak, but that morning she was white as a sheet. The long gray hair that normally flowed over the shoulders of her nightgown seemed to be dull and lifeless. Her breath was coming in great heaves and gasps.

My mother gave her a shot and she began breathing more regularly. My mother told Boone her heartbeat was erratic, but she seemed to be stabilizing. Around mid-afternoon, Dr. Fordham arrived. After taking her vital signs, he removed a vial of medicine from his satchel.

"Give her a shot of this now," the doctor said, handing my mother the vial. "Take her heartbeat and respiration hourly. If she goes into convulsions, give her another shot," the doctor said.

Throughout that night, Miss Mary slept peacefully while my mother and Boone waited at her bedside. In the early morning hours, my mother went to a small anteroom to sleep for a few hours, giving Boone strict instructions to call her if Miss Mary's condition changed.

All that night, Boone stayed in Miss Mary's room, dozing in the rocking chair and keeping the fire going. Intermittently, he would awaken and check on Miss Mary, then go back to the rocking chair to doze again.

The next morning about daybreak, Boone awakened my mother. The old woman was gasping for breath again. My mother took her pulse.

"Her heartbeat is down to thirty-eight times a minute," my mother said, turning to Boone. "We better get the doctor."

Boone nodded his approval. With that, my mother called Crick and told her to go across the woods to the Chalfants' place.

"She's going to die!" Crick screamed frantically. "Oh, I know Miss Mary's going to die. Oh, Miss Mary, we love you so! God, please don't take Miss Mary."

"Stay calm," my mother ordered firmly. "Go over to the Chalfants' place. Get them to take you to Moody's chapel and call the doctor."

"Oh, Lord Jesus, in all your mercy, please don't take Miss Mary away from us," the farm woman wailed. "Oh, please dear Jesus..."

My mother got up, took Crick by the shoulders and shook her. "Keep quiet!" my mother said authoritatively. "Go call the doctor!" she said again. Crick, sobbing like a child, left the room.

After Crick left, Boone sat on the side of the bed and held his wife's hand. My mother gave her a shot and the old woman took several deep breaths. Suddenly she opened her eyes. Boone was elated.

"Mary! Mary!" Boone said, excitedly. His tone was almost pleading.

Miss Mary had a soft, peaceful smile on her face. She looked at Boone then turned to the window.

"Look!" Miss Mary said, sitting up in bed and pointing out the window. "Look out the window!"

Boone looked at my mother curiously. My mother held her hand and patted her shoulder.

"Mary! Mary!" my mother said. "It's me, Virginia."

The old woman couldn't see or hear anything my mother was saying. Her eyes were fixed on the window.

"Boone!" Miss Mary said. "Look! Look out the window!"

The old man bolted upright and looked out the window. Not seeing anything, he turned back to her.

"Mary, what is it?" he asked anxiously

"I see my daddy comin' down the road," Miss Mary said calmly, pointing out the window. "Look! Look! Don't you see him?"

Boone looked out the window then he looked back at my mother. They exchanged knowing glances.

"It's him! It's him!" the old woman said with certainty. "I tell you, it's my daddy. I can see him coming."

Boone looked at my mother again.

My mother didn't answer.

"It's my daddy and he's coming to get me," Miss Mary said again, still staring out the window and peering up the road.

Boone, shaking his head slowly and sadly, said nothing. Stone-faced and still holding his wife's hand, he looked at my mother as she placed the stethoscope against Miss Mary's breast.

"He's here now," Miss Mary said with wild-eyed excitement. "And he's going to take me with him..."

Boone looked at my mother expectantly, almost fearfully. Then, without another word, the old woman fell back on the pillow, her frail head collapsing softly in a nest of long gray hair. For a brief instant, her upper body jerked forward. Then she seemed to relax and a peaceful look dawned across her face.

"She's dead," Boone said knowingly, watching as my mother pressed the stethoscope against the old woman's chest. My mother listened for a moment, then sadly removed the stethoscope and nodded in agreement.

"She lost her mind before she died," Boone said.

My mother, folding up the stethoscope, looked at Boone and said nothing.

Crick, who had returned from the Chalfant farm, suddenly rushed frantically into the room. For a moment, she stared at the old woman's corpse. Then, in a sudden flash of hysteria, she broke down, started sobbing and rushed to the side of the bed.

"Oh, Miss Mary!" she said, getting down on her knees. "May God bless you and keep you. May you go straight through the pearly gates and be happy forever and ever with Jesus! Oh, Miss Mary, we loved you so much!"

Boone, irritation in his eyes, looked at Crick on her knees, sobbing and praying at his dead wife's bedside.

"Get out of here with that!" Boone said sharply, ordering the woman out of the room as if he were dismissing an errant dog. Crick, sobbing uncontrollably, left the room like an obedient child.

My mother pulled the sheet over Miss Mary's body. For a moment, Boone—not a flicker of emotion on his face— looked at the sheet draped over his dead wife. Then Boone told my mother he and Nero were going for a walk. I knew he didn't want me to go.

Three hours later, Dr. Fordham arrived and pronounced Miss Mary officially dead. My mother filled out the death report and Dr. Fordham signed it as her official death record.

After the doctor left, I went out to the tool shed to play cowboy on the old saddle Boone had set up. As I bounced up and down in the saddle, the wood piece the saddle was tied to made a loud, clunking sound as it bounced up and down on its support beam. First, I played like Roy Rogers on Trigger, then The Lone Ranger on Silver and finally Gene Autry on Champion. For some 20-30 minutes, I bounced up and down in the saddle, the clunking of the wood piece drowning out all other sounds. Finally, I grew weary of the play-horse. As I took my foot out of the stirrup to dismount, I suddenly heard a strange sound. I stopped and listened. It was a low, mournful, whining sound like a forlorn animal crying for its mate. It was coming from somewhere beyond the barn.

I went to investigate. As I passed through the barn hallway, I checked all the stalls. Then I followed the sound through the barn hallway to the corn crib. There, in front of the corn crib, I saw Nero sitting alone. I could hear the sound coming from inside the corn crib.

I left Nero undisturbed and went around to the back of the log corn crib where the mud chinks had dried and fallen out of the cracks between the logs. I shaded my eyes and peered inside.

There, through the cracks, I could see Boone sobbing like a little child. The old man was sitting among the ears of unhusked corn. He would make a low, wailing sound like an old bitch dog having pups then he would beat his clenched fists into the ears of corn. It crossed my mind to go in and tell Boone he shouldn't be so sad. Somehow, my better judgement told me not to. Finally, I tiptoed away from the corn crib and went back to the house feeling very sad for Boone.

Later that afternoon, the funeral home people arrived and took Miss Mary's body away. Boone thanked my mother for her help with Mary, but asked her to stay on until the day after the funeral to help Crick around the house. Boone said she "knew about things like that" and he would pay her well.

My mother oversaw the funeral arrangements and the following day my mother and I, Boone and my grandmother attended Miss Mary's funeral at the Pilgrim's Rest Baptist Church. Just about everybody in Thompson's Bend was there. My mother said she saw cousins she didn't even know she had. My grandmother wept like a little child when the gravediggers threw the clods of fresh earth in on Miss Mary's casket. It was all very sad.

I'll say one thing for Boone McDaniel, he had an unswerving certainty to his actions. Unlike many men, Boone McDaniel knew exactly what he wanted in his life and he put that desire into action without the slightest hesitation. After Miss Mary was buried on a Saturday afternoon, Boone came home that night, fed the cattle, the hogs and the chickens and went for a walk in the fields with Nero. Around sundown, he returned to the house, had supper and then went straight to bed.

Early the next morning, a Sunday morning, before anybody else got up, Boone put on clean overalls, a clean khaki shirt and went down behind the barn. On his way out of the house, he reached in the back porch pantry and got the .12 gauge shotgun he used to scare the crows out of the vegetable garden. Outside, at the back porch steps, Nero was waiting as usual.

As if Nero knew exactly what was about to happen, he fell in stride behind Boone and they went down behind the barn together.

Boone killed the dog first. A point-blank blast from the .12 gauge shotgun decapitated Nero. Boone then reloaded the shotgun and pulled off his right shoe. Then he sat down on the ground, leaned his back against the side of the barn and held the gun against his left breast. Then he pulled the trigger with the big toe of his right foot.

Apparently Boone had intended for the shotgun blast to go directly into his heart. Unfortunately, he had used the big toe on his right leg, the bad one, to pull the trigger. The shotgun barrel had somehow slipped downward when it discharged and the charge had passed just under Boone's heart and shattered the upper ribs, ripped a huge hole in the bottom portion of his left lung and left his small intestines a mess of ragged, bleeding flesh.

My mother was the first to be awakened by the shot. Instinctively, she jumped out of bed, awakened Crick and together they rushed down behind the barn. There they found the dead dog and Boone lying against the side of the barn with a gaping gunshot wound in his left side. Blood, in a constant stream, was gushing out of the wound down the side of his overalls and onto the ground.

"Oh God! Oh, God!" Crick said hysterically, her face livid white with terror. "I'll go get the doctor."

"No!" my mother said calmly. "Help me get him in the house first."

My mother removed the shotgun and ordered Crick to go back to the house and bring some sheets. Upon Crick's return, my mother worked quickly to pack a sheet into Boone's wound and, using two others to fashion a makeshift stretcher, she and Crick managed to get Boone into the house as I held the doors.

Once inside the house, my mother and Crick managed to carry him into the front bedroom. Then, on my mother's orders, Crick raced off to get the doctor again and my mother began wrapping Boone's wounds to contain the bleeding. Even as I watched my mother tell Crick to rush across the pasture to the Chalfants' home again, I didn't really believe she felt the doctor could do any good. She just wanted to get the hysterical Crick out of the way. She did ask me to stay in the room with her after Crick left.

Boone, bleeding profusely, lay in the same bed Miss Mary had died in. My mother had propped his back up with pillows. He was losing blood rapidly. His breath came in enormous, labored heaves and each time I could see his left lung inflating and deflating like a toy balloon. The wadded-up sheet my mother had packed inside the wound was already saturated with blood and the dark, red liquid of life was trickling down on the bed frame and then on to the floor.

Suddenly, Boone opened his eyes and looked straight past my mother out the window.

"Oh, God…" Boone said, staring out the bedside window. "Oh, great God Almighty!"

"What is it, Boone?" my mother asked anxiously, glancing out the window herself.

"It's Mary!" Boone said, as if he couldn't believe his eyes. "Oh Jesus, I can see her! I can see her! I can see her plain as day! She's comin' up the road," he said. "And she's comin' to get me!"

I saw my mother visibly shiver when Boone said that. Her mother's eyes bulged in a way like I had never seen before.

Suddenly, Boone started shaking as if he was trying to get out of the bed. It was as if he was ready to go to the fields or the barn or somewhere. My mother, still holding one hand on the bloody, wadded-up sheet in his side, put her other hand on his shoulder and tried to hold Boone on the bed.

"Boone! Boone!" My mother said desperately. "You've got to stay in bed."

A massive stream of red, hot blood from the soaked sheet continued trickling down on the floor. Inside Boone's open chest, I could see his left lung inflate then slowly deflate as he sucked in the last giant gasps of precious, life-giving air.

My mother, her eyes still bulging, holding one hand on the wadded sheet in Boone's side and another on his shoulder, looked frantically at me, not knowing, probably even wondering, if I was taking all this in the proper vein.

Then suddenly, Boone's face turned a white ashen color. As he stared out the window, Boone was calm as a cucumber and grinning like I'd never seen him grin before. The only time I had ever seen him really laugh was when he started cackling at Isaiah Dismukes chasing that brood sow. Now he had a truly peaceful, serene smile on his face.

"I'll be glad to see you again, Miss Mary," he said, still smiling and peering out the window. "Oh, Lord God Almighty! I'll be so happy to see you again."

For a brief moment, Boone, still smiling big as day, turned from the window and stared straight into my mother's face. Then a cold deathly glaze formed over his eyes, his hand fell and his crooked body slumped back softly against the pillows. Boone McDaniel was dead.

A VIRTUOUS WOMAN

The Holy Bible and Sex

After her husband died in the fall of 1949, Gladys Georgia McKinney vowed she would never be wed again. After two children and 38 years of marriage, she felt she had done her duty as a wife, a mother and a woman and she was certain that one man was more than enough for her lifetime. So she set up her house and her lifestyle to revolve around her own simple needs and the lives of her daughters and her two grandsons, Billy and Roy. She didn't have to work, but to stay busy she took to canning and making quilts and minding young children for working mothers. Financially, she was quite well off. When her husband died, he left her a good widow's pension from the factory where he worked and she had four rental homes that provided more than adequate income. Also, at his death, her husband had established a trust fund for her and the two daughters and, if push came to shove, she could always draw on that.

For entertainment, Mrs. McKinney had her radio and her Bible. On Saturday nights, she tuned into the Grand Ole Opry on KWOL in Nashville and listened to Minnie Pearl and Grandpa Jones telling jokes and Roy Acuff singing "The Great Speckled Bird." She would spend hours reading the Psalms, the writings of the apostles and Revelations. She said that Biblical teachings and Christian principles were the greatest set of rules ever made to live by. She said she could see nothing wrong with helping your neighbor, being faithful to your spouse and following the golden rule. Although she had attended a small church near her home for many years, she suddenly stopped after her husband's death. The preacher there, she said, like most preachers, had taken the teachings of the Bible and made it into something that it was never meant to be.

"It's when they start preaching that good people go to heaven and bad people go to hell that I start getting worried," she would say. "Most of the time, it's really hard to tell the good people from the bad ones."

Then one day in the spring of 1951, a white Cadillac with a gold-colored Masonic sticker on the bumper pulled into the front yard of the McKinney home. Mrs. McKinney, who was sitting on the front porch shelling Crowder peas, looked over the banister and saw a tall, well-preserved man in his late sixties getting out of the car. Handsome, well-dressed and reeking of mature elegance, he approached the front porch.

"Howdy, ma'am," the man began.

"Good afternoon to you, sir," Mrs. McKinney answered politely.

"Are you Gladys McKinney?"

"I am," she said.

"I've been waiting to meet you," the man said.

Startled, she turned from her pea shelling and examined the man.

"Now, why would you want to meet me?" she asked finally.

"I heard that you were a virtuous woman."

"That I am," she answered proudly.

"Would you mind if I sit a spell with you?"

"Now just hold on!" she answered abruptly. "I don't know you and you don't know me."

There was a long pause. The man didn't move.

"Who are you?" she asked finally.

"My name is Horace Fletcher," the man said. "I'm from Florida and I'm traveling through Alabama looking for land to buy."

Mrs. McKinney examined the man more closely.

"How did you hear about me?" she asked, strong suspicion still in her eyes.

"Mr. Ray Finch over at the crossroads told me about you."

"Oh, yes," Mrs. McKinney said, her eyes lighting with recognition. "What did he say about me?"

"He said you were a widow and you were a good and virtuous woman."

Mrs. McKinney examined the man again.

"Are you an honorable man?" she asked.

"I think so," he answered.

"Okay. I guess it will be all right. Come up on the porch and have a seat," she said finally. "I'll make some iced tea."

With that, Mrs. McKinney got up from her seat, laid aside the pan of Crowder peas and wiped her hands on her apron. As the man reached the front porch, Mrs. McKinney reached down and offered her hand.

"I hope you don't mind," she said. "There's a little bit of pea stain."

"It's okay," he said, with a firm handshake. "It's a pleasure to meet you."

"How do you like your iced tea?" she asked.

"Sweet with extra lemon."

With that, Gladys offered the man a seat on the front porch. Then she picked up the pan of peas and went inside. Some five minutes later, she reappeared on the porch with a serving tray bearing two glasses of iced tea and the fixings. After she had served her guest, she took a seat across from him.

"Now tell me why you want to meet me," Mrs. McKinney said.

"I'm looking for a wife," he began. "I've been a widower for almost five years now and I'm looking for a good woman."

As she listened, Gladys Georgia McKinney was mildly amused by the man's forthright talk of marriage. Although she felt she own marital status was forever fixed, she was intrigued by the man's sincerity.

"It broke my heart to lose my wife," he said, "because she had been such a good wife and mother. But, after the funeral, I knew I had to go on with my life."

During his married years, the man said, he had operated a successful real estate company in Jacksonville, Florida. After his wife's death, he sold the business, he said and now he was "quite well off."

"Now I got lots of time on my hands and I'm looking for a good woman to enjoy life with."

Without even realizing it, Gladys Georgia McKinney found herself listening to the man's every word. In fact, after listening for some twenty minutes, she talked to him about her own marriage, her children and her life after the death of her husband.

During that first day, Mrs. McKinney and Mr. Fletcher chatted for over an hour and drank six glasses of tea, which was all that she had in the house. She explained that she would ask him to have coffee, but she was out of cream. Whether she wanted to admit it or not, Mrs. McKinney had thoroughly enjoyed the visit.

Finally, when he got up to go, Mr. Fletcher asked if he could "call on her."

Although she had enjoyed the man's company, the full force of his intentions still hadn't registered.

"You mean you want to court me?" she asked finally.

"Yes," he said. "That's what I mean."

At first, she didn't answer. She hadn't been in this situation in almost 40 years. In fact, she had never dreamed that she would ever be there again. Part of her was afraid to answer.

"I'm a virtuous woman," she said.

"That's the reason I come looking for you," he said.

Mrs. McKinney, wanting to be sure she knew what she was letting herself in for, gave the man the once-over for the umpteenth time.

"You better come back and have some more iced tea before I answer that," she said finally.

"When?"

Somehow, she was still afraid.

"You really are interested in me, aren't you?"

"I sure am," he said confidently.

There was another long pause.

"What about Saturday afternoon?" she asked. "My grandsons Billy and Roy will be here in the morning, but I'll be free in the afternoon. Say around two?"

"That's fine," he said.

"And I'll stock up on tea and lemons."

He smiled.

"I enjoyed my visit," he said, offering his hand.

"So did I," she said, returning the handshake.

With that, Mr. Fletcher smiled, returned to the Cadillac and pulled out of the front yard. As Mrs. McKinney watched the Cadillac roar out of sight, she inhaled deeply.

At exactly 2 p.m. the following Saturday afternoon, the white Cadillac pulled into Mrs. McKinney's front yard a second time and Mr. Fletcher, decked out in a white polo shirt and gray khaki pants, got out. The moment he emerged from the Cadillac, Mrs. McKinney was at the front door. She was wearing her best flowery dress and she had cleaned up her house spotlessly for the visit. She had made a giant pitcher of ice tea and bought plenty of lemon and some sugar cookies. She had even put two Bible books and a weathered copy of Life magazine on the coffee table in the sitting room.

"Good morning, Mrs. McKinney," the man said, shaking her hand warmly.

"Good morning, Mr. Fletcher, she greeted. "Please come in."

With that, Mr. Fletcher went into the McKinney household. This time, they talked three hours about anything and everything. They talked about how President Truman was doing. They talked about Europe after the war, the morals of the new generation and their families, their friends and their interests.

Around 5 p.m., Mr. Fletcher said he had to get back to the Southern Pines Hotel in Hamilton and make some calls regarding some property he was looking at.

"Can we have a real date next time," he asked. "The man at the hotel says there is a little catfish restaurant down by the river that serves good fresh fish."

"You mean Claude's," Mrs. McKinney said. "His wife Margaret is a friend of mine."

"That's it," he said, remembering. "We could get dressed up, drive down and have some fresh catfish."

"I think I would like that," Mrs. McKinney said, this time without hesitation.

So the following Wednesday night, Mrs. McKinney joined Mr. Fletcher for her first date in almost 40 years. When they entered the catfish restaurant, owner Claude Duncan and his wife Margaret, greeted them at the door.

"Why, Gladys," the woman said, "it's so nice to see you. And who is your friend?" she asked.

"This is Horace Fletcher," Mrs. McKinney said.

"So happy to meet you," she said.

Once they were seated and served, Gladys ate five pieces of catfish with cole slaw, hushpuppies and tartar sauce. Finally, when they were finished, Margaret was at the door to say goodbye. After shaking Mr. Fletcher's hand again, she turned to Gladys.

"He's so handsome," she whispered. "Have you been dating him long?"

"Oh, we're just friends," Gladys said.

"Close friends?" the woman pried.

"Just friends," Gladys replied with a polite smile.

After they returned to her house, Gladys and Mr. Fletcher sat in the Cadillac in the front yard for over two hours talking. Finally, when Mrs.

McKinney said she had to go inside, she offered her hand. Mr. Fletcher took her hand then kissed her on the mouth. Mrs. McKinney was totally taken aback at the kiss. As she looked at Mr. Fletcher, she was afraid of what she felt inside. Quickly, she said, "Good night," and darted into the house.

During the second week, Mr. Fletcher was at the McKinney home on Wednesday, Friday and Saturday nights. After he asked to return on Sunday morning, Mrs. McKinney said he would have to make it Sunday night because she was having her regular Sunday morning brunch with her daughters.

Mrs. McKinney loved both of her daughters dearly, but, Virginia, the oldest, was by far the most stable and sensible. After she graduated from nursing school, Virginia had married Robert Johnson, her high school sweetheart. Immediately, the young couple set up housekeeping, had a child and settled down as prominent members of the community. After high school, Gail, the younger daughter, had attended a small college in North Alabama briefly, then dropped out. Following her return to Hamilton, she was married briefly, had a child and was then divorced. Since then, she had been through a string of fast-moving, wealthy, often-married men. Although her divorce settlement had been quite generous—she had received an immediate $5,000 cash settlement—Gail had spent the money in only a few months on expensive clothing, weekend excursions to Birmingham and gifts for her male friends. Now, alone with a small child, she had to work at a local department store to make ends meet. Many times, Mrs. McKinney had said she didn't understand where Gail got her wild says, but she would "just give anything if Gail would get her life under control."

The following Sunday morning, as usual, the two daughters arrived at their mother's house for brunch. For the occasion, Mrs. McKinney had prepared scrambled eggs, silver dollar pancakes, home fries, peach preserves and some special coffee she had ordered in the mail. Near the end of the meal, the mother explained that she needed one of the daughters to take her to the dress shop downtown.

"What's the occasion?" Virginia asked.

"I've met a man," the mother said.

The two daughters looked at each other then perked up interestedly.

"A man?" Gail asked. "What do you need with a man...at your age?"

"I can do what I like," Mrs. McKinney replied sharply.

"Now don't you two get started," Virginia intervened.

"It's not Howard Bishop, is it?" Gail pressed, referring to a local grocer who had tried to court Mrs. McKinney immediately after her husband's death.

"No," Mrs. McKinney said quickly. "This man is wealthy and very nice looking."

"Do we know him?" Virginia asked.

With that, the mother explained her relationship with Mr. Fletcher.

"I think I smell love in the air," Gail commented flippantly, winking at her sister.

"I told you we're just friends," Mrs. McKinney said.

"Sounds like more than good friends to me," Gail said with a sly grin.

There was a long pause.

"That's enough of this," the mother said. "Which one of you can take me to the dress shop?"

"I'm going shopping on Wednesday," Gail said. "I'll take you."

"Will you two please try to keep from fighting," the older daughter requested.

Over the next two weeks, Mr. Fletcher became a standard fixture in Gladys Georgia McKinney's life. Suddenly, virtually every facet of her life had become directly or indirectly centered around Mr. Fletcher and their time together. For hours, she would clean, scrub and sweep so her house would be spotlessly clean for his visits. Then she would fuss around endlessly about what she was going to wear and what she was going to serve him. During those two weeks, she and Mr. Fletcher made the rounds of all the little restaurants in the community to, as she put, "see and be seen." Also, they went shopping together, took long walks along the river and once even went to worship services at the little church she hadn't attended in three years.

During the brunch with her daughters the following Sunday morning, the mother reported the events of the past two weeks.

"You're in love," Gail observed.

"Oh, don't be silly," Mrs. McKinney said.

"You have a glow about you," Gail added.

The mother looked at her older daughter for an opinion.

"She's right, mother." Virginia said. "You've changed."

The mother was thoughtful for a moment.

"I have to admit I really like Horace," she said blissfully. "I've never known another man quite like him."

The two daughters were listening.

"When your father courted me in 1913," the mother continued, "The world was different. Very different. And I was very different."

She stopped. Both of her daughters were all ears.

"I have to admit I've become very comfortable with Horace," she said.

There was a long pause.

"You're calling him by his first name now," the younger daughter said.

"Yes, I guess I am," she said wistfully.

"Are you sleeping with him?" Gail asked with a sly grin.

"No!" the mother said sharply. "Even if I was, it's none of your business."

"It was only a question," Gail said innocently.

"Nothing is ever 'only a question' to you," the mother countered.

"Come on, you two," the older daughter said.

The mother and younger daughter were quiet for a moment.

"Mother, how much do you know about this man?" the older daughter asked.

"I know everything I need to know."

"You sure he's not after your money," she pressed.

"Oh no! He's very well off himself."

"I wouldn't jump into anything until I knew where I was going to land," the older daughter cautioned.

"I know what I'm doing," Mrs. McKinney said confidently.

"I hope so," the older daughter added.

By Saturday night of the fifth week, Horace and Gladys had become regulars at Claude's Catfish House. When they entered, the manager's wife recognized them instantly and ushered them to their regular table. Gladys loved the fresh catfish and explained to Mr. Fletcher that it was nice to "have somebody else do the cooking."

After dinner that night, they drove to the public park at the edge of the river. Then, hand-in-hand, they went for a stroll.

"I'm sixty-six years old and I don't want to spend my last years alone," Mr. Fletcher said. "All my kids are grown and have families of their own."

He stopped at a small bridge over the water to look into the water. Then he turned to Gladys. For a moment he looked into her eyes, then he embraced her and kissed her.

"I love you, Gladys," he said. "Will you marry me and be my wife?"

Gladys Georgia McKinney inhaled deeply. Somehow, she had been expecting this.

"I sure do like you, Horace," she said. "I've had so much fun over the past month."

"I've enjoyed it too," he said solemnly.

"It feels so right to have a man in my life," she said. "It's been so long I had forgotten what it was like."

"Then marry me," he said.

With that, he kissed her again.

Gladys was about to swoon. She had never swooned before in her whole life, but now she was on the verge. Again, she took a deep breath and tried to compose herself.

"I can't answer that right now," she said. "It's not that I don't like you. It's just that I'm afraid..."

"What are you afraid of?" he asked. "If two people are in love, they should be married."

He looked curiously at her.

"It's not your children, is it?"

"Oh, no," she said.

"Then what is it?"

"All of this has been so sudden..."

"That's the way love is, Gladys."

"I know. I know," she said, trying to gather her thoughts.

"We could be so happy as man and wife," he said again. "Please say you'll marry me."

She was still trying to compose herself.

"You may be right," she said, "but I can't give you an answer right now."

"You think about what I said," he suggested, taking her hand and starting back toward the parking lot.

"I will," Mrs. McKinney promised. "I will."

At the brunch with her daughters the following Sunday morning, the daughters couldn't wait to hear the latest.

"He wants to marry me," Mrs. McKinney announced. "He wants to take me back to Florida to live with him on his ranch."

The daughters looked at each other.

"Mother," the younger daughter said, "You've only known this man for a month."

"I know," Gladys replied, "But the whole thing feels so right."

She turned to her older daughter for an opinion.

"What do you think, Virginia?"

"I think you're rushing things."

"Maybe you're right," Mrs. McKinney said thoughtfully.

"Okay," the mother said decisively. "I want you two to meet him. Then tell me what you think."

"That's a good idea," Virginia said. "Bring him out to my house so Robert can meet him."

So the following Saturday night, Mr. Fletcher escorted Gladys to dinner at the older daughter's home. Also in attendance were Gail and her son Roy, Virginia's husband Robert and their son, nine-year-old Billy. During the dinner, the participants exchanged polite table talk and enjoyed a meal of roast turkey. Afterward, the group retired to the sitting room where they were entertained with the harmonica playing of Virginia's husband. Finally, Horace and Gladys said goodbye and left.

"Oh, he's gorgeous," Gail gushed during the mother-daughters brunch the following morning. "You're so lucky to have met a man like that," she continued. "He's quite a catch."

Mrs. McKinney looked at her older daughter.

"Oh, he seems very nice," Virginia offered. "He's almost too good to be true."

Gladys looked at her older daughter, but said nothing.

"So…," Gail asked, "Are you going to accept the proposal."

Gladys didn't answer at first.

"If I marry Horace and move to Florida, will you two bring Billy and Roy down to see me?" she asked.

"Of course," the daughters said.

"I want to see them at least two weeks out of the year," the grandmother added.

"That's no problem," the daughters answered.

With that, both daughters waited to hear their mother's response. There was a long pause.

"Then I'm going to marry Horace," Mrs. McKinney said finally. "And we'll have to change the trust."

The two daughters froze at the mention of the word "trust."

"I've already talked to the lawyer," the mother continued. "He said if I get married again, then the money in the trust must be divided three ways among us."

"How much is in there?" Gail asked quickly.

With that, Gladys reached for an envelope on the table and unfolded it.

"According to the latest bank statement, there is $118,432.21," Gladys said.

Gail inhaled deeply as her mother read the figure.

"We've got to go down to the lawyer's office and sign the papers," Mrs. McKinney said calmly.

On the morning of the following day, the mother and two daughters went to the lawyer's office in Hamilton and signed the papers to split up the family trust.

As they were going down the stairs from the lawyer's office, Gail said, "I can really use that money."

"You won't take care of it," Mrs. McKinney said accusingly. "It was because of you your father had it put into a trust."

"What's that supposed to mean?" Gail asked.

"It means you have no respect for money," the mother said coldly. "You'll just blow this money away like you did the money from the divorce settlement."

"If it's mine, I can do what I damn well please," Gail shot back.

"You have no sense of personal responsibility," the mother said, glaring at her daughter. "You have no respect for money, no respect for yourself."

"Let me tell you something," Gail said angrily, raising her voice, "I don't have to answer to you or..."

Suddenly, Virginia screamed in frustration. The mother and younger daughter, startled at the loud scream, forgot their argument and remembered where they were. They had reached the bottom of the stairs and other people leaving the lawyer's office were staring at them.

"Come on!" Virginia ordered angrily. "This is no place for family arguments."

Back at the McKinney home that night, Gladys told Mr. Fletcher that she would be happy to accept his marriage proposal. The man smiled happily and kissed his bride-to-be. For the next hour, they discussed the plans for the wedding and decided to be married the following weekend. With that, Mr. Fletcher suggested they go have some fresh catfish to celebrate.

Gladys Georgia McKinney was delirious with joy when she and Mr. Fletcher left the restaurant that evening. As the Cadillac cruised through the warm Alabama night, she felt she had made one of the most important decisions of her life and she was on the brink of a new and wonderful beginning.

"You make me so happy, Horace," she said.

Horace smiled at her.

"Now that everything is final and we're going to be married," Mr. Fletcher said, "why don't you come spend the night with me down at the Southern Pines."

Gladys wasn't sure she had heard correctly.

"What?!" she asked.

"Why don't you come and spend the night with me tonight?"

"I'm not sure I can do that, Horace," she said.

"We ARE going to be married," he said.

Mrs. McKinney looked at her future husband, trying to get her thoughts together.

"Yes, but we haven't actually said our vows yet."

"Gladys, we need to know some things about each other before we actually tie the knot," he continued. "We need to know how sexually compatible we are."

She looked at him and said nothing.

"I was married to a man for thirty-eight years," she explained. "We never had any problems with those things."

"Suppose you don't like me," he said.

"I'll like you," she said confidently.

"Suppose I don't like you..." he said.

The woman looked at him. There was a long pause. She was still trying to get her thoughts together. The Cadillac pulled into the front yard of her home.

"So?" the man asked, turning to her.

"Maybe you're right, Horace," she said. "Tomorrow night I'll spend the night with you."

"I love you, Gladys," he said.

"I love you too, Horace," she said.

The following afternoon, when the Cadillac pulled up in her front yard, Gladys, carrying a packed bag, got into the car with Mr. Fletcher.

Some twenty minutes later, they arrived at the Southern Pines hotel. Once they were settled in the room, they sat on the bed and began kissing. After several minutes, Gladys stood up and took off her dress. Then, as she started to return to the bed, she glanced into the bathroom mirror and saw herself dressed only in a slip.

"What's wrong?" he asked.

"I don't feel right about this, Horace," she said, turning from the mirror.

"Gladys, we're going to be married."

"I know," she said thoughtfully. "But I just don't feel right about this."

He got up from the bed, took her in his arms and began nuzzling her bosom. She pushed him away.

"Let's get married first," she said. "Then we'll have sex."

"That's not the right way to do it," he protested.

"That's the way I do it," she shot back.

"Gladys, the wedding is a week away. I want you now. I love you."

He started to nuzzle her bosom again. Again, she pushed him away.

"You said you wanted me because I was a virtuous woman. If I have sex with you before we're married, I'm no longer a virtuous woman."

"Gladys, I need to know what you're like in bed," he said.

"Well, you won't be finding out until we're married," she said decisively.

With that, she got up from the bed and started pulling on her dress.

"I want to go home," she said.

He looked at her disbelievingly.

"I SAID I wanted to go home," she said firmly.

In the Cadillac riding back to her house, they rode silently.

"I don't know why we can't agree on this, Gladys," he said. "We seem to agree on everything else."

"You want to destroy the part of me that you said you appreciated the most," she said coldly. "When I first met you, you said my virtuousness was the main reason you wanted me. Remember?"

"Virtuousness is just a word, Gladys."

"No, Horace," she said firmly. "Virtuousness is a principle. The Bible says that a virtuous woman is one who has only been bedded with her husband. You aren't my husband yet."

"All that Bible stuff is fine and dandy," he said, "but principles don't have anything to do with me and you getting into bed and making love with one another."

"It has EVERYTHING to do with it," she said firmly.

The man didn't respond.

As the white Cadillac pulled into the front yard of the McKinney home, Gladys started to get out.

"When can I see you again?" he asked.

For a long moment, she looked coldly at the man, saying nothing.

"Come by tomorrow morning around ten," she said finally.

"Ok. Good night, Gladys," the man said.

The woman didn't look back and continued walking to her front door.

The following morning, Gladys McKinney was waiting on the front porch and saw the Cadillac coming down the road at the appointed time. When the car pulled up in the front yard, she stepped off the front porch.

"Good morning, Gladys," the man said.

"Good morning, Horace," she replied, walking to the car. "There's no need to get out."

"What is it?"

"I want to say goodbye."

"What?"

"I said this is goodbye."

The man couldn't believe what he was hearing.

"Gladys, are you serious?"

"I'm very serious."

"You're making a big mistake."

"This is goodbye, Horace."

"Gladys, we can just forget about spending the night together before we're married," he said. "That's just something I thought we needed to do."

"No," she said crisply. "I don't trust you any more. This is goodbye."

"Gladys, I can't believe you're doing this."

"Well," she said, inhaling deeply, "I am."

"Is there anything I could do to change your mind?"

"No."

For a long moment, she looked at the man.

"Bye, Horace," she said coldly. With those words, she quickly turned and started walking back to the house. The man knew the conversation was at an end. Behind her, Gladys Georgia McKinney heard the Cadillac's engine start, then roar out of her front yard for the last time.

At the brunch the following morning, Mrs. McKinney wasted no time breaking the news to her daughters.

"The wedding is off," she announced as she served coffee.

The two daughters looked at their mother.

"What?!" Gail asked disbelievingly.

"I told Horace goodbye."

"What happened?" Gail asked.

"It's something I had to do," the mother answered. "It's not anything you girls would understand."

The two daughters looked at each other.

"Mother, you've lost your mind," Gail said sharply. "If that man were my age, I would latch on to him myself."

"You'd latch on to anything," the mother said sharply. "You don't have any principles."

"I know how to be a free woman," Gail shot back.

For a moment, the mother and daughter glared at each other.

"Now, don't you two start," Virginia said, raising her voice.

"Mother," Gail said, calmer this time, "We signed the papers."

"Well, we'll just have to UNsign them," Mrs. McKinney said, "I've made my decision."

Gail looked to her sister, who was sitting quietly, for help.

"What really happened?" Virginia asked.

"I'm not sure I can tell you."

"Tell us anyway," the older daughter pressed.

Both daughters looked at their mother.

"Well...," Gladys started.

"Go ahead," the younger daughter goaded.

"He wanted to bed with me before we were married."

"And...?" the younger daughter asked.

"I refused."

With that, the younger daughter burst into spasms of delirious laughter.

"You refused to marry him because he wanted you to crawl in the sack before you were married?" Gail asked, unable to control her laughter.

"What's wrong with that?"

"You're old-fashioned, mother," Gail said, still giddy with laughter. "Kids nowadays crawl into the sack on the first date. This is the fifties."

"I have to have my principles," the mother said.

"Mother," Gail continued, "Willard and I was doing it in the back seat of his Dodge on the third date."

"Well...that's you and Willard," she said. "This is me this time."

"You're way behind the times," the younger daughter said, giggling in girlish delight.

"Maybe so," the mother said firmly, "but I did what I believed in and I'm glad I stood up for my principles. That's more than you can say for yourself!"

The younger daughter, her face red with rage, got up from her chair and glared at her mother. Instantly, the mother, equally angry, arose to confront her daughter.

"That's enough," Virginia shouted quickly, coming between her mother and her sister. "I'm not going to listen to this."

With that, the mother and daughter, still glaring angrily at one another, retreated to their chairs.

Three days later, the mother and two daughters, all three calmer now, went back to the lawyer's office and changed the stipulations of the family trust again, but the issue of "Mr. Fletcher" was not over.

Five months later, Virginia made an unannounced visit to her mother's house late one night.

"I'm surprised to see you here on a weekday," the mother said. "Especially this time of night."

"This is important," the older daughter said, opening her purse. "This can't wait until Sunday."

"What is it?" the mother asked.

With that, Virginia withdrew a folded newspaper clipping from her purse.

"I saw this in the Birmingham News yesterday," she said, handing the clipping to her mother.

"Look at the bottom of the page."

With that, Gladys McKinney's eyes glanced across the bottom of the newspaper page where she saw a photo of a man and a headline which read "Aging Romeo Charged with Murder."

Gladys Georgia McKinney looked closely at the photo.

"Oh, my goodness! That's Horace!" she said, staring at the photo in disbelief.

"Read the article," the daughter instructed.

Mrs. McKinney began reading: "ATLANTA—Atlanta police charged a 67-year-old Florida man with first degree murder today after his wife of only six weeks was found dead in the bathtub of their luxurious suburban home.

"Horace Fancher, a native of Pensacola, Fla., was arrested and charged with the murder of 57-year-old Emma Faye Griffin after Fancher called police and reported that his wife had apparently fallen in the bathtub and drowned while he was away shopping.

"Fancher, who is being held without bail, became a suspect in the woman's death after a coroner's autopsy revealed that the victim had died of strangulation rather than drowning.

"After police investigated Fancher's background, they discovered that, only days after his marriage to the victim, he had taken out a $150,000 insurance policy on her life.

"Investigators also discovered that Fancher had been married to at least seven women in five southern states over the past ten years. Five of those women died mysteriously within a year of their marriage to Fancher.

"'Fancher, a well-dressed, slick-talking Romeo who drove a white Cadillac and posed as a real estate developer, was an expert at seducing older, well-to-do women," according to one homicide detective.

"'Once he had gained a woman's trust and conned her into marriage, he would quickly locate her assets, then devise some means to bring about her death,'" Detective Tom Harley told the News.

"The police investigation also revealed that Fancher had used a string of aliases throughout the southern United States over the past ten years which included the names Horace Fletcher, Herman Fletcher, Herman Fancher, Horace Fisher and Herman Fisher.

"During their investigation, police discovered that Fancher has bank accounts in four Atlanta banks totaling more than $1.4 million."

Mrs. McKinney looked up from the article.

"I suspected something like this," she said. "I KNEW there was something fishy about Horace, but I just couldn't quite put my finger on it."

"I'm glad you made the right decision," Virginia said.

The mother looked at her daughter thoughtfully.

"Has Gail seen this?"

"No."

"Then don't mention it to her."

"What are you going to do?" Virginia asked.

"I'm going to show this to her next Sunday," the mother said. "And I want you to stay out of it. You understand?"

"Mother, there is no need…"

The mother interrupted her.

"Just stay out of it," she said firmly. "This is something I have to do."

Virginia could see that her mother meant business.

"Okay…?" the mother pressed.

The older daughter nodded in agreement.

The following Sunday, the mother and two daughters had their usual Sunday brunch. Near the end, Mrs. McKinney turned to her youngest daughter.

"Gail, I have something to show you," she said.

With that, she produced the newspaper article and handed it to Gail. The mother and older daughter sat silently as Gail read the article.

"So I made a mistake," Gail said, looking at her mother sheepishly. "That's how the cookie crumbles."

"So much for Christian values," the mother commented sarcastically. "So much for standing up for what you believe in. You weren't quite as smart as you thought, were you?"

The youngest daughter, hurt to the quick, stood up and faced her mother.

"I'm not some crazy old woman that's still stuck in the thirties," the daughter shot back angrily. "At least I'm a free woman."

"And look what it's made of you," the mother said, standing up to face her daughter. "A divorced woman with a small child you're having to raise by yourself."

"Fuck you!" Gail said angrily, glaring into her mother's eyes. "Fuck you!"

With a single motion, the older woman brought her right hand around squarely on her daughter's cheek. The sound of the loud slap reverberated throughout the house. Gail's right cheek turned a bright crimson color.

"That hurt!" she shouted, putting her hand to the reddened cheek.

"I meant for it to hurt," the mother shouted back angrily.

"You bitch!" the daughter shouted in fiery rage. "You crazy old bitch! You're not my mother. You're just a crazy old bitch! You hear me! I'll never speak to again."

Tears were streaming down her face.

"Bitch! Bitch! Bitch!" She screamed, glaring at her mother.

Then, still holding the reddened cheek and crying hysterically, Gail grabbed her purse and bolted for the door. The mother and older daughter looked at each other as they heard the door slam.

"I should have done that when she was ten," Mrs. McKinney said calmly. "Maybe she would have turned out differently."

With that, the issue of "Mr. Fletcher" was closed forever. For more than a year, the youngest daughter didn't speak to her mother. Then, some 15 months after the slapping incident, Virginia told her mother that Gail was in dire financial straits and had asked to borrow some money. With that, Mrs. McKinney gave the requested amount to the oldest daughter to give to Gail. A month later, Gail called her mother and said thanks. The mother said she was welcome and said no more. Two weeks later, the older sister told her mother than Gail wanted to make up and start attending the Sunday brunches again. The mother said that would be fine. When Gail arrived at her mother's home the following Sunday morning, the mother and daughter hugged each other and apologized. After that, Gail was gentler and less offensive toward her mother and, two months later, found a successful man and settled down in marriage. Whether Gail had learned that wealthy, fast-moving men were not always honest and aboveboard remained to be seen, but the fact that the episode brought some stability into her life made Mrs. McKinney very, very happy.

During the years that followed, Mrs. McKinney never gave another thought to remarrying. She lived out the last 33 years of her life with her Bible and her radio in the small house where she and her husband had lived. The family trust remained intact until 1984 when she died at the age of 90, never having married again and having had sex with only one man in her life. At her funeral, the minister said that Gladys Georgia McKinney had been a truly virtuous woman and a virtuous woman was a genuine rarity during those times.

ANNIE

"I'm not barren," she said.

Billy and Roy were just two mischievous boys—probably meaner than most 11-year-olds—but still just bored, country kids looking for some adventure and excitement. Having grown up together in the small farming community near Hamilton, the two youngsters were more like brothers than first cousins. Their grandparents, John and Gladys McKinney, had migrated to that part of north Alabama in 1922 and homesteaded two 40-acre plots of land from the U.S. government. Over the years, the McKinneys had built a house and a barn, cleared and farmed the land and raised two daughters. As their offspring grew up and married off, the McKinneys gave their newly wedded offspring plots of land on the homestead to build homes and raise their own families.

So when Billy and Roy's mothers were married, they settled on the McKinney family homestead in houses which were within a stone's throw of one other. As a result, Billy and Roy had been knowing each other and playing together since the day they were born. After their grandfather died in 1949, the boys' grandmother requested that their parents arrange for one or both of the boys to come spend nights with her because she hated being alone at night. The parents approved and the two boys were delighted.

At home, Billy and Roy were well-behaved 11-year-olds because their fathers were strict disciplinarians and expected them to toe the line. But once they were away from their parents at their grandmother's house, they loved to engage in every form of mischief imaginable. They knew their grandmother would let their boyishness run wild and she would engage them in forbidden conversations.

Although the two 11-year-olds found many forms of entertainment during those nights at their grandmother's house, their favorite pastime was "spying" on the residents of their grandmother's rental houses.

Mrs. McKinney had three rental houses on her property. The best one was a two-bedroom, white frame home across the road from the grandmother's house which rented for $35 a month and she called it her "Good House." The boys' grandmother kept the house in good repair and the tenants were mostly factory workers who were reasonably well to do, drove a nice car and had enough personal pride to keep the premises clean and presentable. Billy and Roy seldom "spied" on the residents of the "Good House" because they had to cross the road to get to it and the only place they could "spy" was in a muddy field some 30 yards from the house itself. Also, it was the number one source of rental income for their grandmother and they didn't want to disturb that.

Their grandmother's second rental home was a concrete block house located just down the road from the grandmother's home and she always referred to it as the "Block House." This structure was quite downscale from the "Good House" and, for many years, a family of Shaws, a man, his wife and their three daughters, had occupied that dwelling. The "Block House" was usually rented by tradesmen types—cabinet-builders, plumbers, brick layers and such who worked steadily and could afford to pay the $25 a month rent. Roy especially loved to sneak around and spy on the Shaws at night because he had a crush on Mary Alice, the oldest girl in the Shaw family.

When Billy and Roy spied on the Shaws, which was quite often, they would hide in the tall grass just beyond the wild plum bushes near the Shaw's back porch. In the summertime, the boys knew the Shaws would have visitors and, after dinner, the men and the boys would sit on the front porch and talk and the women and the girls would sit on the back porch and drink ice tea and gossip.

When the women were drinking ice tea, Billy and Roy knew they would come out to the plum bushes to pee every thirty or forty minutes. The two 11-year-olds would duck down low in the high grass and wait. Then, they would watch and listen in the darkness as the women would squat and urinate, still laughing, talking and giggling among themselves.

One night, Billy and Roy were hiding and listening to the women peeing in the plum bushes when Roy, knowing that his beloved Mary Alice was among the group, became overcome with excitement and started giggling. Roy couldn't contain himself and the women, not dreaming there was a soul within ten miles, screamed in fright. Quickly they jumped up, jerked up their panties and scampered out of the grove of wild plum bushes in chaos. Billy and Roy, frightened that the men would come to investigate, raced back across the field to their grandmother's house. Billy, leader of the two, had warned his cousin again and again that he shouldn't become so excited while they were "spying" because, he said, using a term he heard in a radio spy show, it "blows our cover."

Their grandmother's third rental house was a small, ramshackle structure under two big oak trees that stood on the opposite side of a cornfield behind the grandmother's house. That home, which their grandmother called the "Little House," was more of a shack than anything else. There were three rooms, a living room and bedroom in front and a full-length single room in the back which served as a combination kitchen-dining room. The "Little House" was always in very poor repair and the people who rented it were invariably people who lived on the economic edge. If someone came along and offered to pay their grandmother anything at all to rent the "Little House," Mrs. McKinney would strike a deal.

Thus, over the years, there had been a succession of strangely colorful ne'er-do-wells who had rented the "Little House" and Billy and Roy had "spied" on every one of them. There was an older couple, the Turleys, who smelled of axle grease and always had several old, abandoned cars littering the front yard. The husband claimed to be a part-time mechanic, part-time electrician, part-time sawmill worker, part-time this and part-time that, but he never went to a job. His wife, a huge, bespectacled woman with bad breath and a hairy wart on the end of her nose, made tacky plastic roses in the kitchen all day and sold them to churches. Some mornings, when Billy and Roy were at their grandmother's house, they would hear a shotgun blast from across the cornfield at the "Little House" and their grandmother would explain that Mr. Turley was killing wild birds for the couple's breakfast.

At one point, a one-legged traveling salesman, his insane wife and their skinny, undernourished son had lived in the "Little House." Some afternoons, Billy and Roy would hear loud, hysterical screams coming from across the cornfield and they would race through the cornstalks and peek over at the "Little House." In the front yard, they would see a young, very unattractive woman, shouting to the sky and throwing herself on the ground, screaming, "Take me Lord! Oh God, please take me into your loving arms, sweet Jesus!" All the while, her little, undernourished son would stand on the ramshackle porch crying hysterically as he watched his mother scream and plead and flail her body against the ground.

Once, during the Christmas holidays, Billy and Roy gave the undernourished little boy a piece of coconut their grandmother had carved from a freshly broken coconut shell. Billy and Roy wanted to play a trick on the little boy so, before they gave it to him, they both peed on it.

The hungry little boy eagerly took the piece of coconut, inspected it, smelled it, then bit off a piece and began chewing. He chewed for over a minute, saying nothing.

"How does it taste?" Billy asked the child with an air of expectancy.

"Okay," the little boy said seriously, chewing the crunchy, fresh coconut fruit.

"Does it taste good?" Billy asked again.

"It's okay," the hungry child reiterated, taking another bite. "A little salty, but…okay."

With that, Billy and Roy looked at each other, giggled, then darted off into the bushes and laughed themselves silly at their mischievousness.

Over the years, the list of tenants in the "Little House" who had provided entertainment for Billy and Roy during the nights they spent with their grandmother had grown quite large. Although there had been a long list of memorable adventures, far and away the tenant who had provided more entertainment than all the others was Annie Atkinson.

The first time Billy and Roy saw Annie was late one afternoon in January of 1952 when she walked into the yard at their grandmother's home and asked to speak to "the woman of the house." Annie, looking very stern and severe, was wearing a black, high-collar Victorian dress with ankle-high, button-up shoes and carrying a black umbrella with ruffles around the edge. A mass of long, white-gray hair had been swung up majestically on top of her head and she walked with a definitive air of dignity, grace and pride. In many ways, she looked starkly out of place in the little North Alabama farm community.

When the boys' grandmother came to the door, she invited the woman inside. Annie explained that she wanted to rent the "Little House" down under the oak trees. She told the boys' grandmother that she would pay the rent each month as soon as she got a check from her husband. If he didn't mail the check, she said, he would bring the money during one of his periodic visits.

As she negotiated with their grandmother, Annie glanced into the front bedroom and saw Billy and Roy. Although the two boys appeared to be reading Lash LaRue comic books, they were actually eavesdropping on every word of the negotiations. They had seen Annie from the moment she had walked into the yard and, as she talked with their grandmother, they hoped with all their hearts that their grandmother would rent the "Little House" to this strange woman.

"When does your husband send the check?" the grandmother asked.

"Second or third of the month," Annie replied, pushing her wire-rimmed glasses up on her nose proudly.

"Then I'll expect the rent no later than the third day of the month," the grandmother explained.

"Soon as I get the check," the woman said, "I'll bring it to you."

Both women grew quiet and the boys' grandmother studied Annie.

"'Oh, please say 'yes', Grandma,'" the boys begged in their hearts as they listened. "'Please...Please...Please say 'Yes'.'"

"Okay," their grandmother said finally. "I'll let you have it for ten dollars a month, but you'll have to clean the windows and watch for the old black cat."

"Black cat?" Annie asked.

"There's an old black cat with the mange that comes to the Little House from time to time. If you feed it, it'll start coming over to my house."

"I won't feed it," Annie promised.

The grandmother seemed to be satisfied.

"And you have to watch for rats," she added. "I'll give you some strychnine and, if they get real bad, you'll have to put it out."

"I'll take care of that, too," Annie promised.

"Okay," the grandmother said, "I take you at your word."

With that, Mrs. McKinney shook hands with Annie. The deal was done. Then, proud and haughty as ever, Annie pulled a $10 bill out of an aging, frilly black purse and handed it to the boys' grandmother. Annie said that was the first month's rent and announced that she would be moving into the "Little House" the following Saturday. As she got up to leave, she glanced into the front bedroom again and saw Billy and Roy with their heads seemingly buried in two Lash Larue comic books. As the door slammed behind her, Roy and Billy darted to the window and watched as Annie strode back across the yard and out to the dirt road with her severe Victorian look and her ruffly umbrella.

The following Saturday morning, as promised, an old pickup truck loaded with Annie's belongings pulled into the front yard of the "Little House." From the cornfield, Billy and Roy watched as the Negro man driving the truck helped Annie unload five suitcases, an old steamer trunk, a wood table and chairs, a weathered sofa, a cookstove, a single bed and a wind-up Victrola. As they watched, Billy and Roy agreed they should give Annie time to get settled in before they started "spying" on her.

Over the next few weeks, Annie and Mrs. McKinney became quite close friends. Annie would come to visit their grandmother at night and the two women would play a card game called High Low, Jack and Game. During those sessions, Billy and Roy would sit in the corner and watch the games and listen to the women talk.

At first, Billy and Roy kept their distance from Annie. Annie was different from any woman the boys had ever seen. She was dressed in clothes that made her look like something out of the old Liberty magazines they had seen in their grandmother's closet. Annie had a way of tilting her head and peering at the two boys through her thick glasses in a manner that made them shiver. The stare she gave them would bore a hole in stone and when she affected the look through the thick glasses, the lenses would magnify her eyes into huge gleaming lights that made her look like some glassy-eyed demon from hell. When she turned that look on Billy and Roy, they would look away and quickly jump up and run outside to play.

As a result of the visits, the boys' grandmother became something of an expert on Annie. Mrs. McKinney told the boys that Annie had been a stage actress in North Carolina in her younger days and she had appeared in plays all over the South. Annie had grown up in a wealthy family near Atlanta and had had great expectations as a young girl. After her father died, however, the family discovered that her father was deeply in debt and when she left the family in 1931, she was destitute. As a result, she took odd jobs wherever she could. The boys' grandmother warned them that, while Annie appeared innocent enough in her old-fashioned clothes, there was a deadly side to her that would come out if provoked. She told the boys that Annie carried an ice pick in her frilly purse and she would stab them if they bothered her. This was all Billy and Roy needed to delve further into Annie's private life.

That night, the boys went to "spy" on Annie for the first time. After they had crossed the cornfield, they ducked down inside the broom sage patch at the edge of the field, then, staying low, made their way to within 30 feet of Annie's house. Then they raised their heads to peek over the broom sage. The curtains were open and the light was on.

"I can see Annie," Billy said authoritatively, peering at the window.

"What's she doing?" Roy asked.

"She's at the cookstove," Billy said. "Come on."

Billy motioned for Roy to follow him.

In an instant, the two darted out of the high broom sage and dashed across the yard to a huge oak tree less than 15 feet from the house. They waited for a moment.

Billy peered around the side of the oak tree at the house. He motioned to Roy again and, in a flash, the two boys were under the floor. While the corners of the house were built on stone foundations, the rear of the house was much higher off the ground than the front. This meant there was a crawlspace three to four feet high under the floor on the house's back side. Underneath, there was a big crack in the wood flooring under the dining room and a small crack in the floor under the kitchen area. For years, these two vantage points had been Billy and Roy's favorite places for "spying."

In the darkness under the house, Billy peered through the small crack in the kitchen floor. As he peered through the crack into the house, he could see Annie standing naked at the cookstove.

"My God!" Billy whispered.

Minding a pot on the stove, he could see Annie standing naked, her small breasts sagging and deposits of cellulite hanging high on both thighs.

"My God!" Billy whispered excitedly again.

"What is it?!" Roy whispered eagerly.

"She's naked, butt-ass naked..."

"Let me see," Roy said urgently.

"What a minute!" Billy said impatiently.

"No, I want to see," Roy said. "Let me see..."

Billy motioned to his cousin to remain calm. Above him, Annie, stirring the contents of a pan with one hand, was fondling her breasts with the other. She had the look of a woman who was in dire need of a man.

"Jesus!" Billy said, his eyes big as saucers.

"Let me see!" Roy said impatiently. "Let me see!"

Billy moved away and his cousin put his eye up to the crack in the floor. As he watched, Roy started snickering as he stared at the naked woman. Then, unable to control himself, he doubled over with excited laughter.

"Shhhhhh!" Billy said urgently, putting his finger to his lips.

"Ha! Ha! Ha!" Roy giggled. Now he was laughing so hard he couldn't control himself.

Suddenly, the two boys heard a loud thumping on the wooden floor above them. Roy muffled his laughter and both boys grew deathly quiet.

"Billy! Roy!" Annie called from above.

Both boys were deathly quiet.

"Billy! Roy!" she called again. "Are you boys down there?"

From above, Annie stomped the floor again.

"Billy! Roy!" the boys heard Annie demanding loudly, "I know you two are down there."

The boys were quiet.

"You two better get out from here!" she screamed. There was a pause. They could hear Annie, very agitated, trying to catch her breath.

"If you don't get out from here, I'll tell Mrs. McKinney and she'll whip your butts. You hear me!" the woman shouted.

The two 11-year-olds looked at each other. Instantly, Billy motioned to Roy to flee. Stealthily, the two scooted out from under the house, then raced back across the cornfield and were on their grandmother's back porch in minutes.

"Have you boys been sneaking around Annie's house?" the grandmother asked the boys two days later.

"Oh, no!" Billy lied. "We haven't been anywhere near the Little House."

"Roy?...," the grandmother, looking very stern, asked the other grandson.

"Oh, that's right, Grandma," Roy lied. "We haven't been near the Little House."

"Now don't you boys lie to me," the grandmother said sternly. "Annie said she saw you and Billy running through the broom sage patch two nights ago."

"Oh, it wasn't us," the boys said in unison.

"Okay," the grandmother said finally, seemingly satisfied. "Maybe it was a dog or something she saw. Annie's eyes aren't real good."

Several days later, the two boys were fishing in the creek behind their grandmother's house. After they had baited their hooks, they were walking along the edge of the cornfield when they glanced over at the "Little House."

"Look," Billy said, pointing. "There's a man at Annie's house."

The boys could see Annie sitting on the front porch. Across from her sat a small, sallow-faced, bespectacled man wearing brogans, overalls and a blue denim shirt buttoned at the top.

"Who is that?" Billy asked.

"Let's go ask Grandma," Roy said.

Back at the grandmother's house, the two boys found her peeling apples when they burst into the kitchen.

"There's a man over at Annie's house," Billy reported breathlessly.

"That's Journey," the grandmother said calmly, looking up from her apple peeling. "He's her husband."

Billy looked at Roy with a knowing smile.

"Well, he's sort of a husband," she said on second thought, "but not really a husband."

The grandmother explained that Annie and Journey had been married for seven years, but he only came to visit from time to time. Journey was an "okra man," the grandmother said, who provided fresh okra to the local grocery stores over in Calhoun County. Once Journey had rented a plot of land from a farmer, he would pay to have the land plowed, fertilized and planted in okra. After the crop grew to maturity, Journey would hire workers to pick the okra and deliver it to the grocery stores, the grandmother said.

"Annie doesn't see much of Journey between March and October because he's with the okra crop," the grandmother continued. "She hates being alone. That's why she comes over to visit with me."

The grandmother grew quiet as she peeled an apple. The boys were waiting for their grandmother to finish.

"Grandma...," Billy asked curiously, "what did you mean when you said he's not a real husband..."

The grandmother looked up from her apple-peeling.

"Journey's a 'sexual," she said.

"A what?" the two boys asked together.

"A 'sexual. A queer. He likes men."

Billy and Roy looked at each other.

The grandmother stopped her narrative briefly as she cut a core from a large apple. The boys were listening.

The grandmother explained that Annie had told her that, although she and Journey had been married seven years, they had never had male-female sexual relations. She said Journey had never had sex with a woman because he had to have a man's "juices" to stay alive.

The grandmother explained, "When Annie and Journey were living in Calhoun County, Annie said Journey had an okra patch right behind the big army base there. On weekends, the whores would come in from the nearby town and the soldiers would take them out in the pine thickets near the okra patch at night.

"After the soldiers were finished," the grandmother continued, "they would hang the congers on the pine trees. Annie said, on Monday mornings, Journey would slip out of the house early and go over and gather the congers off the pine limbs."

The grandmother stopped again.

"What are congers?" the boys asked.

The grandmother tossed a long apple peel into the pan, then she looked up at the boys, seemingly irritated.

"It's what a man uses when he...," the grandmother suddenly stopped herself. "There are some things you boys don't need to know at your age..."

The grandmother returned to the apples.

"What are congers?" Billy asked again.

"I told you...," the grandmother broke herself off again. "There are some things...now y'all get on out of here and go play."

The two 11-year-olds looked at one another, not understanding the subjects their grandmother was describing.

"Now you boys get on out of here," she ordered again. "I've got to finish these apples."

Later that afternoon, while they were fishing back at the creek, they devised a plan.

"Let's go spy on Annie and her husband tonight," Billy suggested.

"We can't!" Roy said. "We promised Grandma."

Billy looked at his cousin mischievously.

"We might see Annie naked again...," Billy pressed.

Roy chuckled at the thought.

"Yeah," he agreed, giggling gleefully.

"But we've got to be careful," Billy counseled. "Grandma will have a fit if she finds out."

That night, very carefully and very stealthily, the two boys went about their appointed mission at the "Little House." As the sun went down, they were waiting in the cornfield and, by the time deep darkness fell, they had moved into the broom sage patch.

"The coast is clear," Billy said, peering over the broom sage.

With that, the two darted out of the broom sage to the oak tree, then scooted into the crawlspace under the backside of the "Little House." Through the big crack in the dining room floor, Billy could see one leg of Journey's overalls as he sat at the table.

"They're eatin'," Billy whispered in the darkness. "Spaghetti and meatballs. I can smell 'em."

The two boys waited. Some ten minutes later, they heard Annie clearing the table, then washing the dishes. Finally, things were quiet. They listened.

"Now stop that!" Journey said abruptly. "I don't like that..."

"Journey, I need you," Annie said urgently. "I need your seeds."

"You know I don't like to do it with a woman," he said. The boys could hear the irritation in his voice.

"You're my husband," Annie pressed. "Just do it to me until I get a child. I'm forty-four years old and I'm not barren."

"I told you no," the man replied. "We've talked about this a hundred times. When we got married, we had an agreement."

"I know," Annie answered. "But I'm so alone. I'd love to have a child."

"When we got married," the man continued, "you said all you wanted was companionship."

"But I never see you," Annie countered. "You're always gone. If I had a child, I'd have someone to be with me."

The man didn't answer.

"The child could be ours,' Annie started again. "It would belong to just the two of us."

"Now, what would I do with a child?" the man asked defensively. "A child would just be in my way. I don't have time for a child."

"You wouldn't have to do anything," Annie said. "I'd take care of it. I just want someone to love…somebody that I can hold on to…"

There was another long pause.

The man didn't answer.

"Please don't leave me again," Annie pleaded.

"I have to go back and take care of the crop," the man said. "I've got thirty acres of okra. I can't just plant it and leave it."

Another long pause.

"You're going back to Chester, aren't you."

The man didn't answer.

"I knew it," Annie said bitterly. "I hate that man. Oh, I hate him so…"

Above them, the two boys could hear Annie weeping softly. Somehow, the two boys had never even dreamed that such a strange woman could shed tears. They waited, hoping to hear more. Some ten minutes later, they heard Annie's feet moving across the floor.

"She's going to bed," Billy whispered, peeking through the big crack. "And he's still at the table."

Under the floor, the two boys could hear Annie crying softly in the bedroom. Fearful they might be discovered, the boys quickly and quietly scrambled out from under the floor of the "Little House" and raced back across the cornfield.

The following week was the last week in February and the March rent was due. On the third day of March, Mrs. McKinney went to Annie's house to inquire.

"I'm sorry," Annie said, "but Journey hasn't sent me the check yet."

"When do you expect to get it?" the grandmother asked.

"He said if he wasn't back in two weeks, he'd mail it. I'm sure I'll be getting it soon," she said.

The grandmother studied the woman.

"You agreed to pay the rent by the third," the grandmother pressed.

"I know," Annie said apologetically, "but I won't have it until Journey gives it to me."

"Okay," the grandmother said finally. "But once your husband comes back, I'll be expecting my money."

"You'll get it, Mrs. McKinney," Annie promised.

The following week, just before dark, Billy and Roy were back at the

"Little House" to get the latest on Annie. Once they were in the broom sage patch, they peered over at the "Little House."

"Look!" Billy said. "It's the old black cat."

On the front porch, the two boys could see the old black cat their grandmother had warned Annie about. It was licking its paws as if it had finished a meal.

"Grandma's gonna be mad about that," Billy said. "Grandma hates that old black cat."

Then he turned to his cousin.

"Come on!" he said.

Moments later the two boys were in the crawlspace at the small crack under the kitchen floor where they had seen Annie and her nakedness. Billy peered through the small crack into the kitchen area, but could see only the bottom of the cookstove and the kitchen ceiling. The house was quiet. The two boys listened.

"Journey," they heard Annie say, "do you want some more canned ham. It's very tasty."

The two boys bolted upright when they heard Annie call her husband's name.

"Journey?!" Billy whispered, looking at his cousin.

The two boys could hear Annie walking across the floor to the living room.

"Journey, darling," Annie said. "Let's hear some Guy Lombardo."

The two boys could hear the clicking sound of the old Victrola being wound up. There was a moment of silence, then they could hear the scratchy sounds of the song "Canadian Sunset" wafting through the house.

For several minutes, there was only the sound of the Victrola playing. Finally the song stopped.

"I've always loved Guy Lombardo," Annie said. "His music is so calm and soothing."

"Who is she talking to?" Billy whispered.

Roy shook his head and shrugged.

Again, Billy stuck his eye up to the crack in the floor. Still all that he could only see was the bottom of the cookstove and the ceiling. Then he motioned to Roy that he was going to the big crack under the dining room.

Once he was in the new position, he was instantly startled by what he saw. Frantically, he motioned for Roy. With that, Roy scooted to the other end of the house.

"It's Journey," Billy whispered. "He's there."

Roy peered through the crack in the floor. Above him, he could see the leg of a man dressed in overalls and brogans seated at the table.

"It IS Journey," Roy said, turning to Billy.

Billy peered through the crack again.

"Yep, that's him," Billy noted conclusively.

In an instant, the two boys jumped up from their hiding place and started back across the cornfield. Billy stopped.

"Should we tell Grandma about the black cat?" he asked.

"If we do, she'll know we been back at Annie's house for sure," Roy concluded.

"Yeah," Billy said resignedly, "And she'll have a fit…"

Two days later, Mrs. McKinney and her two grandsons made the long walk from her house to the mail box out at the main road. After she has retrieved her mail, she saw Annie at her own mailbox. She waved.

"Annie!" the grandmother called.

"Hello, Mrs. McKinney," Annie answered.

"I'm still waiting on this month's rent."

"I told you," Annie said apologetically. "I'll give it to you as soon as Journey gets back."

"When did you say that will be?"

"About ten days now," Annie said.

There was a pause.

"I believe that's the week of the twenty-third."

"I think that's right," Annie said.

Satisfied, the grandmother, mail in hand and the two grandsons in tow, started walking back to her house.

"Journey's still over there," Billy offered innocently.

"How do you know?" the grandmother asked, turning to her grandson suspiciously.

"Me and Roy saw him going in the house," Billy lied.

"It's not Journey," their grandmother said.

"But it is, Grandma," the boys insisted. "We saw him."

"It can't be!" she said. "He's over in Calhoun County."

"No, it's him," Roy confirmed, "We saw him."

The grandmother stopped. Her frustration showed in her face.

"Will you boys just stop this foolishness," the grandmother said, eyeing them sternly. "Is there no end to your tricks?"

Billy looked at Roy and shrugged, saying nothing. Quietly, the two boys walked with their grandmother back down the dirt road to her house.

The 23rd day of March, 1952, fell on a Sunday. When the boys' grandmother awoke that morning, she checked her calendar and noted that this was the day Annie had promised to have the rent. After Annie hadn't appeared at her house by late afternoon, the boys' grandmother asked them to go over to check on her. She said she would go herself, but she had a terrible case of rheumatism in her left leg and shoulder and could hardly move. She told the boys to tell Annie this was the day she had promised the rent.

With that, the two boys made their regular trek through the cornfield to the broom sage patch and peered over at the "Little House."

"Look!" Billy said pointing.

Roy raised his head.

Annie, who was walking across the front yard to the road, was dressed up in the same severe Victorian outfit she was wearing when she had rented the "Little House." She had her frilly purse and she going somewhere.

"Let's tell her what Grandma said," Roy offered.

"No, wait!" Billy said thoughtfully. "Let's wait until she's gone, then see who that man is."

The two boys waited in the broom sage until Annie was out of sight, then, moments later, they were in the crawlspace under the house.

Breathlessly, the two boys stopped and listened.

"I don't hear anything," Billy said. "Come on!"

Expertly, they moved through the crawlspace to the other end of the house to the big crack. Then Billy peered up into the dining area. As before, all he could see was the leg of a man's overalls at the kitchen table.

"I say it's Journey," Billy said decisively. "And he hasn't moved."

"What are we gonna do?" Roy asked.

"Come on!" Billy said.

With that, the boys scooted out from under the house. Outside, they stopped to listen again. Everything was quiet. Billy tiptoed to the kitchen window, but the curtain was drawn except for a small crack. Through the small crack, Billy could see the back of a man's head seated at the table. He turned to Roy.

"It IS Journey," he said, indicating for his cousin to take a peek.

Roy peered through the crack in the curtain.

"Why's he sitting at the table that way?" Roy asked.

"Let's find out," Billy said.

With that, the two boys bounded around the side of the "Little House" to the front porch. For a moment, before stepping on the front porch, they stopped and listened. There were no sounds. Then, very quietly and cautiously, the two boys tiptoed across the porch to the front door. Billy stopped and listened. Hearing nothing, he gently nudged the door. It swung open.

"Yikes!" Billy said suddenly, responding to a powerful stench that emanated from inside the house.

Through the open door, the two boys could see all the furniture—the old sofa, the Victrola, a stack of old 78 rpm records as well as the weathered steamer trunk—they had seen Annie and the black man unloading some two months earlier. Then, like expert cat-burglars, the two boys tiptoed into the living room. Everything was quiet. The stench their noses had sensed on the front porch was almost unbearable now. Instinctively, they stopped to gather themselves before looking in the dining room. Both boys knew that something horrendous was awaiting them. But, they also knew that nothing could stop them.

Billy, the leader of the two, looked in first. For a moment, he stood transfixed, frozen stiff by what he was seeing. Then Roy, standing at his cousin's side, peered wide-eyed and he likewise was transfixed by the sight. Suddenly, the two 11-year-olds—unable to contain themselves any longer—screamed in uncontrollable fright and ran out of the house.

"Grandma! Grandma! Grandma!" they screamed at the top of their lungs as they raced through the broom sage patch and across the cornfield. "Grandma! Grandma! Grandma!"

The grandmother, who was still nursing her rheumatoid leg and shoulder, had heard the boys' screams long before they reached the cornfield. In fact, she was standing on the back porch waiting when they bounded into the back yard.

"Great God!" she shouted, holding her rheumatoid shoulder. "What's wrong with you kids?"

The two 11-year-olds, their faces lily-white with fear, were gasping for breath.

"What's wrong?! Tell me what's wrong!" the grandmother demanded again.

"Journey's there!" Billy said, panting for dear life and pointing toward the "Little House." "Journey's there!"

"Now just calm down and talk to me," she said, somewhat calmer herself.

"Journey's at Annie's house," Billy said breathlessly, "and the black cat's eating him!"

"What?! The black cat's eating him?!" the grandmother blurted out disbelievingly. "Is this another one of you boys' tricks?"

"No grandma...It's true," Roy said, still trying to catch his breath. "I mean the truth. I swear...Journey's been there all the time..."

Now thoroughly agitated, the grandmother—who had forgotten her rheumatoid shoulder and leg—demanded that they calm down and talk sense to her. The boys, who had never been so frightened or breathed so hard in their whole lives, told their grandmother what they had seen. The grandmother listened patiently and waited until the boys had finished.

"This better not be one of your tricks," she warned Billy, still not believing the story.

"It's not," Billy said urgently. "I swear it's not."

With that, the grandmother ordered the two to follow her to the "Little House."

When she opened the door, the same powerful stench swept over her and she took off her apron and put it to her nose. Then, showing no sign of fear, she walked straight into the dining room.

For a moment, she gasped at the scene before her. The old black cat, with its back legs on the table and front paws resting on Journey's chest, was nibbling at his lower lip. The grandmother wasted no time taking charge.

"Shoo! Shoo! Get out of here!" she ordered, swinging her hand angrily at the cat.

The hungry animal, seeing the threatening woman, turned from its meal, jumped off the table and darted out the door.

"My Lord!" she gasped in disgust, now seeing the full scene.

Putting the apron closer to her mouth and nose, she moved closer.

The boys, white with fear, their eyes big as saucers and holding their noses against the stench, watched as their grandmother inspected the corpse.

Journey's face was bloated and red and the skin around his throat had a stretched, shiny look like the skin of a dog that had been killed on the highway and had been rotting for several days. The black cat had eaten most of the soft tissue around the man's nose and his lips and the grandmother and her two grandsons could see little nibbles the cat had taken out of his cheeks and eyelids. Dressed in Liberty blue overalls and a blue denim shirt buttoned at the top, Journey was sitting perfectly upright in the dining chair. Although his glasses were slightly askew, he was seated as if he were ready to eat. On closer inspection, the grandmother and the two boys could see that Journey had been tied into that exact seated position with several pair of women's long, wool stockings.

The grandmother, still holding the apron to her nose, examined Journey's eyes and shook her head sadly.

"Looks like Journey got more of that strychnine than the rats did," the grandmother said. "I guess Annie just didn't want to be left alone any more."

For another long moment she examined the scene then suddenly turned to her grandsons.

"You boys come on!" she ordered. "This smell is gonna kill me dead."

The grandmother, still holding her nose, turned and strode out of the "Little House" with Billy and Roy, still frightened out of their wits, right on her heels.

When they returned home, the grandmother told the boys to go across the road and tell Mr. Shaw to come bring his car because she had to go to town. By the time Billy and Roy returned with Mr. Shaw, their grandmother was ready. She had washed up, put on her best black dress and was wearing her light-blue, pillbox hat. She got into Mr. Shaw's car and ordered the two boys to stay put until she got back.

An hour later, the grandmother returned, except this time she was riding in a sheriff's car and they drove straight to the "Little House." The grandmother, holding a knit handkerchief to her nose, escorted the three deputies inside the house and showed them Journey's rotting carcass. Thirty minutes later, a red ambulance arrived and they carried Journey out of the "Little House" in a clear plastic bag.

When Annie came home later that afternoon, the sheriff's car was there waiting for her. Annie went right up to the house as if she had somehow been expecting it. As she walked across the yard, the deputies got out of the car and approached her. She seemed a little surprised, but she didn't put up any fight when the deputies told her she was under arrest for murder.

Naturally, Billy and Roy were there to witness the proceedings. They watched from the edge of the broom sage patch as the deputies put chrome-plated handcuffs on Annie's wrists. As the deputies led Annie around the side of the sheriff's car, she looked up and saw Billy and Roy watching. Instinctively, she somehow knew the two boys were the forces behind her downfall.

Annie snarled at them.

"Vermin, you are!" she shouted at them angrily. "Do you hear me?! Vermin! Pestilence...!"

She shook her handcuffed wrists at the two boys in livid anger.

Then one of the deputies pushed Annie's head down and she got into the back seat of the sheriff's car. The deputy slammed the door. As the sheriff's car pulled away from the "Little House" and out on the highway, Billy and Roy watched sadly.

As with "sexual" and "congers," the two boys didn't know what the words "vermin" and "pestilence" meant. So, as the sheriff's car faded into the distance, Billy and Roy stood at the edge of the broom sage patch and sadly waved goodbye to Annie for the last time. Of all the renters in their grandmother's "Little House," Annie had provided more fun and entertainment than all the others. Billy and Roy would miss her terribly. They were just two 11-year-old boys—meaner than most probably—but still just two bored, country kids looking for some adventure and excitement.

A GIL MCDOUGALD

Memory for a Lifetime

The greatest thrill of William Vernon Johnson's lifetime took place on the morning of December 5, 1953. It was on that morning, much to his surprise, that God surveyed planet earth, reached down from heaven and tapped him on the shoulder. At least that's the way Billy felt on the day it happened.

One afternoon in late April of 1953, when Billy was 12 years old, he and his cousin Roy had been with his father at a local grocery store buying candy and bubble gum. Once they were back in the pickup truck, Billy watched as Roy opened his package of bubble gum and pulled out several cards which featured full-color photos of major league baseball players.

"Let me see those," Billy said curiously.

"Now you have to give them back," Roy said.

"Oh, I will," Billy replied.

As he flipped through the cards and the heroic faces of baseball's best-known players flashed before him, Billy Johnson felt a magical excitement like he had never known before. Upon examining the backs of the cards, he found a detailed history of each player's achievements in baseball. Billy was already a big fan of Mutual's Game of the Day, the radio program that featured a major league baseball game each and every day of the week. Now, as he gazed at the cards, he knew they would add a new dimension to the live radio broadcasts, making them more realistic than ever. Billy was hooked.

From that moment on, every time Billy was near a candy counter, he would look for the bubble gum section and then for baseball cards. Once he found them, he would buy up to ten packages at a time just to see which new players he would receive. In the packages, which cost a nickel, he would get six random baseball cards and two flat, pink slabs of bubble gum. The enclosed bubble gum was usually so old that it had become a hardened slab of petrified goo and was, for all practical purposes, unchewable. But the bubble gum was not important; the real prize was the baseball cards.

After only a month, Billy had two old shoe boxes crammed full of baseball cards. For endless hours, he would sit on the floor and sort through the stacks of cardboard, keeping exact tabs on the status of the collection. At any given time, he knew exactly how many Mickey Mantles, Duke Sniders, Minnie Minosos, Warren Spahns, Ted Kluszewskis, Sal Maglies, Monte Irvins and Red Schoendiensts he had on hand. Also, he kept running tabs on which players he had on each and every team and, if he needed certain players to complete a team, he knew exactly who they were.

Very quickly, Billy decided that his favorite team was the New York Yankees. In the past four seasons, with Casey Stengel as manager, the Yankees had won the American League pennant and the World Series and, once the 1953 season opened, the Yankees appeared to be headed for another pennant and an almost certain world championship. With that, Billy Johnson decided that his primary goal in life was to collect all the players in the Yankees' starting lineup.

When he made the decision, Billy already had several of the Yankees' most popular players. After some trading with cousin Roy and his school friends, the list began to grow and, by late May, he had collected most of the players in the Yankees' starting lineup. These included Yogi Berra behind the plate, Billy Martin at second, Phil Rizzuto at short, Hank Bauer in right, Mickey Mantle in center and Gene Woodling in left. Also, he had collected the top four Yankee pitchers: Ed Lopat, Allie Reynolds, Whitey Ford and Vic Raschi. Now all he needed was first baseman Joe Collins and third baseman Gil McDougald.

First, Billy set about the task of finding a Joe Collins. Cousin Roy didn't have one. His school friend David Faucett had a Joe Collins, but he was also a Yankee fan and refused to give it up. Even after Billy had offered him $10 and a slightly used catcher's mitt, David still refused. Another school friend Tim Barker, who had over 2,000 cards, said he had had a Joe Collins, but he had swapped it for pitcher Mike Garcia because he didn't like the Yankees. Tim was a Cleveland Indians fan.

Then one day, Billy was over at his friend Jimmy Hodges's house and noticed he had a small stack of baseball cards. With his friend's permission, Billy flipped through the cards and, lo and behold, there was a Joe Collins. Billy asked his friend what he wanted for it.

"Nothing," Jimmy said.

"You mean I can have it?" Billy asked nervously.

"Sure," Jimmy shrugged. "I don't care about baseball cards."

"Thank you! Thank you! Thank you!" Billy said gratefully.

Back at home that night, Billy added the newest treasure to his collection. Now, all he needed was third baseman Gil McDougald—a single card—and his collection would be complete. It would be the most memorable quest of his life.

Since he had started his collection, Billy had never seen a Gil McDougald. His friend David Faucett, who was also looking for a Gil McDougald, said he had never seen one either and didn't know of anybody who had. David said he wasn't sure that one even existed.

"You might be wasting your time," Tim Barker said. "I've never seen one mentioned in baseball magazines. On some players, no cards were ever printed."

Billy absolutely refused to believe that. There had to be a Gil McDougald somewhere in the world and he was going to get it to make his collection complete.

Three weeks later, school was out for the summer and Billy was relentless in his pursuit. With money he had made cutting grass, he made a point to buy at least five packages of bubble gum every week in hopes of getting a Gil McDougald. Sooner or later the odds would have to catch up with him, he thought. Also, he checked constantly with his collector friends asking if they had a Gil McDougald or had ever seen one.

By mid-July, Billy had enough cards to fill up five shoe boxes. Late into the night, he would browse through the cards, memorizing the players' faces, details of their personal lives and their baseball statistics. During the hot summer afternoons while he listened to Mutual's Game of the Day, he kept his cards close at hand and, as each player performed on the field, he would pick up the corresponding card and gaze at it. The cards were a perfect visual aid to the radio broadcasts.

On August 3, Billy tallied his collection. He had 822 baseball cards, including the full starting lineup of the Boston Braves and the Chicago White Sox. Meanwhile, he had an overabundance of certain individual players. When Billy calculated the totals that day, he had 28 Mickey Mantles, 31 Duke Sniders, 21 Al Kalines, 12 Warren Spahns, 16 Lew Burdettes, 23 Ted Kluszewskis, 27 Wayne Terwilligers, 19 Clem Labines and 41 Marv Thornberrys.

In late August, a week before school was due to start, he sold his catcher's mitt and on old bicycle and netted $18.50. With his father, he went from one grocery store, service station and drug store to the next buying all the packages of baseball bubble gum they had in stock. In one store, Billy bought a full, unopened box of baseball bubble gum—a total of 50 packages—for $2.50 plus tax.

When Billy returned to the pickup truck with the unopened box of bubble gum, his father looked at him.

"Are you sure you know what you're doing?"

Billy looked at his father.

"I'd give anything in this world to have a Gil McDougald," he said.

His father looked at him for a moment, then said nothing.

Back at home, it took Billy almost three hours to go through the full box as well as 32 other packages he had purchased. Once he had all the new packages opened and organized, he had an incredible willy-nilly array of baseball talent, but still no Gil McDougald. Almost all of the new cards were duplicates of those he already had.

On September 29, the day before the 1953 World Series opened, Billy had a total of 1,312 baseball cards. He now had the full starting lineup of four major league teams, the Boston Braves, the Chicago White Sox, the Pittsburgh Pirates and the Washington Senators. On three other teams, the Boston Red Sox, the Philadelphia Phillies and the Brooklyn Dodgers, Billy needed only one or two players to have the complete starting lineups. Meanwhile, as before, he had stacks upon stacks of various individual players. These included 36 Mickey Mantles, 39 Duke Sniders, 19 Willie Mays, 22 Jackie Robinsons, 17 Junior Gilliams, 15 Don Newcombes, 12 Sal Maglies, 17 Ralph Kiners, 24 Ted Williams, 28 Ted Kluszewskis, 31 Wayne Terwilligers, and an amazing 59 Marv Thornberrys.

On the following day, September 30, the 1953 World Series between the Yankees and the Dodgers opened in Yankee Stadium. In the first game, Billy Martin hit a bases-loaded triple in the first inning that gave the Yanks the lead. After the Dodgers tied the score in the sixth, Joe Collins homered in the seventh and gave the Yankees the go-ahead run and the 9-5 win. In game 2, Mantle homered in the eighth inning and the Yankees won 4-2. In the third game, Carl Erskine struck out 14, including Mantle four times and the Dodgers won 3-2.

Brooklyn won the fourth game 7-3 after Duke Snider drove in four runs with two doubles and a homer. The fifth game was an 11-7 slugfest in which Mantle hit a bases-loaded homer in the third and both teams set a series record of 47 total bases. In the sixth game, Martin, the series hero, got his twelfth hit in the bottom of the ninth and scored Bauer for a 4-3 Yankee win. The win gave the Yankees their fifth consecutive World Series crown, an all-time record. Now, more than ever before, Billy wanted to complete his collection of the Yankees' starting lineup. All he needed was a Gil McDougald.

The following afternoon, Billy asked his father to take him around to the stores again to buy more bubble gum packages. With $3.40 he had saved, Billy bought 52 new packages, but, once they were opened, it was the same story. He was duplicating again. This time, when he figured the totals, he had an amazing 43 Mantles, 41 Duke Sniders, 38 Ted Williams, 26 Junior Gilliams, 31 Ted Kluszewskis, 37 Wayne Terwilligers and 64 Marv Thornberrys. Not a single Gil McDougald in the lot. He was heartbroken. Of the $18.50 he had reaped from the sale of the catcher's mitt and the old bicycle, more than $15 had been spent in pursuit of a Gil McDougald. And for what?, he asked himself.

By early November, Billy had a total of 1,634 baseball cards. Long before that, he had moved the collection to the family trunk so he would have room for storage and organization. At that point, he had the complete starting lineups of three more major league teams, the Boston Red Sox, the St. Louis Cardinals and the Chicago Cubs. As for individual players, the list had continued to grow. At that point, he had 48 Mickey Mantles, 47 Duke Sniders, 44 Ted Williams, 37 Junior Gilliams, 34 Ted Kluszewskis, 41 Wayne Terwilligers and an incredible 71 Marv Thornberrys. How in the world could he have 71 Marv Thornberrys, he wondered, and not a single Gil McDougald?

On the second weekend in November, his father had taken him into town to see a horror movie. While he waited for his father to come pick him up, he bought a package of baseball bubble gum at the corner drug store. He really didn't expect to get anything worthwhile. There was an Earl (Matt) Batts, a Wayne Terwilliger, an Eddie Matthews, a Bobby Avila and two Marv Thornberrys.

Four days later, he was with his father at the supermarket at the crossroads. While his father went inside to buy groceries, he went next door to the drug store and bought two packages of baseball cards. There was a Bobo Newsome, a Stan Musial, an Enos Slaughter, two Jackie Robinsons, a Robin Roberts, an Eddie Matthews, a Ted Williams, a Lew Burdette and three Marv Thornberrys. As he started back to the pickup to meet his father, he threw the three Marv Thornberrys into a trash can. His father saw him.

"Those weren't important?" his father asked, as Billy got into the pickup.

"I've got 85 Marv Thornberrys," Billy said.

His father chuckled.

"How long is this going to take?" he asked.

"Until I find one," Billy said.

That night, William Vernon Johnson reassessed the task he had set for himself. Maybe he should give up, he thought. Maybe Tim was right; no Gil McDougalds were ever printed. Again he thought about giving up, but, in his heart, he knew he couldn't.

A week later, back at school, he asked his friend Tim Barker again if he had seen or heard of a Gil McDougald.

"There a kid I know in Greenville that has over seven thousand cards," Tim said. "He's in a wheelchair and he spends all his time collecting baseball cards. If anybody has got one or knows of one, it's Morris Thompson," Tim said. With that, he gave Billy the kid's address in Greenville.

The following Saturday, Billy and his father drove the 26 miles from Hamilton to Greenville, Alabama, and met Morris Thompson. Billy got his hopes up when the kid said he thought he had a Gil McDougald, but they would have to go through his collection to find it. Morris said he didn't pay much attention to the Yankees because he was a Philadelphia Athletics fan. With that, Billy and the other boy spent three hours going through almost 8,000 baseball cards, but there was not a Gil McDougald.

"Sorry," the kid said finally, looking up from his wheelchair. "I thought I had one, but I don't know what happened to it."

"But you have seen one?" Billy asked for reassurance. "You have actually held on in your hand?"

"Oh, yeah!" the other kid answered.

Billy wanted to be sure they were talking about the same thing. "Now you're sure you had a Gil McDougald," Billy asked.

"I think it was a Gil McDougald," the other youngster said. "It sure did look like him."

"What color was his hair?," Billy asked.

"Blonde, I believe," the kid said.

"McDougald has blonde hair," Billy said, recalling photos he had seen in baseball magazines.

Afterward, as he and his father drove back to Hamilton in the pickup, his father, weary from waiting three hours, turned to him.

"Still not ready to give up?" he asked.

"I can't give up now," Billy said. "At least I know now there is one out there somewhere."

"You 'think' there is one out there," the father said, "Morris said he wasn't sure."

"Yeah, I know," Billy said, "But I have to believe there is one out there somewhere."

His father chuckled at his son's resolve.

On the following Saturday, a cold, rainy day in early December, Billy's father announced he was going into Hamilton to the feed and seed store. Billy, who had just gotten out of bed, said he wanted to go. Hurriedly, he pulled on his clothes and jumped into the pickup truck with his father.

Once they arrived at the feed and seed store, Billy announced he wanted to go down to the corner to buy some baseball cards. Also, since he hadn't had time to eat breakfast, he wanted to get a hamburger. His father said he would have to hurry because he wanted to get back to turn the cattle out to pasture. With that, Billy raced down to the corner drug store, put a nickel on the counter and grabbed a package of baseball bubble gum. Then he went next door, ordered a hamburger and fries and headed back to meet his father.

As he plopped down breathlessly in the truck seat, he was ravenously hungry, but he thought he should go ahead and open the baseball cards. With that, he opened the package and started rapidly flipping through the pieces of cardboard. There was an Enos Slaughter, a Del Crandall, a Ted Williams, a Preacher Roe and a Clem Labine. The last card in the package was one he had never seen before, so, figuring it was a nobody, he glanced at it without looking at the name, then tossed the cards aside on the truck seat. With that, he wasted no time unwrapping the hamburger. Then, as he took the first bite of the hamburger, he suddenly stopped, remembering the last card.

"Oh, my God!" he said. Suddenly, in his mind's eye, he recalled the face on the last card and it had a strong resemblance to the pictures of Gil McDougald he had seen in baseball magazines. Quickly, he laid the hamburger on the seat and picked up the cards again. As he flipped through the cards a second time, he could hear his heart pounding in his ears. Then, as he turned up the last card, he stared at the most beautiful thing he had even seen. The last card—which he had thought was a nobody—featured the smiling face of a blonde, baby-faced Gil McDougald. Even at that point, Billy still couldn't believe it. As he stared at the card, he thought perhaps his eyes were playing tricks on him. So he looked away, then back at the card. Still disbelieving, he looked away a second time, then back at the card. Lo and behold, it WAS a Gil McDougald!

"Yippeeeeeee!!" he yelled at the top of his lungs. It was a cry of pure, unadulterated joy.

His father, startled at the outcry, turned to him.

"What is it?" he asked.

"I did it!" Billy said. "I got a Gil McDougald."

His father smiled.

"It's about time," the father replied.

As he sat in the front seat of the pickup truck and read about McDougald's personal life and his accomplishments in baseball, Billy was living the greatest thrill of his life. Inside, he felt as if God had looked down from heaven and said, "I have one and only one Gil McDougald to give to someone on this earth and you, William Vernon Johnson, have been chosen to receive it. Take it and use it well."

It was an absolute miracle. Billy had dreamed the impossible and it had come true.

✳✳✳

Over the years, William Vernon Johnson used that moment as a benchmark for other experiences in his life. Once when he was 42 years old, several years after his second divorce, he had met a beautiful Jewish woman in Atlanta, Ga. She was a tall, shapely brunette with long legs, high, firm breasts and a master's degree in anthropology. From the very first moment Billy set eyes on her, what he wanted more than anything else on this earth was to take her to bed and bathe in that brunette loveliness. The night before he took the Jewish woman he wondered how the experience would compare to that cold, wintry day in early December of 1953. The morning after, however, he knew that nothing—absolutely nothing—could ever compare to the sheer joy and sense of fulfillment he felt when he opened the package of bubblegum-smelling baseball cards and saw a smiling, baby-faced Gil McDougald smiling back at him.

FRANKLIN'S

Country-Style Drug Dealer

For as long as I could remember, all the "good people" in our little community said that the Tallapoosa County sheriff's office was going to shut down Franklin's. It was a shame and a disgrace—an absolute abomination of God—to have a place like that in their midst, they said. In fact, the last thing they needed in their community, and they always whispered the word when they said it, was a "bootlegger."

Along Highway 31 outside of our little town, a mere stone's throw from the St. Clair County line, there was an innocent-looking roadside service station called Franklin's. From all indications, the small weather-beaten wooden building and accompanying gas pumps appeared to be just one more of the tens of thousands of little service stations along Alabama highways which sold gas, cigarettes, candy, soft drinks and snacks to passing motorists. The difference was that Mr. Tom Franklin, a tall, stone-faced man who operated the business, sold beer out of a refrigerator.

In Tallapoosa County, the legal sale of alcohol had been banned since 1930. Shortly after prohibition ended, the Baptists in the county rose up as the dominant political force and vowed that alcohol would never destroy their community and their families. Although the county's pro-alcohol forces claimed that the legal sale of alcohol would provide tax money for schools and roads, the Baptists always managed to muster more votes in each and every election. As a result, by 1953, they had kept the county legally dry for more than 23 years.

Then in 1954, the people of adjoining St. Clair County voted to bring in legal alcohol. So, six months after the new St. Clair County law went into effect, Mr. Franklin opened his business just across the river in Paloosa County.

Once word got out about Franklin's, the "good people" raised the alarum about the dangers and the evils the little service station represented for their county.

At my school, the teachers said alcohol was the major cause of all of the various forms of human suffering which included insanity, divorce, automobile accidents, murders, rape, mayhem, robbery and the list went on and on and on. They added, again in whispered tones, that Franklin's, the major "purveyor" of alcohol in the county, represented the potential for all these iniquities, and he and his business were due to be shut down at any time.

One of my best friends at school was Gerald Franklin, a nephew of Mr. Franklin's. Although I never mentioned it, I always felt sorry for Gerald because I believed that some day the sheriff was going to arrest his uncle and throw him in jail for selling beer.

In the little church where my mother took me on Sundays, the preacher, Rev. Cecil Mize, always referred to the little service station as "the house of the devil."

"That little service station may look innocent enough from the outside," Rev. Mize would say, his voice reaching a fever pitch, "but inside it's a den of iniquity where devil drink and all the other abominations of God are festering.

"The day will come when God, great God almighty, will smite Franklin's and all other houses of sins into eternal damnation," he would say, his fist crashing down on the pulpit in front of him.

At the sound of Rev. Mize's fist slamming against the pulpit, I would always tremble at the thought of God, a stern-faced, bald-headed man with a long beard, striking the little service station with a deadly bolt of lightning and causing the small wooden building, all the metal signs and the gas pumps to go crashing to the ground.

Despite all the talk about the evils that Franklin's represented, many of the men in the community kept their mouths shut about the illegality of the place and would quietly venture over several times a week to do business with Mr. Franklin.

On Saturdays, which was my Uncle Fred's day off from the local steel plant, he would slyly announce that he was going down to Franklin's, buy a six pack of Falstaff and relax for the weekend.

"Uncle Fred," I would say, "I'd be careful. The sheriff is going to raid Franklin's."

"Naw," my uncle would say. "The Baptists can vote it out, but they can't keep it away from the people that want it."

Even my father would go down to Franklin's from time to time. I knew my father liked to drink a beer every now and then. Especially in the summertime. In late August, when it got hot and there was little work to do on the crops except watch them grow, my father and I would venture over to Franklin's so he could buy a few beers.

At first, my father hid it from me. When I was eight or nine, we would go into Franklin's and, while I was at the candy rack, my father would order some "oil" from Mr. Franklin. Once my father had paid, we would return to the pickup truck and my father would place the brown paper bag with the "oil" in the back of the truck. For several years, I never knew the difference.

Then, one day when I had just turned 11, my father and I stopped at Franklin's. As usual, we went inside, did our shopping and returned to the pickup.

As we started out, I absently looked inside the bag my father was holding. I froze when I saw what was inside. There were six brown bottles inside that said "Budweiser." Instantly, I looked up at my father.

"It's beer," he said sheepishly. "It's okay."

With that, he tucked the brown paper bag under his arm and we walked out. This time, he put the "oil" in the truck seat right between us. I guess he was sick and tired of lying to me.

Both of us remained silent as the pickup pulled out on the highway. Finally, my father looked at me.

"Don't say anything to your mother. Okay?"

I knew my mother would have a hissy fit if she knew my father was drinking beer. But I trusted my father.

"Okay," I promised.

After we rode for a while, I looked over at my father.

"Daddy, everybody says that the sheriff is going to close up Franklin's."

"No," my father said. "That's just something the Baptists like to say. They'll never close it."

"But isn't beer against the law?" I asked.

"Yeah," my father said, "But that doesn't mean Franklin's will be closed."

I thought about what my father had said and, from that moment on, every time we stopped at Franklin's, each stop was a man-to-man secret exclusively between my father and me.

One Saturday morning in August of 1953, when I was 12 years old, my father and I had stopped at Franklin's. As we started back to the pickup, I glanced outside the window and saw two Tallapoosa County sheriff's cars pull up in front. Getting out of the cars was Sheriff Collier, three deputies and the Rev. Cecil Mize.

Oh, God! This is it! I thought frantically. They're going to arrest Mr. Franklin and my daddy and throw them in jail for having beer! Everybody has been saying it and now it's going to come true and my daddy is going to be right in the middle of it.

I froze as Sheriff Collier, the three deputies and Rev. Mize entered the little store.

"Stay where you are, Johnson," Sheriff Collier said to my father, who was still holding his brown paper bag of beer.

All-business, the sheriff, with Rev. Mize in tow, brushed past my father and confronted Mr. Franklin, who was standing at the counter.

"Mr. Franklin," the sheriff began, "You know that I am the sheriff of Tallapoosa County."

"Yes, sir," the storekeeper answered calmly.

"And you know that I am sworn to enforce all the laws of this county."

"Yes, sir."

"This citizen here," the sheriff continued, pointing to the reverend, "claims that you're selling alcoholic beverages out of that refrigerator."

Everybody in the room looked quickly toward the white, innocent-looking appliance in the corner.

"It's not true," Mr. Franklin said. "All that's in that refrigerator is soft drinks."

"I'll have to look," the sheriff said.

I held my breath as Sheriff Collier walked behind the counter and opened the refrigerator door. For a moment he stood and gazed inside. Nobody could see inside the refrigerator except the sheriff.

"I don't see anything in here but soft drinks," the sheriff said, peering inside the refrigerator.

"There's beer in there," the preacher said confidently and started behind the counter to see for himself.

"Wait! Hold it!" the sheriff said, holding up his open palm to the churchman. "You can't come back here. You're not a member of law enforcement."

"But…," the reverend protested.

The sheriff turned to one of his deputies.

"Deputy Clark," he said, "Come back here."

The deputy walked behind the counter.

"Deputy Clark, do you see any alcoholic beverages in there?" the sheriff asked, holding the refrigerator door open.

The deputy looked inside the refrigerator.

"No, sir," he shrugged. "Nothing but Coca-Cola and Royal Crown."

With that, the Sheriff closed the refrigerator door.

"We're sorry to bother you, Mr. Franklin," the sheriff said authoritatively

"Come on, preacher," the sheriff said. "You are wasting my time."

"But I KNOW there's beer in there," the preacher protested.

"You know no such thing!" the sheriff countered. "I've seen for myself. So has the deputy here. Now come on!"

"But, but…," the preacher protested.

"I said to 'Come on!'" the sheriff said again, raising his voice more aggressively. Rev. Mize, seeing that the sheriff's mind was made up, knew it was futile to protest further.

With that, the sheriff, the deputies and the preacher walked out the front door and left the premises. I breathed a huge sigh of relief.

Back in the family pickup, I tried to make sense out of what I had witnessed. I had seen it, but I didn't understand.

"Daddy, what happened?" I asked. "Why couldn't he see the beer?"

"He didn't want to see it," my father said, with a sly smile.

"Why wouldn't he want to see it?" I asked.

"If he had admitted it was there, he would have to close the place down."

"So why would he not want to close the place down?" I asked.

"Because he wouldn't get his cut every month."

"What do you mean he 'wouldn't get his cut'."

"The sheriff gets money from Mr. Franklin every month to let him stay open."

I looked at my father disbelievingly.

"Mr. Franklin gives the sheriff money every month to not arrest him and close his business?" I asked.

"That's right," my father said. "Otherwise, why didn't he see the beer?"

I looked at my father, not believing what I was hearing. I knew there was something terribly wrong here, but I couldn't fathom exactly what it was. I knew that it certainly did not fit in with all the things I had been taught in school, in church and in social studies class. I had been told that I should look up to and respect men of the law. I was also told that Sheriff Collier was an honest, upright man and I had always believed that to be the case. If the sheriff was taking money from Mr. Franklin, then he had to be taking money from other people that weren't being arrested. If he was that kind of person, then why was he ever elected? And how could so many "good people" in the county be fooled? There was something terribly wrong here, I thought.

"I told you they'd never close it," my father reminded me.

And he was right. The "good people" of Tallapoosa County never did close Franklin's. At least not legally, that is. Franklin's continued to do business in the county until 1969, when the pro-alcohol forces in Tallapoosa County finally won an election. With that, Franklin's was no longer needed in Tallapoosa County because the drinkers there could now buy beer at their local supermarket.

But as luck would have it, in the same election, the Baptists in neighboring St. Clair County led a mighty charge against alcohol which resulted in that county being voted dry. The political situation was now reversed. With that, Mr. Franklin moved his business just across the river to the St. Clair County side and started all over again.

JOHNNY DAYTONA

Childhood Heroes Die Hard

The year was 1949. Harry S. Truman was president; Jersey Joe Walcott was the heavyweight champ; Hank Williams's "Your Cheatin' Heart" was the top pop song and Billy Johnson was eight years old and living with his parents on a small farm in the pine-studded hills of North Alabama.

During late November of that year, the youngster's days were mostly preoccupied with his studies as a third grader at the local country grammar school. After school each day, he would return home, help his father with farm chores, have supper with his parents, do his homework, then go to bed. The following day, the cycle would repeat itself.

During that period, the highlight of Billy's week was Saturdays. This was the day he would go with his father into the nearby town of Hamilton to attend to family business. With great anticipation, the eight-year-old always looked forward to those Saturday trips in the family pickup with his father. He loved the excitement of driving the 12 miles into town and reading the road signs along the route. Once in town, he was always fascinated by the local townsfolk and he loved to see all the downtown stores built side-by-side, each and every one offering its own particular goods and services. Most of all, on these trips, Billy looked forward to going to the local Wrenn's ice cream parlor and getting a double-dip chocolate cone.

On one particular Saturday afternoon, the father and son had driven into town to pay the electric bill, then stopped by the local hardware store to buy some paint. After they left the hardware store, Billy asked his father when they were going to Wrenn's. The father explained that he wanted to stop by the family lawyer's office first, then they would go for ice cream.

As the father and son walked back up the street from the lawyer's office to the family pickup, the father stopped abruptly in front of a dark, windowless building on one of Hamilton's back streets. It was an older, often-remodeled structure with a single, triangular-shaped window high on the building's door. Above the door, a neatly painted sign in black letters read "Al's Billiard Parlor."

The father turned to his son.

"Let's go in here a minute," the father said.

With that, the father opened the door and Billy Johnson, close behind his father, entered a pool hall for the very first time.

Inside, the eight-year-old suddenly found himself in a world unlike anything he had ever seen before. There was a lively buzz of men's voices in the place. A heavy pall of cigarette and cigar smoke hung in the air. All around him, scruffily dressed men—both young and old—moved mysteriously under bright, fluorescent lights playing a game in which players wielded pointed sticks and punched a white ball around a felt-covered table which knocked colored balls into pockets. As Billy surveyed the surroundings, his father turned to him.

"Wait right here!" the father ordered, indicating a row of seats along the wall. "I'm going to the back."

Obediently, Billy took a seat, then watched eagerly as the men around him played this strange game, laughed, talked, joked and cursed among themselves, using all types of tobacco and spitting into foul-smelling spittoons. Some had tattoos. Most cursed openly. The younger ones seemed to enjoy striking a pose in which a cigarette dangled jauntily from their lips and the smoke curved upwardly and gloriously around their face.

Eight-year-old Billy watched as one young player with ducktails, a crudely drawn tattoo of a naked woman on his forearm and a cigarette dangling from his lips, punched the white ball with a pointed stick.

"God damn it!" the young man said angrily, watching the white ivory ball roll around the table. "I cut it too much. Son of a bitch!"

As his eyes and ears sucked in the surroundings, eight-year-old Billy suddenly felt a delicious, forbidden excitement about this strange place. He had never heard language like that used openly and he was keenly aware that there were no women in the place. In fact, he sensed that women were not even allowed in such a place. He liked that.

After some five minutes, his father returned from the men's room and motioned for him to go. Obediently, the eight-year-old arose from his seat and followed his father back out the front door.

Back in the family pickup some twenty minutes later, Billy licked his double scoop chocolate ice cream cone as the pickup bounced along the dusty, country roads back to the family farm.

The son, knowing he could talk to his father about such things, asked about pool halls. His father said pool halls were an evil place and law-abid-ing people didn't go into them. His father explained that a pool hall could be a very dangerous place where a young, unsuspecting boy could run afoul of the wrong types of people.

Although his father spoke of pool halls as if they were to be feared and avoided, William Vernon Johnson remembered how his father had reminisced to his uncle Lester about playing pool as a young man and how he had loved the game. After the father's explanation, the eight-year-old sensed that, although pool halls were fraught with some special evil, there remained a certain forbidden glamour about them that somehow demanded honor and respect in a very macho, back-street way.

Months later, as the youngster thought back on the incident, he re-membered how the spirit of the pool hall had held an immense appeal to a secret part of him. A pool hall was a man's private sanctuary, he sensed, a very special place where a man could say or do anything he liked and have no fear of a woman's disapproval. It was a place where a man's maleness could run free and wild. He liked that and, for years afterward, he would remember the heavy smell of smoke, the raucous call to "rack" and the forbidden, evil looks of the young men with their tattoos and dangling cigarettes. More than anything, he would remember the distinctive sounds of the clicking ivory balls.

***

The year was 1955. Dwight Eisenhower was president; Rocky Mar-ciano was heavyweight champ; Bill Haley's "Rock Around the Clock" was the top pop song; and William Vernon Johnson was 14 years old and liv-ing with his father in the suburbs of the little north Alabama town. Dur-ing the previous year, Billy's father had been hired at the local steel plant and, as a result, he rented the family farm and moved Billy and himself into town. Suddenly, Billy Johnson became a "city boy." He enrolled at Hamilton Junior High, began paying more attention to his personal hy-giene and availed himself of the youth services in the little town.

One June afternoon, a neighborhood friend invited Billy to go to the newly opened Boys Club in the town. The friend—who was an avid chess player—told Billy the Boys Club was a fun place and they could play chess and ping pong and basketball and all sorts of other neat games.

So, later that night, Billy went with his friend to the Boy's Club. Once inside, Billy followed his friend into the game room where several young

87

boys were gathered around chess boards studying the situations and plotting strategies. Within minutes, Billy's friend, who had brought his own chess board, chose an opponent and began setting up the pieces. As Billy watched, his young ears suddenly picked up the distinctive clicking of ivory balls somewhere nearby. The sound stirred something deep inside him.

With that, Billy instinctively followed the sound of the clicking and, in a nearby room, he found several teenage boys playing eight-ball on an aging, dilapidated pool table. The felt was old and stained; some of the balls were missing; there were only three cue sticks and one piece of well-used chalk. Despite this, William Vernon Johnson had found his own special heaven. That evening he gladly paid his 75 cents to join the Boys Club and, for the next year, he didn't miss a chance to go to the Boys Club and play pool.

During that first year, Billy discovered the incredible fascination the game and the environment held for him. It was at the Boys Club where he learned the basics of pool playing. He learned the basic stroke, the correct way to form a bridge, the use of english, the proper use of powder and chalk and, of course, the ever-present concept of getting "position." After some eight months of constant practice and dedication, 14-year-old Billy became one of the best eight-ball player at the Boy's Club and handily won eight-ball tournaments over most of the older and more experienced boys.

Later the same year, Billy also discovered the YMCA, the other male-oriented organization in the town. Many Saturdays, as a diversion from the Boys Club, Billy and his high school friend Jimmy Stevens would catch a city bus to the other side of town to play there. At the "Y," as they called it, he and Jimmy could play all the pool they wanted for 90 cents an hour. It was fun and the tables were good, but something was missing. The YMCA was a pool hall without the thuggery and the down-and-dirty macho quality which he felt any self-respecting pool hall should offer. The regulars at the "Y" were mostly bronzed, young athletic types with crew cuts and shining white tee-shirts and were delighted to tell others about how Jesus Christ had saved their souls from the eternal flames of hell. Billy loved the access to the game, but the religious angle somehow didn't fit in with his personal tastes.

Then, when he turned 15 in April of 1956 and entered his first year of high school, an incredible thing happened. In his biology class, his friend Jimmy told him he had played pool the previous Saturday at one of the local pool halls. Billy knew that Jimmy, like himself, was underage and asked how he gained admittance to play in a real pool hall. His friend said it was easy.

So, after school that day, Billy was introduced to his first playing experience in a real pool hall—The Funtime—by his friend Jimmy Stevens. The Funtime was a small four-table affair in the back of Willard's Barber Shop on one of the town's back streets. The barber shop was a combination barber shop/shoe shine parlor which had been a long-standing tradition in the town. At some point, the barbershop owner had decided that his customers should have some sort of diversion while they waited their turn for a haircut. As a result, he installed the pool tables in a vacant area behind the barber shop.

When Billy and Jimmy arrived at the Funtime that afternoon, the house man, a small, balding man named Shorty stopped them as they started from the barber shop into the billiards area. Shorty started by saying he knew they were both underage and he could get into big trouble with the police for letting them come in. He added, however, that he would let them play if they observed the rules. Shorty explained that they had to stay quiet, couldn't gamble, couldn't argue, and couldn't say "fuck" if there were ladies up front in the barber shop. William Vernon Johnson agreed to obey all the rules.

Over the next few months, it became a ritual on Saturday mornings—and most school day afternoons—for Billy and his friend Jimmy to go to the Funtime and play pool.

One Friday afternoon after school, Billy and Jimmy were enjoying a game of eight-ball at the Funtime.

"You gonna go see Johnny Daytona tomorrow night?" Jimmy asked off-handedly.

"Who?"

"Johnny Daytona," Jimmy said again. "You don't know who Johnny Daytona is?"

Billy shrugged.

"He's the local slick," Jimmy said. "…And boy is he good."

"You mean he's…like a hustler?"

"Sort of," Jimmy said. "He's does exhibitions and stuff."

"If he's so good, why isn't he famous."

"He IS famous," Jimmy said defensively. "He beat Mosconi at nine-ball."

Billy stopped, not believing his friend.

"Willie Mosconi? THE Mosconi?"

"Yep. THE Mosconi," Jimmy replied confidently. "My daddy says that Johnny Daytona is the best long-rack nine-ball player that ever lived."

"And what is this thing tomorrow night?" Billy asked.

"It's an exhibition," Jimmy explained. "People pay to watch this guy play pool."

Billy studied his friend.

"But you're underage," he said. "How are you going to get in?"

"My daddy's going to take me. If you're with an adult, you can get in."

"Can I go?"

"Sure," Jimmy said. "Seven o'clock at the Smokehouse."

Billy couldn't wait.

The following evening, Billy caught the bus across town and arrived promptly at 6:45 p.m. at the Smokehouse billiard parlor on the north side of town. After he got off the bus and walked down the side street, he could see a folding billboard standing outside the front door of the Smokehouse. On both sides, in huge letters, the billboard read "Billiards Exhibition!! Here Tonight!!"

Billy peered at the small print: "See the greatest pool player alive in exhibition here tonight. Mr. Johnny Daytona will play three games of 100-ball straight pool for the crowd's enjoyment. Exhibition begins at 7 p.m. Admission is $2 per person."

Stapled to the billboard was a glossy photo of a dapperly dressed, well-coifed little man holding a pool cue. As Billy stared at the photo and the sign, an electrical excitement shot through his veins.

As promised, Jimmy Stevens and his father arrived just before 7 p.m. Jimmy's father was a quiet, middle-aged factory worker who fancied himself a local pool player of some renown. At the pool hall door, Jimmy's father told the house man that Billy was with him and his son.

"How old are these two?" the doorman asked.

"They're both sixteen," Jimmy's father said.

"That one don't look like he's more than fourteen," the doorman said, pointing to Billy.

Billy froze at the words, fearful that he would be denied entrance.

"He's sixteen," Jimmy's father said firmly. "If there's any problem, I'll vouch for him."

The doorman rolled his eyes, took the money and motioned the three inside.

Inside, all the pool tables had been closed for the night. One table—the center table—had been well dusted and rows of chairs were placed around the perimeters of the table for some 40-50 spectators.

Once the spectators were seated, the house man announced the star of the show and a short Italian man—dapper in a white shirt with a red velvet cravat and a black vest with gold braiding—made his entrance amid a burst of applause and catcalls. Johnny Daytona, all business, smiled for his fans, acknowledged the applause and motioned for the house man to prepare the balls for play.

As the house man racked the balls, Johnny Daytona unzipped a genuine leopard-skin cue case and withdrew two pieces of a cue stick. The crowd watched interestedly as Johnny Daytona expertly joined the two pieces and screwed them tightly together. Once assembled, Billy could see a string of small diamonds encrusted around the handle of the cue stick and characters that appeared to be some sort of oriental writing.

"Check out his cue stick," Jimmy whispered. "It's from Hong Kong."

By the time Johnny Daytona had assembled his special cue stick, the balls had been racked and the spectators watched expectantly as their hero stroked the cue ball for the break. From the very first moment Billy watched this little Italian man put down a bridge and stroke the cue ball, he knew he was in the presence of genius.

For just over an hour and a half, Billy watched eagerly as Johnny Daytona played three games of 100-ball straight pool. During that time, Billy's eyes took in every nuance as the dapper, little man moved around the table, chalked his cue, studied his shots and manipulated the ivory balls almost at will. As he watched, he couldn't believe the little man's personal style and virtuosity. He had a stroke and surety with the cue stick that was near God-like. His knowledge and control of english was nothing short of miraculous. And he had a repertoire of shots—kick shots, cut shots, rail shots, bank shots and masse shots—that were unbelievable. During the 90-minute exhibition, Johnny Daytona ran 300 balls and missed only twice. William Vernon Johnson was totally enthralled.

After Johnny Daytona had pocketed the last ball of the twentieth rack, the room burst into wild applause. Billy Johnson, totally overcome with the little man's virtuosity, clapped the loudest. Once the performance was finished, Johnny Daytona acknowledged the applause, casually re-packed his Chinese cue stick, shook hands with the house man and walked out the front door.

After he went home that night, Billy relived every minute of the exhibition in his dreams. He remembered every shot, every movement the stylish little Italian man had made. Looking back, Billy couldn't believe what he had seen. Seeing this little man practice his craft so expertly represented an artistry and craftsmanship that he found absolutely magnificent. It was an act to end all acts. Billy had seen a truly great artist at work and he knew he would never forget him.

During the weeks that followed, Billy felt an overwhelming desire to learn everything he could about Johnny Daytona. The following day after school, he went to the Funtime alone. The tables were idle and Shorty, the house man, was reading the paper so Billy asked him about Johnny Daytona.

"Oh, he's the greatest," the little man said in his off-handed way. "Johnny is not only a great pool player, but he's a born gambler. He can rattle an opponent better than anybody I know."

"What do you mean…'rattle'?"

"Johnny can break another man's concentration," the little man continued. "I've seen him do it. He can make his opponent lose his nerve."

Billy Johnson was listening intently, making mental notes.

"And you can't rattle Johnny," Shorty continued. "He's always calm and cool. I've seen men try to rattle Johnny and end up getting rattled themselves. When the big money is on the line, nobody can touch Johnny Daytona for staying cool."

Billy was taking in every word.

"What about his family?

"Nobody knows much about his personal life," the little man continued. "He lives somewhere outside of town. He has a wife and he drives around in a big Cadillac. They call him Johnny Daytona because he's from Daytona Beach, Florida."

"What does he do when he isn't playing pool?" Billy probed further.

"That's all he does," Shorty answered.

"But where does he practice," Billy asked. "Does he have a table at home?"

"Oh, no," the little man replied, "He's good friends with Barney Goldstein. He practices over at the Stag."

The Stag. Billy Johnson said the word to himself. He loved the sound of the word. The very sound triggered visions of macho glory in his 15-year-old mind.

After school the following day, Billy and his friend Jimmy rode the bus across town from the local high school to the Funtime.

As they stepped off the bus and started walking up the street to the Funtime, Billy turned to his friend.

"You ever been in the Stag?"

"Yeah," Jimmy said, after a moment's hesitation. "With my father. They're real strict at the Stag if you're a minor."

The two continued walking.

"What's it like at the Stag?"

"Oh, it's a big time pool hall," Jimmy said expertly. "They have really good tables. They have gambling. It's run by some gangster guy from up north."

They walked silently for a few minutes.

"Let's go to the Stag," Billy said suddenly.

"Are you crazy?" Jimmy said, stopping and eyeing his friend with disapproval. "They'll run us right out in a minute."

"You ever tried?"

"No…but I'm not stupid," Jimmy shot back. "I know they won't let me in unless I'm with my father."

"Come on," Billy said. "At least we can try."

"No," Jimmy said firmly. "I told you they'll run us out."

They started walking again toward the Funtime. After several paces, Billy stopped again.

"Look!" he said. "I want to go to the Stag."

"Well, go on!" Jimmy said. "I told you I'm not going."

"Why not?" Billy protested.

"I'm telling you now the house man won't let you in," he said, anger rising in his voice. "Can't you get that through your thick head?"

Billy and his friend looked at each other.

"Look," Jimmy said finally, "If we're going to play pool today, we're going to the Funtime. I'm NOT going to the Stag."

Billy inhaled deeply, then shrugged.

"Okay," he said finally.

The two teenagers turned and started walking toward the Funtime.

They walked quietly for some five minutes. When they had reached the front door of Funtime, Jimmy turned to Billy.

"Look!" he said. "If you want to go to the Stag so bad, you can go with me and my daddy next time we go."

"When will that be?" Billy asked excitedly.

"Tomorrow night," Jimmy said. "Daddy likes to bet on the Yankees."

The following night, Billy went into the Stag—the premier pool hall in the town—for the very first time. It was a moment to be remembered and, from the instant he walked in, he knew this was the pool hall he wanted to call his own. In Billy's mind, the Stag was everything a pool hall should be. The owner and proprietor at the Stag was one Barney Goldstein, an unsmiling, white-haired, Jewish man from New Jersey who looked like a gangster from a George Raft movie. A longtime professional gambler, Barney was a quietly mysterious man who wore silk shirts, alligator skin shoes and a watch with diamond studded numbers that rumors claimed cost $17,000. All the regulars at the Stag looked up to Barney and referred to him as "The Silver Fox."

Barney's right hand man at the Stag was Bobby Cash, a local gambler who handled Barney's bookmaking operation and oversaw the pool hall business. Bobby Cash hired and fired the rack boys, made sure the coke machines stayed full and kept new felt on the tables. Most importantly, Bobby took the bets for Barney in a little room in the back of the pool hall. Bobby Cash, a no-nonsense, bearish-looking man who was always chomping on an unlighted cigar, kept records of all the bets in a little black book.

Although the Stag was actually little more than a front for the gambling operation, it remained a very well-maintained billiard parlor. There were eight regulation-sized tables. The felt and the rails were changed regularly. The balls matched and generally the cue sticks were straight and had good tips. At the back of the Stag—near the air conditioner—was what the local guys called the gentleman's stand. After a game, a player could wash your hands and face and freshen up a bit. The nearby air conditioner was a giant five-ton unit that cooled the pool room during the hot, sweltering Alabama summers.

As Billy sucked up the flavor of the Stag, he knew this was the pool hall of his dreams. Not only was the Stag the place where his hero played regularly, but it reeked of the sweetly mysterious, macho underworld quality he had sensed when he visited his first pool hall with his father seven years earlier.

After school the following day, Billy was alone when he caught the bus from the high school into town. As usual, he got off at Fourth and Broad Streets. Today, however, instead of walking the block to the Funtime, he went in the opposite direction toward the Stag. As he walked the five blocks to the Stag, he tried to gather his courage. Within minutes, he stood at the front door. As he looked up at the door, the premises loomed before him, monstrous and gigantic. For him, the Stag was something to be loved, yet feared. Finally, he took a deep breath and went inside.

Inside the pool hall was quiet. Only one table was in use. Billy looked around. Then he reached into one of the cue racks and took down a cue stick. Immediately, Bobby Cash, chomping on an unlighted cigar, strolled over.

"Didn't I see you in here the other night?" Bobby Cash asked roughly.

"Yes, sir," Billy said meekly.

"And you were with an adult?" the older man stated authoritatively.

Billy nodded.

"You got identification?"

Billy fumbled in his pocket and produced a high school identification card.

The man examined the card.

"You ain't old enough to come in here," he said.

"Please, Mister, I won't cause any problems," Billy said, almost pleading. "I just want to come in and watch."

"I can't allow that," the older man replied. "You have to be sixteen years old to come in here. You won't be sixteen for another four months."

Bobby Cash handed the identification card back.

"Look..." Billy started again.

"Come on, let's go," Bobby Cash interjected. He took the cue stick from Billy's hand, then motioned toward the door.

Billy's head dropped.

"Go on now," the older man said. "When you're sixteen, you can come in here. Until then, don't come back."

Billy inhaled deeply. Then he turned from the older man and, brokenhearted and dejected, walked out of the Stag.

Billy had tried and failed. He had never dreamed that a mere birthday could separate him from something he loved so much.

The next four months were some of the hardest of Billy's life. More than anything else, he wanted to become a regular at the Stag. He wanted to rub elbows with gangsters and gamblers. He wanted to learn to curse, gamble, be macho and bond to his fellow males at the Stag. Also, he wanted to work on his game at the same place as his hero Johnny Daytona. He had outgrown the Funtime and he needed some new territory.

So, instead of rubbing shoulders with gangsters, gamblers and hustlers, he had to spend the next four months with factory workers, drunken truck drivers and an assortment of ne'er-do-wells at the Smokehouse. The Smokehouse—where he had seen Johnny Daytona play for the very first time—was the middle ground among pool halls in the little town. You could play at the Smokehouse when you were 15, but you had to stop if the police came in. The regulars said that the local police chief was a cousin of the owner and, as long as there were no ruckuses, the chief just looked the other way. During those four months, Billy played at the Smokehouse, but at every chance, he would go to the Stag with Jimmy Stevens and his father to watch his hero Johnny Daytona.

The happiest day of his life was April 14, 1957, the day he turned sixteen years old. His birthday was on a Friday and the following Saturday morning, he showed up at the Stag. When Bobby Cash asked to see his ID, Billy displayed it proudly and was told he could come into the Stag whenever he liked. Bobby Cash told him he had to mind the felt, not use too much chalk or powder and he was not supposed to talk about the "operation" they had in the back. Billy said his lips were sealed.

Over the next two years, Billy became a regular at the Stag. He learned firsthand all the various levels of male bonding he had lusted after in previous years. He learned to smoke and drink and curse and tell dirty jokes and openly discuss the full range of naturally macho subjects which included women's genitals, the latest pennant contenders and, of course, politics. He learned to bet a three-team parlay on the Yankees, the Cubs and the White Sox and he learned to play the true gambler's game, long-rack nine-ball. During those two years, Billy was a frequent visitor to the vacant room above the pool hall where the older men would gather on Saturday nights to drink beer and watch sex movies. It was a learning period.

Most importantly, he spent endless hours watching his hero Johnny

Daytona shoot pool. Every Wednesday night from 7 p.m. until whenever, Bobby Cash would reserve table number four—the best table in the house—for Johnny Daytona to come into the Stag and practice. Billy was there each and every Wednesday night.

In all of his life, nothing had ever amazed Billy Johnson in quite the same way as Johnny Daytona. The sureness with which the little Italian man stroked the cueball; the intelligence and forethought that went into his positioning; the dynamics of his personal style, the way he addressed the cue ball, the gold and diamond cufflinks, the smart, firm cool way he stroked the cue ball—all of this contributed to an incredible magic for Billy. In Billy's mind, Johnny Daytona was truly the maestro.

Billy's heart would soar with gladness when he saw Johnny stroking the cue ball low because he knew the maestro was about to show his mastery of english. Johnny Daytona had a natural sure stroke and he could make the cue ball rocket around the table at his command. The single display of cue ball wizardry that Billy adored the most was a simple, 45-degree cut shot in a corner pocket with the next ball at the opposite end of the table. The shot itself was easy enough to make but the spectacularity of the shot was in how much english—pure, unadulterated spin—-Johnny Daytona could get on the cue ball. Most players would shoot the shot with a tiny bit of right top english, let the cue ball run to the forward rail, then spin to the opposite end of the table.

Not Johnny. Johnny never did anything like anybody else. That was part of his genius. When Johnny shot the shot, he would use loads of bottom english. When he shot the shot, the cue ball had so much spin that it looked like it had stopped. In truth, the cueball had so much english on it that it was actually spinning on the felt like a spinning tire. Finally, when the rapidly turning cue ball slowed down enough to grasp the felt, it would dart off in a dazzlingly wild curving motion like it had an invisible string attached to it. To watch Johnny Daytona perform the shot made Billy's heart soar with gladness and awe.

During those two years, Billy collected a mental catalogue of all the shots he had watched Johnny pull off. Every now and then, Johnny would pull off a shot that was to become one for all time.

One day during the late summer of 1959, when Billy was 18 years old and a senior in the local high school, he watched his hero run thirteen racks of straight pool and, in the process, pull off the most magnificent straight pool shot he had ever seen. It was the pool shot to end all pool shots. Johnny had pocketed the fourteenth ball in the rack and had the last ball in a terrible place behind the rack. When the other fourteen balls were racked, the next ball Johnny had to make was directly behind the rack. Johnny examined his predicament. He checked the angles, pointed his cue stick in imitation shots and examined the new rack from every angle. Finally he was ready to shoot.

"Four ball, right corner," Johnny said calmly.

Billy had heard Johnny call the shot, but he didn't believe it.

"Jesus Christ, this man must be crazy," Billy thought to himself. The shot Johnny was calling was to kick two rails into the back of the rack, cut the four ball in the corner, then break open the rack! It was an impossible shot, Billy concluded. Absolutely impossible! Billy got up out of his seat to witness the shot.

Johnny laid down his bridge and stroked the cue ball. As Billy watched him, he felt in his heart there was no way to make the shot. With that, Johnny shot the cue ball two rails and the rack broke from the inside corner. As the balls clinked around the table in ping pong fashion, the purple four ball rolled out of the stack and went into the left corner pocket exactly as Johnny had called. Billy let out an incredible whoop of joy. He had seen it, but he would never have believed it. He could have kissed Johnny Daytona. Never would he have thought to play the cue ball off the stack and then into the four ball. The imagination, the vision, the sheer genius that lived inside Johnny Daytona was too much for eighteen-year-old William Vernon Johnson.

***

The year was 1964. Lyndon Baines Johnson was president, The Beatles' "I Want to Hold Your Hand" was the top pop song; Cassius Clay was the new heavyweight champion, and Billy Johnson, at age 23, had graduated from Hamilton High School and was in his last year of journalism classes at Alabama State, a small college some 35 miles north of his hometown. During the week, he lived on-campus at the college and pursued his studies, but on weekends, he would return to his hometown, go to the Stag to play pool, talk to his friends and watch his hero.

Early one Saturday afternoon in May of 1964, a big red-faced, middle-aged man from Kentucky who called himself the "Duke of Paducah" came into the Stag. When he first came in, he invited one of the regulars to a friendly game of short-rack nine-ball for $1 a game. During the game, a crowd gathered around to watch the red-faced man shoot. It didn't take long to see how good he was. After he had won seven straight games, the regular hung up his cue, noting that the "Duke" was too good.

With that, the red-faced man announced to the crowd that he was the world's best long-rack nine-ball player and he was looking for a big game. Immediately, the regulars pointed him to Bobby Cash.

"How big a game?" Bobby asked.

"A $10,000 winner-take-all match," said the red-faced man boastfully.

Bobby Cash studied the man, saying nothing.

"Unless, of course, that's too strong for your blood," the red-faced man said sarcastically.

"Let me make a call," Bobby said.

Some thirty minutes later, Johnny Daytona, impeccable in a gray silk suit, brightly polished shoes, black turtleneck shirt and leopard skin cue case in hand, strode through the front door of the Stag. Always the perfect gentleman, Johnny Daytona shook hands with the "Duke of Paducah." The red-faced man said his game was long-rack nine-ball and he would put up $5,000 and his opponent would match it. For the $10,000, they would play up long-rack nine-ball until one of them won seven games. That player would take all the money. Johnny said okay, but he explained that he wanted a ten-minute intermission after the fourth game. The "Duke" approved.

With that, the red-faced man counted out $5,000 in five stacks of $100 bills. Johnny Daytona wrote a personal check for $5,000, gave it to Bobby Cash and received $5,000 cash in return. Both men then handed their money to Bobby who counted it again, placed it in a white envelope and put it in his office safe. Bobby Cash announced that he would judge the play, call the winner after each game and pay the final winner. Bobby Cash flipped a coin and Johnny got the first break.

Johnny broke and made the six ball on the break. Then he ran the one, two and three balls and missed a bank shot. With that, the Duke started to show his stuff. First, he made a nice cut on the four ball and had perfect position on the five. His next problem was, after he made the five ball, he had to get to the other end of the table to shoot the seven. He made the five, but he didn't get enough english on the cue ball to run back up the table so he was left with a very difficult bank shot. He missed, leaving Johnny in perfect position for a runout. Johnny had won the first game.

"Johnny Daytona has won the first game," Bobby Cash announced to the gathered crowd.

Bobby Cash racked the balls and Johnny broke for the second game. On the break, Johnny made the two ball, but he didn't have a shot on the one. So he played safe.

Then the Kentucky slick had a chance to show his stuff. He made the one ball on a beautiful kick shot, then was positioned perfectly on the three. From there, he had easy cut shots on the five, six and seven balls. He missed the eight, but left Johnny an incredibly tough bank shot which Johnny missed. Then the Kentucky slick banked in the eight and had an easy shot on the nine. The Kentucky slick had won the second game.

As the Kentucky slick chalked his cue to break for the third game, the Stag regulars examined him closely. The slick had a good eye and a smooth stroke and he was not afraid of a long shot. Also, he was a good banker and kicker, but he used far too much bottom english. In fact, he loved bottom english so much that he acted as if top english did not exist. In many cases when top english would have been the correct english, the slick would use bottom.

The "Duke of Paducah" broke the rack for the third game and made the six ball, but didn't have a shot on the one. With that, Johnny banked in the one ball, then handily ran through the two, three and four balls.

As Johnny chalked his cue in preparation to shoot the five ball, the Duke interrupted him.

"I'll lay you $500 you can't run 'em," the slick said daringly.

"We already have a bet," Johnny said.

"I like side bets," the Kentucky slick said.

"Let's stick with the bet we already have," Johnny replied firmly.

The slick smiled.

All the regulars knew that the slick was trying to play with Johnny's head. It was a tactic hustlers used to cause an opponent to lose his concentration. It's called "rattling." If you could "rattle" your opponent, you could break his nerve. You caused him to lose his confidence and his concentration.

Johnny said nothing and made the five ball in the corner. Johnny then ran the seven and eight balls and played safe. After the hustler played safe on the nine, Johnny made and unbelievable two-rail bank shot and Johnny had won the third game.

After Johnny again failed to make a ball on the succeeding break, the hustler came roaring back. After he ran the one through five balls, he played safe. Then Johnny cut in the six and seven, made a beautiful kick shot on the eight ball, but left himself with a very difficult bank shot on the nine. Johnny tried to play safe, but the Kentucky slick made an incredible rail shot on the nine to win the fourth game. The score was 2-2.

As agreed, Bobby Cash called the intermission at the end of the fourth game. At the intermission, Johnny went to refresh himself up at the gentleman's stand. The Kentucky slick went into the men's room and didn't return until two minutes before the intermission was to end. When the Kentucky slick came back out for play to resume, he was a little louder than before and smelled of whiskey.

The Duke broke the rack for the fifth game, but failed to make a ball. When the balls had stopped rolling, the cue ball was at one end of the table and the one ball was at the other end. The one ball was makeable, but it was a very difficult shot.

"Now that's what I call safe," the slick started again.

He looked at Johnny.

"I don't think you can make that shot," the slick said.

Johnny didn't reply.

"Want to make a side bet on that shot?" the slick asked.

Johnny said nothing. Calmly, he laid down his bridge, shot and missed the one ball and returned the cue to the opposite end of the table. The shot Johnny left the Duke was almost identical to the shot Johnny had missed.

The slick looked at the shot, then at Johnny.

"I'm going to kick your ass now," he said threateningly. "You're not only afraid to bet, you're afraid to shoot."

"Go!" Johnny said calmly waving his hand as if he were offering an invitation.

The slick then ran the one through six balls in a spectacular display of shooting skill. Then he had a nice cut on the seven ball and handily made the eight.

When it came time to make the nine ball—the money ball, the Duke appeared to have a relatively easy shot. As the slick chalked his cue, Johnny suddenly spoke up

"What were you saying about a side bet?" Johnny challenged.

The Duke laughed derisively.

"You think I can't make that nine ball?"

"A thousand dollars says you can't make it," Johnny said calmly.

With that, all the Stag regulars watching the contest sprung to instant attention. All eyes were on the Kentucky slick.

The red-faced man chuckled to himself. Then he laughed out loud. Now it was his time to put up or shut up. The slick looked over at Bobby Cash.

"You heard him," the slick said.

Bobby Cash nodded and walked over to the table to take the side bet.

The Kentucky slick reached in his pocket and pulled out a wad of crisp $100 bills and counted ten on the table. Johnny counted out ten $100 bills of his own. The bet had been made.

For the Kentucky slick, the shot in question appeared to be relatively easy, but William Vernon Johnson and the other Stag regulars knew otherwise. The nine ball was dead on the rail and some twenty inches from the right corner pocket. Stag regulars knew that the right corner pocket on that table was very tight and, if the slick didn't put top english on the cue ball which would make the nine ball cling to the rail, the ball would move away from the rail and hang up in the pocket. Billy Johnson sensed his hero's strategy perfectly.

The slick studied the shot. Then he laid down his bridge and stroked the cue ball carefully and confidently. As usual, he used bottom english. All eyes watched as the Kentucky slick stroked the cue ball and the nine ball headed down the rail toward the pocket. As regulars suspected, the bottom english threw the nine ball away from the rail, then caused it to career rapidly between the two cushions and stop in the middle of the pocket. The nine ball failed to drop.

A sudden gasp erupted from the onlookers. The "Duke of Paducah" inhaled sharply, then turned white as a sheet. For a moment, he stared at the nine ball disbelievingly and said nothing. From the look on his face, it was if his whole world had suddenly crashed down around him.

Johnny said nothing. In fact, he didn't even look at the slick. Very calmly, he chalked his cue and dropped the nine ball in the pocket.

"Johnny Daytona has won the fifth game of the match and the $1,000 side bet," Bobby Cash announced to the crowd.

On the following break, Johnny made the five ball, then ran the one and two balls and missed the three. From all indications, the Duke was set up perfectly to run the rack. After he made the three ball, he had an easy cut shot on the four ball. Everybody could see that his next shot—a relatively easy one—was to cut the five ball in the side pocket, then use reverse english off the rail to come back up the table on the six. From there, it looked like an easy runout for the Kentucky slick. The whole table was set up for him. With that, the slick chalked his cue, put down his bridge and shot the five. He missed the five ball! A very routine shot on the five and the Kentucky slick had missed it.

Under other circumstances, missing the five ball would have been taken in stride, perhaps explained away as a lapse of consciousness. A mental mistake, as they say. But in this case, it had far-reaching implications for the Kentucky slick. Although the Kentucky slick tried not to show it, William Vernon Johnson and the other Stag regulars knew that the "Duke of Paducah" had been rattled.

The side bet at the end of the last game—which the slick had been asking for—had broken his concentration. He had tried to break Johnny Daytona's nerve by asking for a side bet. Then, at the appropriate time, Johnny had not only taken him up on the offer, he had beaten him at his own game. The slick had tried to rattle Johnny, but had been rattled himself. The Stag regulars sensed that the Kentucky slick had designed his own defeat.

With that, Johnny controlled the table and ran the five through nine for the win.

"Mr. Johnny Daytona has won the sixth game of the match," Bobby Cash called out to the crowd.

On the following rack, which was the seventh game, Johnny broke and made the seven ball. After he had run the one, two and three balls, he noticed that the four ball was jammed up against the rail with the eight ball extremely close. In fact, the eight ball was so close it didn't appear he could make the four with a good hit.

After Johnny made the three, the slick asked, "How are you going to make the four?"

Johnny Daytona, chalking his cue, examined the shot.

"I can make it," Johnny said confidently

"Not with a good hit," the Kentucky slick added quickly.

All the Stag regulars knew the "Duke of Paducah" was desperate. He had already lost $1,000 and now he was about to lose $5,000 more and it was all his own fault.

Johnny looked at the four-eight positions again.

"It's close, but I can make it," Johnny said again.

"I don't think so," the Kentucky slick said.

With that, Johnny Daytona calmly motioned to Bobby Cash.

Bobby, watching the game and chomping on an unlighted cigar as usual, came over and examined the shot.

"If he makes the four, it will have to be a good hit," Bobby said.

"I want to see this," the Kentucky slick said aggressively.

As the crowd, Bobby Cash and the Kentucky slick all watched, Johnny cued the cue ball. Then he shot and made a perfectly good hit and the four ball rolled into the hole. The eight ball moved only slightly after the cue ball struck the four.

"Bad hit! Bad hit!" the "Duke of Paducah" shouted as the four ball dropped into the pocket. "My shot!"

"Good hit!" Bobby Cash said authoritatively. "Close…but a good hit."

"You're crazy!" the Kentucky slick said angrily. "There is no way that was a good hit."

"I'm the house man," Bobby said. "I said it was a good hit."

"Bullshit!" the red-faced man shot back angrily. "There is no way in hell he could have made a good hit on the four ball."

"Play the game!" Bobby Cash said roughly to the slick. "I've made the call."

The Kentucky slick looked angrily at Bobby, then at Johnny.

"You called it that way cause he's your Goddamn friend," the Kentucky slick shot back, chalking his cue. "It was a bad hit and you know it."

Bobby Cash glared at the Kentucky slick. Then, teeth clenched tightly on the unlit cigar, he walked over to the Kentucky slick with a pool hall swagger that had been practiced over many years. Then he got right up in the Kentucky slick's face.

"You son of a bitch!" Bobby said angrily. "I said it was a good hit! And it stands. You got that?!"

Everything was quiet in the pool room as Bobby glared angrily into the Kentucky slick's face. You could see that the slick didn't want to mess with Bobby. Especially on his turf.

Bobby Cash motioned for Johnny to keep shooting. The rest of the rack was easy for Johnny. The slick had been "rattled" and then tried to cheat to cover it up. All the cards were now stacked against him.

Johnny quickly ran the five, six and seven balls. Then made a beautiful bank shot on the eight. As he prepared to make the nine ball for the seventh game, all the crowd waited. The Stag was deadly quiet as Johnny got ready to shoot the nine.

Then, as if he was about to take a sip of lemonade, Johnny easily stroked the nine ball in the hole and the pool hall was filled with shouts of triumph for their hero.

"Mr. Johnny Daytona is the winner of the seventh game and the match," Bobby Cash announced.

The Kentucky slick, pale as a sheet, said nothing. He turned away from the crowd, hung up his cue and went back to the men's room.

Johnny was putting his cue back in the case when the Kentucky slick emerged from the men's room. At the table where the game was played, Bobby was counting out the winner's money to Johnny Daytona.

"I hope you enjoy spending that money," the Kentucky slick said, his face flushed with anger as he watched Bobby Cash count out the $10,000.

Johnny, unsmiling and dismantling his cue stick, watched the red-faced man closely.

"You lost," Johnny said calmly. "Fair and square…"

"I didn't lose!" the Kentucky slick shouted angrily. "You cheated!"

Johnny didn't reply.

"You a Goddamn cheat!" the Kentucky slick shouted again, the bitter anger in his voice reverberating across the pool hall.

"And you are too, you son of a bitch," the Kentucky slick said, pointing to Bobby. "Both of you are Goddamn cheaters," he shouted again, a new wave of anger flashing across his angry, reddened face.

Johnny continued putting away his cue stick, all the while calmly eyeing the Kentucky slick.

Suddenly, the Kentucky slick shoved his hand in his pocket and pulled out a derringer.

"Look out, Johnny!" somebody shouted.

In the twinkling of an eye, Johnny Daytona reached inside his leopard skin cue-case, pulled out a .38 special and shot the Kentucky slick right between the eyes. There was a sudden pop from Johnny's pistol, then an instant bullet hole appeared in the middle of the Kentucky slick's forehead. It was so quick the Kentucky slick didn't even have time to fire.

The pool hall regulars gasped as the Kentucky slick fell dead on the pool hall floor. The "Duke of Paducah" didn't scream or moan or even stagger. There were no famous last words, no final dying gasps or any of the dramatic stuff. The red-faced man was killed instantly. Just as surely and swiftly as Johnny Daytona could pull off a three-rail kick shot, he had dispatched the Kentucky slick into eternity. The same guy that could put so much English on a cue ball than he could make it actually curve was the same guy that had sent a .38 caliber slug surely and deeply into the Kentucky slick's brain and ended his life forever and ever.

Johnny Daytona, his face still a mask of quiet calmness, walked over to Bobby Cash and handed him the pistol. Shortly afterward, local police arrived and talked to Johnny and the witnesses. They needed little time to conclude that Johnny had killed the Kentucky slick in self-defense.

The whole incident had been too much for William Vernon Johnson. Johnny Daytona had proven that he was not only a great artist, but a man's man who—in the face of death—was cool and fearless to a fault. That night, Johnny Daytona became a composite of every hero that William Vernon Johnson had ever dreamed of. He was Babe Ruth, Clark Gable, The Lone Ranger and Al Capone all rolled into one. Johnny Daytona was Billy's ultimate dream of a real-life hero come true.

***

The year was 1972. Richard Nixon was president; Roberta Flack's "The First Time Ever I Saw Your Face" was at the top of the pop charts; Larry Holmes was the heavyweight champ and Billy Johnson was 31 years old and an associate editor at the local newspaper in Hamilton.

After he received his journalism degree, Billy had returned to the little North Alabama town and begun working at the Hamilton Courier. During the week, his time was spent covering the Tallapoosa County Courthouse, writing features and shooting photo spreads. On the weekends, however, he liked to get away from the newspaper office and relax. During those times, he would invariably return to the Stag, his friends and the game he loved so much.

One Friday afternoon in late August of 1972, he got a call from Bobby Cash who said that a young hustler who called himself "The Dallas Kid" was in town. He said he had heard about Johnny Daytona and he wanted to add him to his list of victims. Bobby said the young slick had challenged Johnny to seven games of short-rack nine-ball for $25,000.

"Is this guy good?" William Vernon Johnson asked.

"Real good," Bobby Cash had said. "You won't believe how much bottom english he can get on a cue ball."

"Really?" Billy again.

"He can suck a cue ball three long rails."

There was a slight pause.

"Jesus!" Billy muttered under his breath. "This I gotta see."

The following afternoon, Billy left the newspaper office at noon. Usually he liked to stay later to make sure the Sunday edition was well underway, but on this particular Saturday, it was too hot to sit in the office even though it was air-conditioned.

The August weather had been unbearably hot over the past few days. On Thursday, the high temperature was 96 and on Friday, it was up to 101 degrees at noon. God had shown some mercy on Saturday morning, but by early afternoon temperatures were well over 100. Some said the thermometer read 103 at 1:30 that afternoon. It was one of those sweltering Alabama summer afternoons when the air becomes so hot and dry that you didn't want to be alive.

When Billy arrived at the Stag at 4:30, a huge crowd of regulars had already gathered to see the big match. While the game table—number 4—was being prepared, both combatants were warming up on other tables.

The "Dallas Kid" was a cocky, baby-faced blonde boy of a man some 20–21 years of age who had a tattoo of a squirrel on his bridge hand. Decked out in western boots, tight jeans and a white embroidered cowboy shirt with a leather belt and a big silver buckle, the "Dallas Kid" was warming up on table number 2.

As the young slick walked around the table warming up, he kept bragging to the crowd: "I'm the best God damn short rack nine ball player in the world. No son of a bitch alive is as good as me. This old man here," he said, pointing to Johnny, "I'm gonna kick his ass forty ways from Sunday."

He laughed out loud.

"That $25,000 is as good as mine," he boasted to the crowd.

Johnny, dressed to the nines in a dapper black sport coat and pants, a white silk shirt and a black vest with gold braids and gold buttons, was listening and warming up on a nearby table. Naturally, Johnny's group of fans, which included Billy, was there to cheer on their hero.

Finally the match was ready to begin. Bobby Cash announced to the crowd that Johnny and the "Dallas Kid" were going to play seven games of short-rack nine-ball for a total pot of $25,000. Each player had put up $12,500 and the first player to win four games took the total ante. The locals had never heard of that kind of money being bet at the Stag before. Short-rack nine-ball was a true gambler's game. With only six balls in the rack, a good pool player who really knew positioning and had some luck could run four racks and never give his opponent a shot. It was a daring, sudden-death game.

After Johnny won the toss, he broke the rack and made the nine ball. Johnny won the first game. In the following game, Johnny made the three ball, then—with an incredible stroke of luck—made the nine ball as an easy combination off the one. In less than two minutes, Johnny had won the first two games.

On the break for the third game, incredibly Johnny made the three, four and five balls. Then he had an easy shot on the one ball and then—it was like a miracle—he had another dead combination on the nine ball. What Johnny was doing was something totally unheard of. Johnny had won three games in five minutes and the "Dallas Kid" hadn't even had a shot yet.

As Billy and the other Stag regulars watched, they knew instinctively that what Johnny Daytona was doing to the "Dallas Kid" was the same thing he had done to all the other slicks who had passed through the little town over the years. The difference was that—this time—Johnny was winning a small fortune in the most incredible way imaginable. If he won this fourth game, he would have won the $25,000 and the slick wouldn't even have had a shot. This was bound to go down in local history as Johnny's greatest performance. This was like Babe Ruth pointing to the upper deck at Yankee Stadium, then whacking the ball to the exact spot he had pointed out.

When Johnny made the two ball on the break for the fourth game, the pool hall fell deathly quiet. As the crowd and the young hustler watched in absolute awe, Johnny Daytona—a perfect portrait of efficiency and concentration—moved expertly through the rack. He ran the one and three balls with simple shoot and stop English. Then he made the four ball on a beautiful bank shot and was left with a little cut on the five ball.

To make the five ball, then get shapes on the nine, everybody knew Johnny had to get a tremendous amount of right top english on the cue ball. But this was Johnny's night and he could do no wrong. As expected, Johnny easily made the five ball and the cue ball slid gloriously across the table to the forward rail, then zipped handily to the other end of the table for an easy shot on the nine ball.

Now all that the local hero had to do was sink the nine ball. Everybody knew that the moment Johnny made the nine, a triumphant yell of approval and affection would erupt from the Stag regulars and Johnny would collect the $25,000. With that single act, the greatest chapter in the continuing legend of Johnny Daytona would have been written.

As calm as ever, Johnny chalked his cue and examined the shot on the nine ball. Then, he put down his bridge and began to stroke the cue ball. Suddenly, a strange, unexpected sound erupted in the quiet coolness of the billiard parlor. It was a loud, hissing sound as if something was about to explode. For a split second, the crowd became instantly alert and looked around to determine what was making the threatening sound. Then, without warning, the roar was followed with an even more powerful, loud hissing sound and huge sparks and black soot shot out across the ceiling.

Suddenly, Johnny Daytona's face—always a mask of quiet confidence—filled with horrific fear at the hissing sound. Without a word or a moment's hesitation, Johnny threw down his Chinese cue stick and rushed for the door. Johnny's move sent an instinctive wave of panic throughout the rest of the crowd and, in seconds, most of the spectators in the pool hall jumped put of their seats and rushed out the front door.

Meanwhile, Billy and the other Stag regulars calmly remained in their seats. In fact, they burst out laughing when Johnny and the others made a mad dash for the door. They knew that the loud, hissing noise was the air conditioner. They had learned long ago that the loud hissing sound, followed by a deafening roar and then a flurry of flying sparks and soot was the air conditioner's overworked compressor blowing a gasket. Billy and the others were beside themselves with laughter at what happened.

"That Goddamn air conditioner!" Bobby Cash said disgustedly, frowning and waving his hand in the air to clear the smoke and soot out of his face.

"You guys better get out of here," Bobby said to the seated regulars. "I got to call the repair man."

Billy and the other Stag regulars got up and filed out of the pool hall.

By the time the pool hall had emptied out on the street, two fire trucks had arrived and six firemen and a fire marshal—all looking very professional in their heavy brown coats and yellow helmets—went inside to inspect the damage.

Outside the Stag, Billy, the "Dallas Kid," Bobby Cash, the other Stag regulars and a crowd of curious onlookers waited, talked among themselves and offered comments about the episode. After a few moments, the fire marshal, in a pall of black smoke, emerged from the pool hall.

"This place is closed," the fire marshal said authoritatively.

"But we had a big game going in there," Bobby Cash protested.

"Too bad," the fire marshal said sullenly. "Nobody goes back in until my department makes a thorough check of all the electrical wiring."

"How long will that be?" Bobby asked.

"At least two weeks…maybe more," the fire marshal said.

This sent a groan through the crowd. They wanted to see the end of the match.

With that, the "Dallas Kid" turned to Bobby Cash.

"I ain't waiting no two weeks to finish the game," he said.

"What are you talking about?" Bobby Cash asked.

"Waitin' two weeks means we can't finish and you owe me the money I put up. He didn't make the nine ball in the last game, so all bets are off."

Bobby Cash inhaled deeply.

"Yeah, I guess you're right," he said.

With that, Bobby reached into his pocket and counted out $12,500 into the young hustler's hand.

The young hustler smiled cockily and stuffed the wad of cash into his pants pocket.

"One more thing," he said, as a parting word, "I'm still the best God-damn short-rack nine-ball player in the world. That old man didn't win," he said emphatically. "He didn't beat me! You understand?! Don't any of you ever forget that!"

"Yeah! Yeah!" Bobby said sarcastically.

With that, the "Dallas Kid" smiled again, turned and strode off up the street past the fire engines, the Stag regulars and the crowd of gathered onlookers.

As Billy watched the "Dallas Kid" stroll back up the street, his thoughts turned to his hero and he began looking through the crowd for Johnny. His eyes ranged through the crowd until finally, he found his hero leaning on an old Cadillac.

Suddenly, Billy was rocked by the shock of his life. As he looked at Johnny, he saw a small, frightened, middle-aged man, with a slightly bleeding cut on his forehead and holding a black, synthetic hairpiece in his hand. In the back of his mind, Billy had always known that Johnny wore a toupee, but he had never really thought about it. Without the toupee, Johnny Daytona was almost totally bald. In the escape from the pool hall, two buttons had popped off Johnny's black, gold-braided velvet vest. And, without a cue stick in his hand, he looked so incredibly small, weak and vulnerable.

It had all been a stage show, Billy suddenly realized. Seeing Johnny Daytona without his toupee, his gold-braided vest and the trademark Chinese cue stick in his hand was like seeing a clown without his makeup. Billy was suddenly aware that the incredible, God-like reverence he had had for Johnny Daytona all those years was nothing but an illusion. A fantasy!

At first, the revelation struck William Vernon Johnson as hilariously funny. On one hand, he found it hilarious that Johnny—like most of the other Stag regulars—didn't know that the roaring, threatening noise was an overworked air conditioner. Even funnier for Billy was the fact that, for all those years, he had never allowed himself to see the real, actual human side of Johnny Daytona. For all those years, something inside him had wanted to overlook the fact that Johnny Daytona had all the same basic instincts—fear, anger, anxiety—as every other human being. Moreover, he realized that, during all those years, he had only seen the side of Johnny Daytona he had wanted to see.

Yet, somehow the incident was infused with a terrible sadness. More than anything, he remembered the look of sheer terror that flashed across Johnny's face only moments before he threw down the Chinese cue stick and dashed for the door. Johnny was, in fact, the first one to the door. All those years he had thought of Johnny as a calm, quietly vicious, steel-willed pool hustler who knew absolutely no fear. Here was the man who could stand all manner of psychological intimidation, then come back with a single, deadly viper-like strike to kill his opponent. Here was the man who had put a .38 caliber slug through the "Duke of Paducah's" forehead as casually as he would say "Hello!" Now, this same man had publicly freaked out and turned tail to a faulty air conditioner!

"Why?! Why!? Why?!" he asked himself. Why couldn't fate have allowed him this one undisturbed fantasy for the rest of his days? Why couldn't he have always remembered Johnny Daytona as this incredible genius who was not only the greatest pool player that ever lived, but the ultimate gentleman and a true man's man. Why did he even have to be there that night to see his hero in such a compromising role? Why did the dream have to be shattered?

With that, Billy looked away from the tired, balding little man holding the toupee. Suddenly all of life had meaning for him. For the first time, he realized that human life is a constant struggle between fantasy and reality...an endlessly defining struggle between the way life is and the way human beings want it to be. The great hero that he had nurtured and protected all those years had suddenly become all too real...all too human. With the realization, a heavy sadness crept into 31-year-old William Vernon Johnson's very soul. It was the end of an era and he knew it. Down deep inside his heart of hearts, he began to weep. In later years, he would learn why they called it the blues.

CHARLEY

Angel Unaware

As William Vernon Johnson stumbled down the hospital steps and strode across the street to the hospital parking lot, he was a man walking in a daze. Some five minutes earlier, he had been told that his father had died on the operating table after suffering a massive heart attack. The information had swept over him like a shower of ice cold water and left a great cloud of depression sweeping his very soul. He had always known that his father would die at some point, but in his mind he kept putting it off year after year after year, hoping against hope that it would never really happen. Now, in August of 1972, his worst fears had been realized.

After his mother died when he was thirteen, his father had become his mentor, his closest friend, his best buddy and his confidante. When he wasn't in school, he was always with his father and they spent endless hours together on the farm mending fences, building barns, tending to livestock and raising crops. Until he went to college, the father and son were always together at night. Whether they were playing checkers, working on a farm implement, listening to the radio or just reading, their nights together were always happy times.

Throughout their lives together, their single-most passion had been the fishing trips they made to the little creeks and rivers in Tallapoosa and surrounding counties. As a small boy, the son would dig earthworms for bait, rig up their cane poles and equip a tackle box. Then, he and his father, armed with poles and bait, would slog along the river banks, looking for a place to drop their hooks. Once settled along the water's edge, the father and son would sit for hours catching perch, bream, crappie and catfish. Many nights, after their excursions, they would return to the farmhouse and cook their catch over an open fire, then sit down to fresh fish, hush puppies, French fries and iced tea.

In later years, William Vernon's father bought a small fishing boat and the father and son would haul the vessel to banks of the Tallapoosa River, then go to their "secret" fishing hole, a place they had dubbed "the tree-tops." Some 15 years before, the Tennessee Valley Authority had flooded 10,000 acres of lowlands near the river and, in the process, had covered more than 8,000 acres of standing trees. Once the forest was flooded, many of the tops of the trees jutted up above the surface of the water. In early March, when the crappie fish went on the bed, they would lay their eggs in the top limbs of the submerged trees. By mid-April, "the tree-tops" would be teeming with thousands of fat, hungry young crappie and the father and son could fill their boat with huge I- and 2-pound crappie in no time.

Two months earlier, the son, who was earning good money as a reporter with the local newspaper, had bought a spanking new fishing boat with all the latest features. The week after the boat was delivered, he couldn't wait to go to "the tree-tops" with his father. But the father had fallen ill and was admitted to the hospital. Now, his father had passed from this world and Billy would never have the chance to use the boat in the way he had hoped.

Billy had reached his car in the hospital parking lot. Once inside the car, he took a deep breath and put the keys in the ignition. As he started to turn the key, he felt a huge hollowness burrowing deeper and deeper inside himself. It was a gnawing, vicious grief. He wasn't sure if that hollowness could ever be filled. His father had been such a huge part of his life for so long, he couldn't imagine life without him. Still in a daze, Billy stared straight ahead over the tops of the other cars at the white antiseptic walls of the hospital building. Suddenly, alone and amid familiar surroundings, something inside Billy exploded and he broke down in giant sobs of uncontrollable grief.

Thirty minutes later, somewhat calmer now, Billy pulled his car into the parking lot of the newspaper complex where he was employed. As he unlocked the door to the editorial department, he would see that the office was dark and seemingly empty. On Saturdays, the morning shift would put the early edition to bed by 12:30 and everyone would be out of the office by I p.m. On this particular Saturday, the only person in the darkened office was Charles "Charley" Ryan, the newspaper's aging Sunday editor. As William walked in, Charles Ryan looked up from his desk.

"Sorry to hear about your father," the older man said sadly.

"Thanks, Charley."

"Are you going to have an obituary?"

Billy nodded.

"Nobody can write it better than you," the older man said.

Saying nothing, the young reporter sat down at the desk across from the Sunday editor's desk, put a piece of paper into the typewriter and began typing.

"Robert William Johnson," he began, "a longtime farmer and merchant in Tallapoosa County, passed away at a local hospital Saturday after a brief illness.

"Mr. Johnson, who was 71, was the father of Billy, a reporter with the Hamilton Courier and the husband of the late Virginia Johnson. Funeral services will be held Monday at Fern-Collier Funeral Home in Hamilton."

Finally, having finished writing, he took the single sheet of paper out of the typewriter. As he reread the copy for typos, huge tears rolled down his cheeks and he thought how stale and generic obituaries were. It was as if he couldn't break through the barriers of journalistic objectivity to say what he really felt in his heart for his father. Finally, having reread the copy, he got up from the desk and placed the single sheet of paper in the basket on the Sunday editor's desk.

Without looking at it, the older man took the copy out of the basket.

"I'm sure it's fine," Charley said. "We'll put it on the front page."

"Thanks, Charley."

With that, Billy turned and walked back out of the newsroom. Once he was outside again, a huge new wave of private grief swept through him and he broke down again in a torrent of private tears. Again, he could feel a huge clot of unbearable grief forming inside himself. It was a grief he wasn't sure he would ever lose.

At the funeral the following day, he remembered how much he hated funerals. Somehow, he didn't want to be there among all the public weeping and wailing. He wanted to be alone with his father—just the two of them—to do something special for him, so he asked the funeral director if he could be a pallbearer. But the director, who had also been his science teacher in junior high, said it wasn't traditional for an immediate family member to carry the casket.

"If I can say so," the director said, "it just doesn't look right. Immediate family members should be at the graveside."

Billy didn't argue. So, during the funeral services, William stood by quietly with his aunts and his uncles and cousins in the family area and listened quietly as the minister spoke all the standard funerary words over his father. For William, it all seemed so hollow and meaningless. How he wished that humankind could simply allow their fellow human beings to bear their grief in private rather than making it a public spectacle for all the world to see. It was as if a funeral was some sort of public proof that the deceased person had been loved in life. His grief for his father was something very personal, very private and a public display somehow defiled the sanctity of that love.

Standing at the altar, William watched as his father's family and friends filed past the open casket. There was his Aunt Hilda, his father's oldest sister who hadn't seen his father in 18 years, wailing the loudest of all. There was Abner Hames, the nearby neighbor who had ruthlessly cheated his father in a land deal, looking very sad and forlorn. The young reporter knew that, if his father were alive to witness the mockery and hypocrisy of all this, he would laugh out loud.

After the funeral services, William followed the coffin and the family to the graveside and watched as the casket was placed in the ground and the grave filled and covered with fresh earth. Then, finally, after he had shaken hands and said goodbye to all his relatives and family friends, he went home and got drunk.

The following Monday morning, Billy reported to the office bright and early. He wanted to throw himself into his work, get on with his life and try to get over the loss of his father. After the obligatory condolences from his fellow workers, the city editor told him that the executive editor wanted to see him.

"How long you been with us now," the executive editor began.

"Almost three years," he replied.

"You've proven yourself as a reporter," the executive editor noted. "Don't you think it's time you learned desk work?"

"What do you have in mind?" Billy asked.

"We need a back-up on the Sunday desk."

"Aren't you happy with Charley?"

The executive editor hesitated before answering.

"We're happy with him," he continued, "But some Sundays are better than others. He still likes to take a nip. On those days, he tends to be slow. He's almost 70, you know."

The young reporter looked at his executive editor.

"You want me to be Charley's understudy?" he asked.

The executive editor nodded.

"That's how you move up with the company," the executive editor added.

"That's what I want," the young reporter replied.

So that afternoon, Billy began his apprenticeship as the newspaper's associate Sunday editor under the tutelage of Charley Ryan. From the first, the young reporter and the older man became fast friends.

"I always liked to take a nip," Charley told his pupil. "When I was a young reporter in Birmingham, everybody would go for a few drinks after the shift was finished. Some people can take a drink, then walk away. Me, I wanted to stick my mouth under the spigot," he would say with a smile. "Some mornings, I wanted to put it on my corn flakes.

"One time I got on top of it," Charley said. "And for four years, I didn't touch it. During all that time, I didn't have a single moment of happiness. Now I like to take a little nip to remind me of what once was."

Charley had been employed at the Hamilton Courier for almost 15 years, but his drinking proved to be a problem. For many years, he had been the paper's state editor and had roamed the mountains and valleys of north Alabama covering town hall meetings, writing human interest stories and doing photo spreads. In the mid-sixties, after Charley had been state editor for eight years, he went on a drinking binge and disappeared for four days. When he returned to the office, there was a new state editor and Charley had been demoted to Sunday editor.

As a newspaperman, Charley was from the old school of the thirties and forties and it showed in everything he did. Especially in headlines. Charley used words in headlines that were in common usage in the early 1900s. Words like "halcyon," "salubrious" and "salad days." In a headline, if Charley needed a shorter word for "planned" he would use "set." If he needed a shorter word for "announced" he would use "told." Charley said, once when he was a young man and just beginning to learn desk work, he had a story about a tiddlywinks tournament that was being held locally. It was only a five-paragraph story, Charley said, but the editor wanted three one-word lines with not more than seven letters per word.

"I worked and worked," Charley recalled. "It was tough, but I finally got it."

Billy reflected for a moment.

"You'll never figure out what I came up with," Charley said. "There is no way you can get tiddlywinks into seven letters."

"I give up," William said finally.

"Winks Tourney Told," Charley said with a sly smile.

Charley's greatest moment as a newspaperman came in 1945 when he was working for a major daily along the South Carolina coast. FDR had been vacationing on an island nearby and the editor asked Charley to go down and try for an interview.

"I didn't think I had a chance in hell of getting an interview with FDR," Charley said. "He had been sick, he was in a wheelchair and he had all kinds of security. But I went to the hotel's front desk anyway and told them who I was and what I wanted. After a while, one of FDR's assistant press secretaries came out and introduced himself. He said that 'The president couldn't do an interview at that moment. However, if I could be at the airport around three p.m., the president could spare me fifteen to twenty minutes.'

"I told him," Charley said with a big laugh, "that I thought I could make it."

Charley said, when the secret service ushered him into a waiting room at the airport and he saw FDR, it was the greatest moment of his life.

"'Now Charles,'" Charley proudly quoted FDR as calling him by his first name, "'you know that our troops must win this great war in Europe. The Italians and the Germans must be beaten back from Western Europe and North Africa and the Japanese must be whipped in the Pacific. This war WILL be won, no matter what the cost.'"

Charley said the editor put a banner headline on his story in big bold letters: "This War WILL Be Won!" and attached his photo and by-line. Charley said he had the story framed and it had been hanging on his living room wall for 26 years.

Nothing made the young reporter happier than getting a big laugh out of Charley. And he learned quickly that Charley loved physical humor. There was a paper cutter at the proofreaders' desk that was used to trim the edges of page proofs and, early on, Billy noticed that he had to be careful of your tie when you used it. If he wasn't minding his tie, the end of it could easily slip under the blade and the cutter would whack it into two pieces when he trimmed page proofs.

One Saturday night, Billy wore an old tie to work. As he and Charley were rushing around to meet the midnight deadline, he and Charley took a page one proof to the paper cutter together. Then as Charley watched, Billy put the bottom of the page into the cutter, then deliberately leaned over far enough to get the end of his tie under the blade. When he slammed down the blade, the end of his tie was instantly whacked off. Billy, examining the blunt end of his tie, pretended to be angry. Meanwhile, Charley burst one of the buttons on his shirt in raucous uncontrollable laughter.

While newspapers were his first love, fishing was the second and Charley made no bones of the fact that he loved to fish for crappie in the early spring. Charley said, even if he wasn't catching anything, he loved fishing.

"God covered the earth with three-quarters water," Charley would say jokingly. "That means God meant for man to spend three-fourths of his time fishing."

Then Charley would look impishly over his glasses.

"Don't it say that somewhere in the Bible," he would ask with a sly smile. "If it doesn't, it should."

Finally, after six months, Billy had learned every phase of desk work. He could lay out pages, write headlines, select and crop photos, write captions and guide the composing staff through the process of building each and every page of the Sunday newspaper. Thanks to Charley, he had learned all the fine points of the craft. He learned that a headshot should never look off the edge of a page. He learned how to "air" out a page to make dark borders or large type stand out conspicuously. Most of all, he learned how to balance a page from top to bottom so the reader's eye movement would be slow and pleasing from top to bottom. He learned to stagger headlines on a page which had no photos in order to break up the eye movement. His apprenticeship under Charley had been a truly great experience and Billy felt that he was now, thanks to Charley, a compleat newspaperman.

At the end of the sixth month, the executive editor called in Billy and told him he had "earned his stripes." With that, the young reporter told Charley he wanted to thank him for his patience, his understanding and his expert tutelage.

"How you going to do that?" Charley asked.

"I want to take you crappie fishing," William said.

Charley smiled happily.

"I'm ready when you are."

So the following Saturday morning, William pulled the tarpaulin off the new fishing boat which he had planned to use with his father. Since his father's death, he hadn't gone near the rig for fear that it might renew his feelings of loss. But, as he pulled the tarpaulin back and looked at the boat for the first time in seven months, he felt strangely calm.

After some thirty minutes of preparation, the boat was ready and Billy hitched the vessel to his car. Then, armed with the same fishing gear he and his father had used, he bought minnows for bait and went to Charley's house to pick him up.

"Where are we going?" Charley asked, loading his gear into the boat.

"The tree-tops," William answered, explaining how the place got its name. "My father and I used to go there. It's a secret place."

By the time the two had reached the headwaters of the Tallapoosa River and launched the boat, both fishermen knew that all the signs were right for catching crappie. It was a cool day in late April. The dogwoods were in bloom; there was no wind and the water was still as glass. At the first point where he saw tree limbs sticking out the water, Billy tied up the boat and the two men started fishing. In slightly less than an hour, they had caught more than forty crappie, every single one being 1- and 2-pound "keepers." The fish were biting so well that both men were using two reels and rods. As they would remove the hooked fish from one line, the cork of the other would be dancing across the water. Charley was catching fish so fast that he didn't have time to put them on a string. He just caught them, threw them in the boat, rebaited and tossed out the line again.

Then, as suddenly as it had begun, the feeding frenzy stopped. Finally, after some forty minutes of not getting a nibble, William suggested that find a new spot. As Billy started the engine, he knew Charley was having a good time.

"Now that's what I call fishing," Charley said happily. "I've never caught so many nice crappie in all my life."

Twenty minutes later, Billy had stopped the boat again and tied up to a new set of tree limbs.

"Let's try it here," he said.

With that, Billy baited two reels and rods and dropped the lines over the side of the boat. Charley, having selected a spot between two tree limbs, was trying to toss his line into the chosen area. On the third try, Charley's line had become tangled in the tree limbs.

"Damn!" Charley muttered under his breath.

Billy had seen his father do the same thing many times.

"Sit still," Billy said expertly. "I'll get it."

With that, he pulled the boat close enough to reach the fishing line. Then he untangled the line from the limb and handed it back to Charley.

"Thanks," Charley said with a grateful grin. "At my age, I can't reach like I used to."

William had seen the same vulnerable smile on his father's face many times.

"That's okay," Billy said.

After he returned to the opposite end of the boat, William took a seat again and looked at Charley. Charley had retrieved a minnow from the bait bucket and, very unsteadily, was trying to place the minnow on the hook. As he watched Charley trying to hook the flip-flopping minnow, he suddenly felt a cold shiver race up and down his spine.

"Oh, my God!" he said to himself, not believing what he was seeing. "Oh, sweet Jesus," he repeated.

As he watched Charley, who like his late father was not quite steady putting a squirming minnow on a fishing hook, William saw his dead father at the other end of the boat.

As he gazed at Charley, he was both amazed and frightened by what he was witnessing. Physically, Charley was almost identical to his father. Both men were small, about five foot eight. They were about the same age, Charley was 69 and his father had been 71 when he died. While his father had been a Welshman, Charley was Irish. Both men had very similar facial features, a flat forehead, receding brown hair, a strong lower jaw and both wore glasses with clear frames that were almost identical. Why had he never noticed these similarities between Charley and his late father before?

With that single thought, an amazing realization blossomed in William Vernon Johnson's mind. Charley was some sort of earth-ghost—a reincarnation, so to speak—of his dead father. During the past six months, Charley had inadvertently served as a substitute for his father. And he didn't even realize it! What an incredible, marvelous gift! Why had karma or life or whatever force that had sent Charley into his world done this? Why couldn't he have learned desk work and gone fishing with the grumpy city editor? Or the hard-nosed unsmiling state editor? Or even the young Czechoslovakian executive editor? How could karma have known that Charley was the absolute perfect substitute for his father? As fate would have it, the only person even close to his father—no, a person virtually identical to his father—had been sent to him in his time of need. Billy had received exactly what he needed in his life and, at the time it was happening, he wasn't even aware of it. Fate had worked in his behalf in the most marvelous way imaginable! It made no sense, but it had happened. Billy' eyes glistened with tears of joy and gladness as he looked across the quiet backwater. His heart was wild with delirious wonderment. His soul was singing.

At the other end of the boat, Charley was studiously watching his cork. Finally, he turned absently to Billy and noticed that the younger man was wiping his eyes.

"You okay?" Charley asked.

"I'm fine," Billy said, looking away. "I think I have something in my eye."

Disinterestedly, Charley turned back at his cork resting quietly on the surface of the glass smooth water. Everything was deathly still.

The following fall, Charley took ill. When he didn't come to work, Billy called his home and Charley's wife answered.

"He's in the hospital," she explained. "It's his heart. The doctors have told him time and time again that he shouldn't drink, but he slips around and…"

She didn't finish. She didn't have to.

"He's not doing well," she said.

"Where is he?" Billy asked.

"He's in the Holy Name of Jesus Hospital," the wife replied. "Room 418."

"I'll go over after work," Billy said.

Late that afternoon, before William got off work, the executive editor came over to his desk.

"Charley died about an hour ago," he said sadly. "We're taking up a collection for flowers. I know you will want to contribute."

Billy nodded.

Once the executive editor returned to his office, William picked up the phone. Charley's wife, trying to choke back tears, answered. After offering his condolences, William came to the point.

"I'd like to make a special request," Billy said.

"Anything," Mrs. Ryan answered. "You have been Charley's best friend over the past year."

"I want to be a pallbearer," he said.

"I'm sure Charley would have wanted that," the wife said.

So, two days later, as Billy and seven other men carried Charles P. Ryan's remains across the finely manicured cemetery grounds to its final resting place, he wept like a little child. All the grief that had collected inside his innermost soul for his father came pouring out in huge, uncontrollable torrents. It was a catharsis he couldn't have imagined six months earlier. After Charley was buried, Billy still missed his father, but that gnawing, lingering grief he feared he would never lose was gone forever. Now, thanks to Charley, Billy was prepared to live his life without his father.

***

The following fall, Billy went to an interview for a sports writing job at the Birmingham Herald, the biggest newspaper in the state. The sports editor explained that, while there were several promising young sports writers available, what he was really looking for was someone who could both cover sporting events and do some part-time desk work.

"You had any desk experience?" he asked.

"Oh, yes," Billy said. "I was trained by the best."

"Who?"

"Charley Ryan."

The sports editor was taken aback.

"Charles P. Ryan? The Charles P. Ryan that once interviewed FDR?," the editor asked.

"That's the one!" Billy said.

A broad smile broke across the editor's face.

"He worked here at the Herald with my father," the editor explained. "I've heard my daddy speak of Charley many times."

"Charley was quite a guy," Billy said.

"That's what my father always said," the editor replied.

The editor looked at Billy.

"When can you report to work?"

Even in death, Charley—the reincarnation of Billy's late father—was there to protect and nurture him.

LENNY

Looking For Love

The first time I laid eyes on Leonard Cohen was in the fall of 1975 during my second week of employment as a sports writer with the Birmingham Herald. One Friday afternoon in mid-October, I was putting the finishing touches on a story when I looked across the city room and saw a medium-build, slightly balding Jewish man with a sad smile, a sheaf of papers in his hand and his shirt-tail hanging out, making the rounds of the reporters' desks.

As I watched, I noticed there was an unmistakable underworld quality about this man. When he walked, it wasn't a true walking motion, it was more of skulk. The man's forward movement was that of a creature who wanted to move from point A to point B, but wanted to draw as little attention to himself as possible in the process. For the unknowing observer, it was a movement that spoke of a quiet evil, yet also inspired a certain yearning to know more about the man. This was the quality that caused me to ask about him from the first.

"Oh, that's Lenny," explained Laura Graves, secretary to the managing editor who, by virtue of that position, knew everybody and all the office gossip before everyone else. "He works on the copy desk and goes around taking bets on all the games."

Being a huge sports fan and an adventuresome soul myself, that short description was all I needed to introduce myself to this strange man and participate in his underworld business. On Friday afternoons, before the big weekend sports events, Lenny would make the rounds with his sheets which listed the teams, the odds, the points, projected winners and losers. You placed your bet, paid your money and Lenny kept a record in his little black book. On Mondays, Lenny would come around again, paying winners, notifying losers and explaining the next weekend's offerings. Usually Lenny took bets on college and professional football games, especially the NFL divisional playoffs and, of course, the Super Bowl. Invariably, he always had a big pool for the World Series and the annual Alabama-Auburn game. In the days prior to that traditional intrastate rivalry, Lenny was the man of the hour because everybody wanted to make a bet on their favorite team.

Lenny however, with his exotic strangeness, managed to take wagering into areas where other book-makers feared to tread. Once in the fall of 1975, after Spanish ruler Francisco Franco took ill, the Associated Press ran a story quoting doctors as saying that the celebrated dictator had only 24 hours to live. Thirty minutes after the wire was received, Lenny was making the rounds of the newspaper office with a pool placing bets on precisely when Franco would die. Naturally, I got into the fray and, when I chose my bit of paper from the hat Lenny was holding, I picked 5:30-6:00 p.m. that night. That evening, the generalissimo died at exactly 5:32 and Lenny paid me $920 for my winnings. It was the most money I had ever won in my life.

If you got Lenny started, especially about football or baseball, he would talk forever. One quiet Friday afternoon when Lenny was making his rounds, he and I started talking sports history. I ventured that the 1953 Yankees were probably the greatest baseball team ever. Lenny's eyes lighted up with wild enthusiasm. No doubt, he said. Not only were they the greatest team ever, there could never be so much talent on a single team ever again. Lenny and I must have talked for more than an hour, reminiscing endlessly about Mantle and Berra and Rizzuto and Martin and McDougald. From that moment on, Lenny and I were fast friends.

At the Whistle Stop, the local watering hole for the reporters and editors, Lenny was a regular. Lenny loved to drink draft beer, play eight-ball and talk about sports. After Lenny had had four or five beers, he took on a very special look. When the Allied Forces swept through Germany near the end of World War II and discovered the atrocities the Nazis had committed against the Jews, there was one world-famous photo taken at Auschwitz which summed up those atrocities like no other. The photo depicts a group of starved Jewish men and women staring forlornly from behind a high barbed-wire fence. In the photo's foreground, there is a single balding, bearded Jewish man—a virtual bag of starved skin and bones—who is gazing directly at the camera with the most pitiful, helpless look imaginable. It was a look that embodied a degree of tortured suffering and quiet terror which few human beings had ever endured and, once you had seen it, you never forget it. When Lenny had had a few drinks and was sitting alone, his face took on the same look as the Jewish man in the war photo. It was as if the spirit of the wretched Jewish man in the photo had somehow become imprisoned inside Lenny.

Details of Lenny's personal life were sketchy. His father, who had been a mid-level executive at one of the large steel mills in Pittsburgh, had moved his family to Birmingham in the fifties and began work for U.S. Steel. Lenny always said that coming to the south was the greatest thing that ever happened to him. Lenny always talked about how he loved southerners, southern cooking and being a newspaperman in Birmingham.

"I'll be here until the day I die," Lenny would say with a big smile.

After his parents had passed on, Lenny, who was in his early forties, lived alone and seemed to have no social life outside of his work, his wagering and the Whistle Stop. As far as anyone knew, Lenny didn't have a love life. He had never been married and he never talked about a girl friend. None of the guys had ever seen Lenny with a woman at the Whistle Stop, at office parties or around town. He never talked about a woman in his life.

On the other hand, Lenny had a wildly insane sense of humor about sexual subjects. Every December, the newsroom wags would take the Associated Press's stock Christmas photo, tack it on the office bulletin board then add their own naughty, signed punch lines. Every Christmas, everybody always waited to see what caption Lenny would add to the photo.

During the Christmas of 1975, the AP's annual Christmas offering was a photo of a beautiful, shapely young woman in a very abbreviated Santa Claus outfit smiling, waving and sliding rear-first down a stair railing.

The first punch line, written by the city editor, a dull married man of many years, was "Mrs. Claus warms Santa's Supper." The state editor, a tall macho-crazed man from south Alabama, signed and scribbled "I'll never cum this way again."

But Lenny, with his free-wheeling mentality and his ability to discover the exotic in the most mundane of circumstances, signed and scrawled "How to snatch a splinter...or vice versa."

Naturally, Lenny's line drew more attention and laughs than all the others. There was something secret inside Lenny that was truly glorious and majestic. Lenny was the true Walter Mitty. Lenny was the guy who, no matter how humdrum his workaday reality became, he always seemed to find some way to live life to the fullest.

In the spring of 1988, the assistant managing editor at the Herald was fired because he wasn't bringing in new customers. When he left the company, he took his secretary with him. The company president promptly hired a new assistant managing editor, but he couldn't find a secretary within the company to the new assistant editor's liking. Finally, after several weeks of advertising and interviewing more than twenty candidates, the new assistant editor found what he was looking for.

The candidate he chose was a statuesque, big-busted Jewish woman in her late thirties with billowing dark hair, handsome shoulders and neck and a proud classy bearing. Her name was Barbara Hoffman and she had been secretary to the editor of a small magazine in North Birmingham. When the new assistant managing editor called her former boss for a recommendation, he praised her to high heaven for her typing skills, her ability to get the right amount of sugar in his coffee and the smooth way she could cool off irate readers. She had been married to an attorney for several years but, at the time, she was separated and divorce proceedings were underway.

So the following Monday morning, when the Jewess took her new job, her desk was just outside the assistant managing editor's office and only one desk away from the copy desk where Lenny, the copy editors, the headline writers and the photo editors all designed and laid out the pages of the newspaper.

At first, the new secretary was quite an attractive addition to the newsroom and the primary focus of attention, especially among the single men. When she strode across the newsroom, all the men glanced up instantly to get a glimpse of her flowing black hair, her graceful stride and her warm, intelligent smile. Several of the single, unattached staff members, upon learning that she and her husband were separated, made half-hearted attempts at dating her, but all were politely turned away.

One morning, some two months after the new secretary had taken the job, Laura Graves pulled me aside.

"Ready for the latest?" she said slyly.

"What you got?" I asked.

"Lenny and the new secretary have got this thing."

"No..." I said disbelievingly. "Lenny and Barbara?"

"It's true," she said with knowing smile. "But, it's all very hush-hush. They're trying to keep it quiet."

"Are you sure," I asked.

"I got it from the horse's mouth," Laura said confidently.

I smiled at that. Laura, since she was secretary to the managing editor, had been Barbara's peer during her training period. As a result, they had become close friends. I knew that Laura knew what she was talking about. And I quickly realized what she was saying was true. Although it was not obvious, Lenny and the Jewess had become very chummy. There were the little signs. Lenny and the Jewess were conveniently showing up together at the water fountain. They were leaving brief little notes on one another's desks. Then there were furtive glances as they moved through the newsroom and slight brushings as they passed in the hallway. Then I noticed that Lenny and Barbara were leaving the office for lunch at the same time. Finally, one afternoon, I saw Lenny sitting in Barbara's car in the parking lot. There was definitely something going on.

I had seen it, but I wanted to hear it from Lenny.

The following Friday afternoon when Lenny made his rounds, I said I liked the Yankees against the Indians.

"I'm offering 7-2 odds on the White Sox–Red Sox game," Lenny said. "Chicago's top reliever is hurt and they are playing in Boston."

"No, I want the Yankees," I said, pulling a ten-dollar bill out of my billfold and handing it to Lenny.

"Be down at the Whistle Stop tonight?" I asked as Lenny scribbled in his little black book.

"Probably," he said absently, still scribbling.

"Can I ask you something?" I said moving closer.

"Sure," Lenny said off-handedly.

"Are you seeing the new secretary?"

Lenny looked around to see who was in earshot.

"Why do you ask?" he questioned, almost embarrassed.

"There's some talk."

"We're friends," Lenny said with a sly grin. "I can't talk right now," he added.

I nodded.

"I'll see you tonight," Lenny said, darting off to talk to the humor columnist on the other side of the newsroom.

That night, at the Whistle Stop, Lenny talked about it.

"Oh, I like her," Lenny said casually, sipping his beer, "but I could never get involved with a woman like that. You can't trust them," he said.

But two days later, Lenny and the secretary left the office within two minutes of each other to go to lunch. That afternoon, when the shift was over, Lenny's car and Barbara's car were parked side by side. When I glanced over at Lenny's car, I could see her inside and she and Lenny were embraced in a long kiss. I hurried past Lenny's car to my own and pretended that I hadn't seen anything.

Some two weeks later, Lenny and I went to lunch together. Lenny loved southern cooking and one of his favorite restaurants was Maude's Cafe on First Avenue North which served "down-home southern cooking."

After each of us had sumptuous helpings of fresh green beans, turnip greens, corn on the cob, black-eyed peas and cornbread, the table conversation turned to more mundane subjects.

"What did you do this weekend, Lenny?" I asked.

"I spent the weekend with Barbara," Lenny said, showing no emotion.

"I thought you said you weren't going to get involved."

Lenny looked at me.

"I'm not really getting involved," Lenny said confidently. "I'm just going to play it by ear."

I looked at him quizzically.

"What does that mean?"

"I'm just waiting to see what happens."

I didn't say anything.

"She's a hell of a woman," Lenny added, almost as an afterthought.

"I can see that," I said.

"And we have a lot of fun together."

"You've been seeing her over two months now," I said.

"Oh, I like her," Lenny said.

"There's nothing wrong with that," I said. "Maybe you should give love a try."

Lenny looked at me then laughed at this as if the suggestion had been some sort of joke.

"Let's have some blackberry cobbler," he ventured, obviously wanting to change the subject.

"Sure," I said obligingly.

I could see that Lenny had the bug more than he would ever dare admit. The look in his eyes, the quiet warmth in his face when he talked about the secretary, belied his standoffish attitude.

While Barbara and Lenny had tried to keep their romance under wraps during the first two months, they went public with it during the third month. It was almost an exhibition and it quickly became obvious to everyone in the office that Lenny and the Jewess were having a torrid affair. Suddenly, they were openly leaving the office together to go to lunch. They could be seen holding hands walking across the parking lot. When the copy editor called Lenny's apartment one Saturday morning, Barbara had answered the phone. Everybody in the office that didn't know about Lenny and Barbara in the past couldn't help but notice what was going on at that point.

Lenny was in love and something incredible had happened to him. For the first time in his life, he seemed so happy with himself and his life. His whole persona took on a certain glow that none of us had seen before. Suddenly, Lenny seemed so proud and positive about himself. Lenny's toilet improved. He started wearing more fashionable clothes. He was paying more attention to his hair and suddenly, when he made his rounds, his shirt-tail was no longer hanging out. Everybody felt the new secretary was having a good influence on Lenny. Now, Lenny was not only the office's answer to Al Capone, he was having this wildly passionate romance with the most beautiful woman in the office. Everybody could see that he was truly in his glory.

The following weekend, I saw Lenny at the Whistle Stop. Lenny had had five or six beers and I could see he was a little tipsy.

"This new running back Alabama's got is going to be one of the greatest," Lenny started.

"Oh, yeah," I said. "I saw the 67-yard touchdown run he made against Florida State."

There was a lull in the conversation.

"How you doing with Barbara?" I asked.

Lenny inhaled. As I looked at him, I could see he was pretty drunk. He had the look of the wretched Jewish man in the World War II photo.

"I don't know," he said sadly. "I never have been able to figure out women."

I studied Lenny for a moment.

"I thought everything with A-OK between you and her," I ventured.

Lenny inhaled again.

"I don't know what I've gotten myself into," he said finally. It was almost a confession. "I don't know what's going to happen now."

"Are you and her fighting?"

Lenny looked at me with hollow eyes.

"I don't want to talk about it," he said, managing a weak smile.

I didn't pursue the subject, but I could see that Lenny was trying to restrain himself from crying.

Two days later, I went to Maude's Cafe for lunch and saw Lenny sitting alone. My old friend looked like warmed-over hell. Obviously, he had been drunk the night before and I could see he was nursing a terrible hangover.

"Lenny, how you doing?" I began.

Lenny looked away as if he hadn't heard.

"Lenny, are you okay?" I asked.

"I'm okay," he said finally.

I dove into a plate of fresh vegetables and started eating.

"What you been up to?" I asked.

"I'm not seeing Barbara any more," he blurted out suddenly.

It was like a bolt from the blue. I tried to not act surprised.

"What happened?"

"It's a long story," he said.

I could see he didn't want to talk about it.

There was a long silence.

"So it's all over," I asked.

"Yeah," Lenny said looking away. "Cold turkey. I'm better off," he said, unable to hide the bitterness.

Suddenly, Lenny got up from the table.

"I got to get back to the office," he said quickly. "See you later."

I nodded.

As Lenny got up from the table, I could see there was something terribly wrong.

When I returned to the office, I made a bee-line for the Laura Graves.

"What happened between Lenny and the new secretary," I asked.

"Oh, she broke it off," Laura said. "She's back with her husband."

My heart sank when I heard that. At that point, I knew that Lenny was battling for his very soul.

The following Monday morning, Lenny didn't come to work. I asked the copy editor where Lenny was.

"Lenny's in jail," he said. "Barbara Hoffman had him arrested and charged with being a peeping tom. She caught Lenny peeking inside her bedroom window and called the police."

"How's he going to get out?"

"He's out. I went down and signed his bond this morning," the copy editor continued. "He'll be back tomorrow."

The following morning, Lenny was back in the office and everybody tried to pretend they didn't know what was happening in his life. Lenny went about his work as usual, made his rounds with the office pool and everybody thought things were back to normal again.

That night, Lenny didn't come to the Whistle Stop. All the regulars asked about Lenny and wanted to know what was happening with him. All of us figured that Lenny was sane enough and smart enough to not get into more trouble. But alas, it was not to be.

The following Monday morning, when Barbara arrived at work, she went straight into the managing editor's office. Some 15 minutes later, she emerged and immediately, Lenny was called in. After Lenny returned to the copy desk, I went straight to Laura.

"Mr. Bloomer laid down the law to Lenny," she said, nodding her head toward the managing editor's office.

"What did he say?" I asked.

"He told Lenny that if he was caught sneaking around Barbara's apartment again, he would be fired."

"Lenny was back again?" I asked.

"Oh, yeah, he's got it bad. Real bad." Laura continued. "He was parked outside Barbara's apartment all weekend. When she came out just before noon on Saturday, she said Lenny had followed her to the hairdresser. Then to her mother's house…then to the supermarket."

"And…"

"When she saw him outside the supermarket, she told him their relationship was over and she wanted him to leave her alone."

"So…"

"Lenny drove off. Then later that night, he was parked out front of her apartment again."

Laura said that the managing editor had almost pleaded with Lenny to stop stalking the new secretary, citing his unique abilities on the copy desk and his years of good service to the company. Laura said Mr. Bloomer made it clear to Lenny that, if Barbara reported again that he was stalking her, he would no longer be employed at the Herald.

"What did Lenny say?" I asked.

"Lenny promised it wouldn't happen again."

I shook my head sadly.

"I hope Lenny has learned his lesson," I said.

"So do I," said Laura.

The following Monday morning, when the Jewess arrived at work promptly at 9 a.m., she went straight into the managing editor's office again. With that, we all knew the end was near for Lenny. After she emerged some twenty minutes later, Lenny was immediately called in. While Lenny was inside the managing editor's office, company security came and cleaned out his desk. When Lenny emerged, company security, bearing his personal possessions, escorted him out of the newsroom for the last time.

When I returned from lunch that day, I knew I didn't have to ask Laura what happened to Lenny.

"What's Lenny going to do?" I asked.

"I don't know," she said, shaking his head sadly. "I know he loved working for the Herald."

For several months, Lenny disappeared. All the guys at the Whistle Stop asked about him, but nobody seemed to know what had happened to him. Somebody said he had gone to Florida. Somebody else said he was back in Pittsburgh living with relatives. Everybody wondered what happened to him, but nobody really knew. Lenny appeared to have fallen off the face of the earth.

Then one night, more than four months after he was fired, Lenny suddenly showed up at the Whistle Stop. All the guys were there and everybody was so happy to see him. They shook Lenny's hand, bought him drinks and wanted to know what he had been doing. Lenny talked about the new running back the Denver Broncos had acquired, the way the Orioles appeared headed to win the American League pennant and how the new quarterback at Alabama was destined to be a top Heisman contender. There was no mention of Barbara Hoffman.

Finally, we asked Lenny if he was working. With that, Lenny said he had landed a job with a group of automotive magazines in San Francisco.

"San Francisco?" somebody asked.

"Oh, it'll be great, Lenny said. "I've always wanted to live in San Francisco and I just love the 49ers."

Lenny said he was going to be executive editor of one magazine, have a staff of eight and have to answer to no one but the publisher.

"Sounds great," I said.

"Oh, I can't wait," Lenny said.

I looked at Lenny. San Francisco didn't sound like Lenny's kind of town. Maybe Atlantic City, Miami or Las Vegas, but not San Francisco. Despite this, all of us congratulated Lenny on his new job and wished him well. Finally, when the bar closed and the crowd moved outside, Lenny and I had a chance to be alone.

"Can you do me a favor?" he asked.

"Sure," I said.

"I need a ride to the airport Saturday afternoon. The movers will have all my stuff out by noon. Could you give me a ride?"

"Sure," I said.

"Say about 1:30."

"I'll be there," I said.

I was happy to be able to do something for my old friend.

On Saturday morning, I arrived at Lenny's apartment promptly at 1:15. His suitcases were waiting outside the door.

"Hi," Lenny said cheerfully. "All I've got are these two suitcases and a carry-on. Can you get these?"

"Sure," I said.

I lifted the two suitcases and carried them to the car.

Some five minutes later, Lenny closed the door behind him and, carry-on in hand, got into the car. With that, I pulled the car out of the driveway into the street.

"Wait!" Lenny said suddenly. "I forgot something."

I slammed on the brakes.

"What is it?" I asked.

"I want to tell you you've been a good friend," he said. "A damn good friend."

"You've been a good friend too," I replied, not understanding, "but we can say goodbye at the airport."

Lenny didn't say anything. He offered his hand.

Still not understanding, I shook Lenny's hand firmly. Then, carry-on in hand, he got out of the car.

"Lenny," I called out the car window, "what's wrong?"

He didn't look back.

"Lenny!" I called out again, louder this time. "Tell me what's wrong!"

He stopped and looked back.

"There's something I forgot to do!" he yelled back.

With that, Lenny turned, walked back up the driveway and went back into the empty apartment. I wondered what he had forgotten. It seemed so important to him. So I parked the car on the street and waited.

After some ten minutes, I began to wonder why Lenny hadn't returned. I looked up at the apartment, but there was no sign of Lenny. I figured he must be on the telephone. With that, I backed up the car, pulled back into the driveway and went to the door.

"Lenny?" I called through the open door.

There wasn't a sound. I didn't understand. Downstairs there was no sign of him.

"Lenny?" I called up the stairs. No answer.

With that, I started up the stairs. As I rounded the stair railing I looked into the first bedroom. It was empty. Then, as I glanced into the second bedroom, I gasped in horror. In one corner of the empty room, I saw Lenny slumped over on his side, a .38 Smith and Wesson revolver in his right hand. In his right temple, I could see a single bullet hole with a small stream of blood trickling down the side of his face and on to the carpet.

Lenny had forgotten he had to end it all. For all those years, his whole life—and the life he loved so much—had been the Birmingham Herald, the betting pools and his drinking pals at the Whistle Stop. The prospect of leaving all this and starting over all alone in a strange town like San Francisco were just too bleak for Lenny. But, as I looked at Lenny's limp body, I also saw something I had never seen before. In life, Lenny had always been a driven man, forever agitated, seeking, hustling. On the copy desk, he was always frantically rushing around handling copy, rewriting headlines and dealing with the composing room. With his betting operation, his mind was always in a frenzy figuring the odds, keeping the books and checking the game schedules. And, after a few drinks at the Whistle Stop, his face would take on the tortured look of the wretched Jewish man in the World War II photo. Now, in death, Lenny's face had a quiet, almost blissful expression. For the very first time, Lenny seemed to be happy and at peace with himself.

VIRGIL

"A Man of God"

From the very first, all that Virgil Collier ever wanted to do in this world was to be a preacher. Talking about God, quoting scripture and spreading the gospel meant more to Virgil than anything else. An avid student of the Bible, Virgil would spend hours explaining the teachings of the apostles, the mysteries in the book of Revelations and the "true" meaning of original sin. By the same token, Virgil took the Bible's teachings to heart and, for the most part, tried to live his life according to Christian principles. Virgil wouldn't lie, wouldn't steal and wouldn't deliberately hurt a fly. In fact, except for one small fatal flaw, Virgil Collier was a Christian in the truest sense of the word.

My cousin Roy and I first met Virgil in the spring of 1951 when he and his mother Ethel, along with his little sister Mary, moved into our grandmother's "block house." Since Roy's house was directly across the road from the "block house," he always met the new tenants before I did. So, one Saturday morning in late March when I went over to Roy's house, I saw Roy and a new kid playing marbles in the front yard. When Roy saw me, he jumped up and raced to my side.

"Who is that?" I asked.

"That's Virgil," Roy said. "He's crazy."

I looked past Roy to the new kid. Despite Roy's warning, Virgil appeared harmless enough so I went over and introduced myself. The new kid said he had 53 marbles, a signed picture of Lash LaRue and he could wiggle his ears. After I asked for a demonstration, Virgil took a deep breath and tightened the skin under the neck. Then, rapidly flexing his facial muscles, he could make his ears wiggle back and forth like a butterfly's wings flapping.

"That's neat," I said, genuinely impressed.

Virgil, Roy and I spent the rest of that Saturday playing together in the woods. We made bows and arrows, set out fishing lines at the creek and watched a family of flying squirrels in an oak tree behind Roy's house. Late that afternoon around 4:30, Virgil said he had to go because his mother would be coming home from work soon.

After Virgil left, Roy turned to me.

"Do you like Virgil?" he asked.

"He's okay," I said, unable to see any harm in the new kid.

"There is something wrong with him," Roy said.

"What do you mean?"

"He's not right in his head," Roy said, putting his index finger to his head and making a spinning motion. "I'm telling you he's not right."

Our grandmother said that, although Virgil's mother couldn't afford it, she had rented the "block house" for a whopping $25 a month. With her job as a cook at a local nursing home, our grandmother said she made only $22.50 a week, but she had rented the house anyway because she wanted a "clean, decent" place for her kids.

The Collier family was incredibly poor. Virgil, who was so skinny that the edges of his shoulder blades touched, seemed to always be hungry. If he was visiting my house or Roy's house and our mothers invited him to eat, Virgil always had something. Virgil's mother kept several chickens in a little wire coop out back of their house and every couple of hours Virgil would go check to see if there were any eggs. If he found one, Virgil would knock a hole in the end, sprinkle salt and pepper inside, then suck out the raw egg. Virgil didn't give a second thought to the exercise; he was hungry. But every time he did it, Roy would look at me and shake his head knowingly.

During that spring and summer, Virgil was 10 years old, the same age as me and Roy, and the three of us played marbles, climbed trees and fished and swam in the little creek that ran across my grandmother's property. Many Sunday afternoons, the three of us would have mud-ball battles at an old abandoned house in the woods. We would make hundreds of round, hard mudballs from the red clay earth surrounding the house, then run and throw them at one another. Although the three of us would always start out as one against the others, near the end of the battle, me and Roy would gang up on Virgil and together we would pelt him unmercifully with the stinging mud missiles. More than once, we sent him home crying to his mother.

Even then, Virgil's religious side was showing.

"Everybody that wants to go to heaven has to do right," Virgil would say. "Someday everybody will face God on his golden throne and answer for all the bad things they did in this world. If God isn't happy with them, they'll burn in hell."

"There's no such thing as hell," Roy would say, reflecting his father's staunch Jehovah's Witness beliefs. "Hell is here on earth."

"It is not!" Virgil would say angrily. "Hell is under the ground where the Devil tells everybody what to do and sinners burn in the eternal fires forever and ever."

"You don't know what you're talking about," Roy would say defiantly.

At that, Virgil's face would turn red with anger.

"You're a sinner!" Virgil would shout, "and God is going to get you. You just wait! Sinner! Sinner! Sinner!" he would shout, pointing at Roy. Then he would turn and run home.

Virgil never had a father. Once day while me and Roy and Virgil were fishing, I asked Virgil about his father.

"My father is in heaven," Virgil said.

"Is your father dead?" I asked, not understanding.

"No," he would say with obvious irritation, "I told you my father is in heaven."

With that, I would look at Roy for an explanation, but he would shrug and shake his head knowingly. I didn't question Virgil further.

The truth was that Virgil never knew who his father was. My grandmother said Virgil's mother, who had never been married, had "bedded lots of men" and once told her that she wasn't sure about Mary's father, but Virgil's father was either a storekeeper who lived over in Calhoun County or a man she met at a truck stop who was on his way to Atlanta. Virgil's mother added that, if the truth was known, she leaned toward the man en route to Atlanta because Virgil had brown eyes just like him.

When the Colliers moved out of the "block house" after only seven months, the new tenants reported that a strange man had awakened them one night scratching on the screen at their bedroom window calling the name "Ethel." After the man of the house threatened to shoot, the strange man ran away. My grandmother said later that the strange man was probably some "no-count" looking for Virgil's mother to "get her another young'un."

Four years later, in 1955, Virgil and his mother and little sister moved back into my grandmother's "block house." Although Mrs. Collier told my grandmother she had a better paying job this time—she was making $32 a week—the family seemed to be poorer than ever. As before, Virgil was always hungry. His little sister didn't have shoes so Virgil collected empty bottles and tin cans to sell to the scrap man to help buy her a pair.

Once the Collier family was settled into the "block house" again, Roy, Virgil and I started spending time together, except this time we did 14-year-old things. We built a "boys only" club house in the woods and tinkered with bicycles. Rather than mud ball battles, we worked off our aggression with coal lump battles. In the wintertime, Virgil's mother had a big pile of coal in the backyard for fires. After school, while Virgil's mother was at work, Virgil, Roy and myself would gather armfuls of coal lumps and throw them at one another. One winter afternoon during a heated battle, we broke out a window pane on the back porch with an errant lump of coal, but Virgil's mother never said anything. Two weeks later on a cold December morning, me and Roy saw Virgil's mother, armed with putty and a putty knife, replacing the window pane.

During the earlier period, Roy and I had seen flashes of Virgil's religious side, but now, at age 14, Virgil carried a small Bible with him wherever he went and he was always quoting it. He was very proud that he could name all the books of the Bible from Genesis to Revelations and it seemed that Virgil had a Biblical quote or story to point up some moral for every situation.

If Virgil wasn't quoting John 3:16: "For God so loved the world that he gave his only begotten son…" then it was Matthew 7:7: "Ask and ye shall receive, knock and the door will be opened, seek and ye will find."

It was also during this period that Roy and I learned Virgil had this morbid attraction for black women. There was a colored woman named La Wanda Jackson who would come to help my Aunt Gail, Roy's mother, with her housework from time to time. If Virgil knew La Wanda was at Roy's house, he always wanted to go over and look at her.

One day, when Virgil, Roy and myself were working on an old bicycle, we went to the work shed at Roy's house to find a crescent wrench. As Roy and I searched, Virgil was peeking through the cracks in the door at La Wanda, who was seated on the back porch peeling peaches.

"She's got nice strong legs," Virgil said, his eyes glued to the crack in the door.

Roy and I, digging through a tool box, looked over at Virgil. He wasn't talking to anyone in particular, probably to himself more than anybody else.

"Her slip's showing," Virgil observed. "I wonder what she would look like with all her clothes off. I think she would be right pretty."

Roy looked at me and shook his head knowingly.

In the fall of 1956, Virgil and his mother and sister moved out of the "block house" for the last time. My grandmother said Virgil's mother had gotten a new job as a housekeeper on a farm down at Moody's Chapel and the pay included a house to live in. It would be five years before Roy and I saw Virgil again.

During the summer of 1960, more than a year after we graduated from high school, Roy and I started hanging out at the Dairy Queen drive-in, a little fast food restaurant at the crossroads where all the local guys would gather on Saturday nights to talk about cars and girls. One night, out of the blue, Virgil showed up driving an old Dodge. When he saw me and Roy among the crowd, he made a bee line for us.

At age 19, Virgil was a strappingly handsome young man, tall, well-spoken and aware. Virgil said he had finished high school and was working at a service station in town. His goal in life was to be a preacher, he said, and he was saving his money to go to the Baptist Bible College up in Nashville. If he could come up with $1200, Virgil said he could work in the college kitchen, attend classes and get a minister's degree in two years. So far, he said he had saved $765 and expected to have the rest the following spring.

"I've been called to preach the gospel," Virgil said proudly. "The Lord come to me in a dream and told me that, if I would give my life to Him, he would take care of all my needs."

I congratulated Virgil on his ambitions and wished him well. Roy smiled politely and said nothing.

One night several weeks later, I was alone when I stopped by the Dairy Queen to get a hamburger and a milk shake. As soon as I pulled in, I saw Virgil in his old Dodge. He came over.

"Billy, don't waste your money here," he said. "Let me take you into town to get some barbecue. You like good barbecue, don't you?"

"I LOVE good barbecue," I said.

"I know a place over in colored town that makes the best barbecue in the world," Virgil continued.

"Let's do it," I said.

With that, we got into Virgil's car and drove to the colored section of the nearby town. As we pulled up in the parking lot, a neon sign reading "Pearl's" greeted us. Once we were inside, I gathered very quickly that Virgil was a regular.

"Howdy, Virgil," a young black woman behind the counter greeted him with a warm smile.

"Hi, Floretta," Virgil said.

"What you having today?" the black woman asked.

"You know I like dark meat," Virgil said, with a sly smile.

"And you want it real hot?" Floretta asked, muffling a quiet giggle.

"You know what I like," Virgil said, with another sly smile.

Later, in the car as we ate the sandwiches, I turned to Virgil.

"You seemed pretty friendly with that black girl in there."

"That's Pearl's daughter Floretta," Virgil said. "Me and Floretta are friends."

The way Virgil said that gave a sneaking suspicion that he was getting more from Floretta than barbecue sandwiches. But Virgil was right; the barbecue at Pearl's was the best I had ever tasted. Negroes had a talent for cooking the meat, making the sauce and putting together the sandwich that white people just didn't understand. I vowed I would return to Pearl's.

And I did. One night about a month later, I dropped by Pearl's for a barbecue sandwich. As I got out of my car, I saw Virgil's old Dodge parked out back, but I didn't see Virgil. I went inside and ordered a barbecue, but the only person inside was Pearl, the older black woman who owned the business. After I got the sandwich and started back to my car, I wondered why Virgil's car was out there but he wasn't, so I wandered over to the old Dodge. In the darkened car, I could see Virgil and Floretta naked in the back seat. They were changing positions.

Two months later, I was at the Dairy Queen one afternoon and saw Virgil again.

"I did it!" Virgil said happily. "I'm leaving next week on a bus for the Bible College up in Nashville."

"That's great," I said. "You'll make a good preacher."

After I said goodbye to Virgil that night, I never dreamed I would ever see him again.

Then one day in April of 1972, after I was named assistant Sunday editor at the Hamilton Courier, I was working in the newsroom when a tall, well-dressed man and woman walked in and asked for the religious editor. Absently, I glanced up at the couple, then back at my work. Instantly, I did a double-take. Standing in the reception area of the newsroom was Virgil Collier. I couldn't believe my eyes. As I looked at Virgil, I sensed that a miracle had taken place. The Virgil Collier I was seeing was not the same one I had known as a child. This Virgil Collier was all slicked up in a tailored suit and tie with long black hair swept back like a million dollars. Virgil was smiling big as day and looked like a man who owned the world. I went over.

"Billy Johnson!" Virgil said happily when he saw me. "I don't believe it!"

"Neither do I," I said, shaking Virgil's hand.

"The Lord works in mysterious ways," he said.

Virgil explained he had graduated from Bible College and had been pastor of a church in St. Clair County for nine years. Now he had a new church, the First Baptist Church of Hamilton, and wanted some publicity for a revival. He then introduced the woman at his side, a small, well-dressed blonde, as "Sister Evelyn," his "prayer woman." Finally, after Virgil and I talked briefly about old times, I guided him and the "prayer woman" over to the religious editor.

After they had finished their business, Virgil came back over to my desk.

"Now, Billy," he said, "I want to invite you to our revival. We're saving lots of souls."

I told Virgil that I wished him well, but that I was very busy with my job.

"Billy, every man needs God in his life at every moment," Virgil said. "Without Him, you're leaving yourself wide open for pain and heartache."

I didn't want to get Virgil started, so I lied and said I had been attending another Baptist church across town. Finally, Virgil and the woman said goodbye.

After they left the newsroom, I glanced out the window and saw Virgil and "Sister Evelyn" getting into a shiny new white Cadillac. As the Cadillac pulled away from the curb, I had to admit that I was glad for Virgil. Again, I figured that was the last time I would ever see him.

In the fall of 1975, I resigned my job at the Hamilton Courier and went to work for the Herald in Birmingham as a sports writer. One morning, about 8:30, I went into the Herald building and got on the elevator to go up to the newsroom on the fourth floor. As I stepped off the elevator, Virgil was waiting to get on.

"Billy," he said, recognizing me immediately.

"Virgil!" I said. "What are you doing here?"

Virgil explained that he had given some photos and an article to the religious editor to announce his upcoming television show.

"Television show?" I asked.

"Yeah," Virgil said proudly, "I'm taping the first one next Sunday. In six weeks, I'm taking the show on the road."

"That's great!" I said. "You're in Birmingham now?"

"Oh, yeah," Virgil said. "I've been the pastor at First United for almost a year now."

"That's great," I said hurriedly. "Well, it's good to see you. I've got to get to work."

"Wait, Billy," Virgil said urgently. "Why don't you come and pay me a visit?"

"I stay real busy," I said.

"You always say that," Virgil said. "You aren't so busy you can't visit an old friend, are you?"

"Well...," I said hesitantly.

"Just for old time's sake," Virgil pressed. "We got lots of catching up to do."

"Okay," I said, not wanting to get Virgil started. He handed me his card.

The following Saturday morning, I drove to Vestavia Hills and the First United Baptist Church on Birmingham's upscale South side. As I drove across the church grounds, I could see that Virgil was now in the preacher business in a big, big way. The church complex, which included buildings for Sunday School classes, a nursery, a catering hall, a Baptismal and the parsonage took up a whole city block. As I guided my car up the long driveway to the parsonage, gardeners on either side trimmed thick rows of rose bushes and flowering shrubs. Once I had parked and started to the door, I glanced inside the garage. Inside, I saw three shiny new white Cadillacs. I rang the door bell.

"Right this way, Mr. Johnson," the butler said, smiling politely and closing the door. "Reverend Collier is waiting."

With that, the butler led me up a small flight of steps to an elegantly furnished living room, then into a small office area where I saw "Sister Evelyn" seated at a desk and talking on the phone. Outside the office, on a patio, I could see Virgil, dressed in a robe, reading a newspaper.

"Billy!" Virgil said. "Welcome to my home."

Virgil got up and shook my hand.

"You remember Sister Evelyn?" he asked.

"Oh, yes," I said, acknowledging the woman.

"Sister Evelyn pays the bills and manages my business affairs," Virgil explained.

The woman smiled at me and waved politely. Then she looked over at Virgil.

"Reverend Collier," she said, "we have a new upstairs maid coming over for a tryout."

"Call me when she gets here," Virgil said. "Right now I want to visit with my old friend."

"Come on, Billy," Virgil said. "Let me show you my place."

With that, Virgil guided me through the parsonage room by room. In the living room, Virgil showed me the Italian leather living room suit the previous pastor had purchased as well as his collection of Biblical artifacts including a set of cups and saucers made during the time of Christ. On the mantle over a huge ornate fireplace, there were various photos of Virgil during his evangelistic career. There was a picture of Virgil graduating from Bible College; another of him shoveling the first spade of dirt for some new church building; and still another of him at the annual Southern Baptist Convention with the elders in the church's ruling council.

Virgil said he'd been pastor at the church for almost a year. There was a 2,500-member congregation, he said, and he ministered at regularly scheduled Sunday services as well as special church functions. Now that he had the TV show, he said he was going to have to work harder than ever.

"I know how to be a good preacher," Virgil said, guiding me up a flight of stairs, then down a hallway to the master bedroom. "Some men are preachers, but they will never be good because they don't how to put on a show. Me, I know how to put on a show."

With that, Virgil flung open two huge walk-in closets full of suits and ties and silk shirts and coats and shoes.

"Look at these, Billy," Virgil said, opening a display box which contained seventeen pair of sunglasses. "This pair right here," he said, pointing to a pair with shiny blue lens, "come all the way from Paris, France."

As we started back down the stairs to the expansive living room, I could see a young black woman, dressed in a short, blood-red outfit with lots of cleavage showing, vacuuming the carpet. I had never seen a house maid dressed so sexily.

"Remember Floretta?" Virgil asked as we walked back down the stairs.

"Oh, yeah," I said.

"Well, now I want you to meet my new friends," Virgil said.

Virgil motioned for the young Negress to stop the vacuum cleaner. Then he walked over and put his arm around her shoulder.

"This is Darnella," Virgil said with a big smile.

"Hello," I said.

The young Negress smiled politely, then snuggled up lovingly to Virgil. Finally, Virgil released the young black woman and escorted me outside the parsonage. There he showed me his swimming pool, his four tennis courts and the four-room air-conditioned dog house for his two prize golden retrievers.

"Being a good preacher has paid off for me," Virgil said proudly. "Now I got everything I ever wanted."

With that, we went back into the parsonage and the kitchen where Virgil introduced me to Callie, another young black woman dressed in tight shorts and wearing a thin top which was knotted over her navel. Virgil walked up to her and put his hand on her thigh. When he did that, the young woman smiled nervously and pulled away. As she did that, Virgil watched with amusement.

"Callie is a good cook," he said with a big smile, "but she does her best work in the master bedroom."

I looked at Virgil, saying nothing. He had to know that I could see through his charade. I thought perhaps he even wanted me to see the truth.

Once we left the kitchen, we arrived back at the office where "Sister Evelyn" was still on the telephone.

"Reverend Collier," she called.

Virgil turned.

"The new upstairs maid is here for her tryout."

"Tell her I'll be right with her," Virgil said.

From a shelf in the office, Virgil hefted down a thick photo album.

"Have a look at this, Billy," Virgil said, handing the album to me. "My mother is still alive and working at a restaurant over in Alabaster."

I took a seat and opened the album.

"My sister made a nurse and now she's married and lives down in Sylacauga," Virgil continued. "Why don't you just entertain yourself with that while I take care of some business."

With that, I continued thumbing through the photo album.

"Just make yourself at home," Virgil said. "I'll be back in a little while."

Virgil and the young Negro woman went up the stairs and I continued thumbing through Virgil's family photo album.

Suddenly, some ten minutes after Virgil and the young black woman had gone up the stairs, I heard loud, flailing sounds coming from the upstairs area, then a woman's screams.

I looked over at "Sister Evelyn."

She smiled.

"It's okay," she said.

Some twenty minutes later, Virgil, still in his robe, came back down the stairs. I could see that he was breathing hard.

"What were you doing up there, Virgil?" I asked.

Still trying to catch his breath, he didn't answer at first.

"I tell you Billy," Virgil said finally, "When you get the power of the Lord running through your veins, something happens to you. Sometimes I get so overcome with the love of the Lord, I have to have a woman or I'll go crazy."

"Virgil, you think a man in your position should be doing things like that?" I asked.

"I don't see why not," Virgil said. "I work hard enough. As far as I'm concerned, I deserve the best of everything."

"Reverend Collier," the prayer woman called.

Virgil looked up.

"You're due to start a prayer session at the hospital in two hours."

Virgil turned to me.

"Well," Virgil said, "I got to start getting ready to administer to the sick and the afflicted."

"I like your place here," I said.

"God has been good to me, Billy," Virgil commented. "When I was growing up, I had nothing, but now I got anything in this world I want."

"You've done well, Virgil," I said.

"We've BOTH done well," Virgil added. "Pretty darn good for a couple of country kids from Hamilton, Alabama."

With that, Virgil escorted me to the door.

"Now Billy, you make sure you watch my TV show on Sunday night at seven," he said. "You're going to see your old friend like never before."

I told Virgil I wouldn't miss it.

As I drove back down the winding, rose-lined parsonage driveway, I realized that Roy was right. There was one part of Virgil that just didn't fit with the other part. Virgil was living two very different lives and felt that he could keep one forever separated from the other. At one level, Virgil wouldn't do anything to hurt anybody else. There wasn't a dishonest bone in his body and he would never cheat, steal or deliberately tell a lie. On another level, he honestly felt there was no contradiction between his role as a churchman and his secret, insatiable lust for black women.

The following Sunday night, I turned on the television and there was Virgil, all slicked up in a blue suit and black and white shoes, his wavy, black hair swept back majestically and talking about how God saves only those who want to save themselves.

"Taking God into your heart is the easiest thing in the world," Virgil said, peering into the TV camera. "But you've got to let it happen. If you want Jesus in your life, you've got to open your heart and let him come inside," he emphasized, drawing a clenched fist toward his heart. "Jesus wants to come into your heart, but you must give him permission."

All the time Virgil was talking, a telephone number flashed across the TV screen in big white letters. It was the telephone number viewers could call to make their "prayer offerings." Behind Virgil, a group of church workers were busily answering a bank of telephones and taking pledges. Virgil was getting tons of money for telling the world all the things he used to tell me and Roy for free.

Finally, after preaching for some thirty minutes, Virgil asked that "all lost souls who need comfort and salvation come forth and receive the glory of God." With that, the choir sang "I'll Fly Away" and members of the church audience began slowly marching down the aisle toward Virgil.

Once they stood in front of him, they bowed penitently and Virgil put his hand on their heads one-by-one and said, "May the Good Lord bless and keep you."

As I watched Virgil touching the people's heads, I knew that his life-long dream had been realized in the most majestic way imaginable. The skinny, always hungry little kid who could wiggle his ears and quote the Bible had come a long, long way. But I also knew that Virgil's insatiable lust for black women would catch up with him some day.

Two months after my visit at Virgil's parsonage, Auburn's head football coach had a heart attack while having dinner one night at a Montgomery restaurant. The following morning, the sports editor called at 4:30 a.m. and asked me to report to the office as soon as possible. I jumped out of bed, showered, shaved and went in. When I arrived at the office just before 6 a.m., I went straight to the editor and he instructed me to get to Montgomery as soon as possible and get the scoop on the stricken coach. With that, I glanced down at the Herald's first edition sitting on the editor's desk.

On the front page, in big bold letters, the headline read "TV Evangelist Arrested in Sex Sting." Under the headline was a big photo of Virgil, dressed in a shiny black leather bustier, and two young black women being led away in handcuffs by police.

The story had a Montgomery, Alabama, dateline. It read:

Montgomery Police arrested one of the South's most famous television evangelists last night after police allegedly discovered the minister, his "prayer woman" and two known prostitutes cavorting in a Montgomery hotel room.

Virgil Joshua Collier, the 34-year-old founder of Virgil Collier ministries and producer of the popular "Old South Baptist Gospel Hour" was arrested without incident at the Essex Motel on Montgomery's upscale south side.

Rev. Collier, who was due to deliver a televised sermon at Montgomery's Civic Auditorium the following night, was jailed and charged with moral turpitude, two counts of soliciting a prostitute and indecent acts against God and nature. Rev. Collier was in Montgomery for the first leg of his televised statewide evangelistic crusade.

Arrested with Rev. Collier was Evelyn Ann Lancaster, 37, of Hamilton, who was Collier's long-time business manager and "prayer woman."

Miss Lancaster was charged with three counts of soliciting a prostitute and one count of renting a public habitation for illicit sexual purposes.

Police said the arrests of Collier and Lancaster grew out of an undercover sex sting operation the city's vice squad had been conducting.

Police Sgt. Homer Dunn, head of the department's vice squad, told the Herald:

"Police officers first observed Rev. Collier's white Cadillac cruising along Confederate Avenue in South Montgomery—an area frequented by prostitutes—around 8:30 p.m.

"Miss Lancaster, who was alone in the Cadillac, stopped and asked a black undercover policewoman who was posing as a prostitute if she knew how to do housework. When the undercover policewoman said housework wasn't in her line, Miss Lancaster told the officer she 'knew' what her line of work was.

"At that point, Miss Lancaster told the undercover officer: 'You don't really have to do housework. Just put on a maid's outfit and pretend. The pay is excellent.'

"When the undercover officer asked how much, Miss Lancaster said $500 an hour. For that amount, Lancaster told the undercover policewoman she was expected to put on a maid's outfit, then be stripped and whipped by Rev. Collier. Suspect Lancaster then told the undercover policewoman that, after the whipping, she was expected to have sex with Rev. Collier. With that, the policewoman got into the Cadillac with Lancaster and fellow officers followed it back to the Essex Hotel.

"Moments after the undercover officer and suspect Lancaster entered the hotel room, police knocked down the door and found Rev. Collier, dressed in a black leather bustier and leather pants, whipping two known prostitutes with a small riding crop.

"The two known prostitutes, who were dressed in maid's outfits and bleeding from the whippings, said Miss Lancaster had promised each of them $1,000 for their services," Capt. Dunn said.

Both Rev. Collier and Miss Lancaster, who are each being held in lieu of $100,000 bail, will be arraigned tomorrow morning in Montgomery County Circuit Court.

As I looked up from the article, one part of me was shocked. On the other hand, another part of me wondered just how Virgil had escaped this exact dilemma for so long. Whatever the situation, it didn't look good for

Virgil. It was the kind of story that everybody liked to hear about, talk about and read about. Worst of all, people would never forget something like this.

Two days later, when Virgil was released from jail, the court levied a total fine of $3,500 and required him to perform 40 hours of community service. That was the punishment of man's law. The law of God—embodied within the ruling elders of the Southern Baptist Council—had a different punishment in store for Virgil. Upon his release, the elders issued a statement saying that Virgil appeared to be guilty of profane adultery, the vilest act a churchman could commit. Also, after reviewing the church's books while Virgil was in jail, the elders found some "questionable" spending practices regarding household employees at the parsonage. Despite all of this apparent evil, the council of elders said they realized that Rev. Collier was popular with his congregation and had brought many new souls to the Lord during his tenure. As a result, the elders said they wanted to be fair and voted to have Virgil go on the television and tell his side of the story before they cast their vote.

So, the third night after Virgil was released from jail, he went on the television airwaves and pleaded his case before God, the elders, the members of the church as well as the state's television audience. Naturally, I, along with everybody else in the state, tuned in to hear what Virgil had to say.

"Well, ladies and gentlemen, the moment of truth is near," the mild-mannered, well-dressed announcer began. "Reverend Virgil Collier, the famous Baptist evangelist who made headlines as a man of God, will defend himself tonight against sexual and financial charges which could mean the end of his career as an evangelist. We now join our live broadcast from the First United Baptist Church in South Birmingham."

With that, the church complex I had visited in South Birmingham flashed across the television screen. Then, as the mournful refrains of "Shall We Gather at the River" grew louder and louder, Virgil, looking very crestfallen and penitent, appeared before the cameras.

"Tonight, my friends," Virgil began, "as I come to you from our glorious auditorium here at the First United Baptist Church, I am carrying a very heavy heart. As some of you know, I have been accused of vile and perverse acts. Some say that Reverend Virgil Collier has engaged in sexual perversity. There is some truth to that. You may also have heard that I took money from the good people of the Southern Baptist Convention. I can assure you there is no truth to that.

"Throughout my life, I've tried to live up to the teachings of the Holy Bible. I never drank, I never cursed and I never smoked. I have never stolen anything in my life. I have never borne false witness and I have always honored the Sabbath day and kept it holy.

"Despite this, I must confess that I am not a perfect man. Many times in the past, I have fallen victim to the sins of the flesh that every living man is heir to. As a result, I have lusted with harlots in foul beds. To some, this may seem like a terrible crime but, if you look closely at Biblical teachings, you will see that the same sin was committed by the greatest servants of God.

"King David, who was God's favorite, lusted after Bathsheba after he watched her taking a bath on her rooftop. King David even sent the woman's husband into the heat of battle so the husband would be killed and he could have Bathsheba to do with as he pleased. Despite these transgressions, God forgave David.

"Abraham, the father of Isaac, lusted after his neighbor's wife at the age of 63 and turned his own wife out of their marital bed so he could lust with his neighbor's wife. Despite these clear infidelities, God also forgave Abraham.

"And, in the old Bible, there was Joshua, one of God's greatest servants. Joshua traded horses to the Philistines in exchange for young, nubile concubines that he wanted to lust with in groups of two and three at a time. It was a great thirst that Joshua had to satisfy. In spite of this, God forgave Joshua and he became one of God's greatest prophets.

"Forgiveness has been a mainstay of Christian religion for all time," Virgil continued. "Even on the cross, Jesus forgave the robber before he died. The robber said, 'I have sinned' and Jesus said, 'I forgive you your sins and will remember you in the day of paradise.' And the robber was forgiven his transgressions.

"Now, ladies and gentlemen, I am asking that you forgive me MY transgression! I have admitted with a pure heart that I am guilty of sin. Like King David, Abraham and Joshua, I have lusted after the sins of the flesh. I know now that I made a grave mistake and I ask, with all my heart before Jesus, that you please forgive me…"

With that, Virgil fell to his knees, clasped his hands and looked skyward. The camera came in close on Virgil's face.

"Oh, God," Virgil prayed, "I have sinned. With true knowledge that I was violating the seventh commandment, I lusted with a harlot, no...two harlots in a foul bed. I was only a weak man living out the lust that myself and all other male creatures on this earth are heir to. Now, I stand before you asking that you forgive me these sins and let me continue your good work."

With that, Virgil, his hands clasped in prayer and huge tears streaming down his cheeks, looked straight into the camera and pleaded, "Forgive me, Jesus, Please forgive me for I have sinned. Please forgive me with your loving grace..."

Finally, the camera pulled back and Virgil's pleading voice faded as the mournful refrains of "Shall We Gather at the River" grew louder and louder. The mild-mannered, well-dressed announcer reappeared on the television screen.

"There you have it ladies and gentleman," he said. "The Reverend Virgil Collier, the famous evangelist who stands accused of adultery, moral turpitude, and perverse sexual acts against God and nature, has asked the forgiveness of both the Baptist Church's ruling elders as well as God himself. Now we have to await the results of the elders' vote."

It had been Virgil's greatest sermon and it had won the highest rating the TV station had ever seen, but it fell on deaf ears. Within an hour, the elders in the State Baptist Society voted 15-0 to oust Virgil from their midst. In an official statement, the elders, citing moral turpitude and other sins "too vile to mention," ruled that Virgil was banned from the Baptist church for all time. The church simply could not abide a man like Virgil, they said. The elders stated that, while the lowly parishioner could be forgiven his sins, church leaders were deemed true men of God and should hold themselves up as examples for all others. Also, regarding Virgil's last televised sermon, the elders explained there was no mention in the Bible of Abraham lusting with his neighbor's wife or of the prophet Joshua trading horses for concubines. This correction was the final nail in Virgil's coffin. As a preacher, Virgil was washed up forever. His reputation as a righteous, God-fearing man who obeyed the laws of the Bible was now a giant heap of ashes. And it was all his own fault.

The last time I saw Virgil Collier was in the fall of 1984 when I was in Hamilton to visit my Aunt Gail who was sick in the hospital. After parking the car, Roy and I were walking down the street to the hospital. As we walked past the finely manicured lawn of the Paloosa County Courthouse, I saw a group of homeless men loitering on the grass under a huge magnolia tree. Nearby, I saw a single, rough-looking man pacing across the grass and shouting to the sky.

Roy stopped and turned to me.

"Know who that is?" he asked, pointing to the man.

I shook my head.

"That's Virgil Collier," Roy said. "Nowadays, he preaches to God and lives with the Bay-Rum hounds."

I moved closer and examined the man.

The "Bay-Rum hounds" were a group of local drunks who, since the county was dry and alcohol could not be bought legally, drank "Bay Rum," a cheap brand of hair tonic, for its alcohol content. The "Bay-Rum hounds," preferring to stay drunk and sleep on park benches or in alleyways or wherever they could, were considered the local "bums" and always seemed to congregate around the county courthouse.

"That IS Virgil," I said.

For a moment, Roy and I stood on the sidewalk and watched Virgil.

Virgil was looking up at the sky, shaking his fist and cursing.

"You're an unfair God, you're unjust God and you're a God-damn liar," Virgil shouted at the sky. "You claim to know all and see all and be all, but the truth is you are a liar and a false God!"

Roy looked at me and shook his head sadly.

"I want to talk to him," I said.

"He's crazy, Billy," Roy said quickly, a warning tone in his voice. "You know that."

"I want to see him anyway," I said.

With that, Roy and I walked across the courthouse lawn to the magnolia tree. Virgil recognized me instantly.

"Billy," Virgil said happily, offering his hand and managing a smile. Virgil hadn't shaved or had a bath in weeks and smelled violently of sweat and dirt and cheap alcohol and urine.

"How ya doing, Virgil?" I asked.

"As you can see, I'm not doing too well," Virgil said. "They took everything away from me that I ever worked and lived for."

I nodded, saying nothing.

"They stripped me," Virgil said sadly. "Just over one small transgression."

Virgil was pitiful.

"In two days time, they took away from me everything I'd spent all my life working for. Remember the house I had? God, I loved it. Remember the Cadillacs? They took those too. And for what? For fornicating with black women."

Virgil stopped and looked at me.

"You can't find work anywhere?"

Virgil shook his head sadly.

"Have you tried to go out of state?" I asked.

"I've tried everything, Billy," Virgil said. "Nobody wants a preacher that's been fornicating with a black woman. No matter where I go, the taint follows me. Everybody remembers. Now I don't care any more."

I nodded understandingly, afraid to say anything.

"Billy, I tell you there is no justice in this world," Virgil said sadly. "There is no peace...no forgiveness."

Virgil's eyes filled with tears and he hung his head in shame.

"Let's go," Roy said urgently.

I nodded and turned to go.

"Take care, Virgil," I said.

Virgil, his head still hanging, nodded goodbye.

With that, Roy and I walked back across the courthouse lawn and continued down the street to the hospital. Behind us, we could hear Virgil still preaching to God.

"You're not fair and you're not honest! You're an unjust God," Virgil shouted to the sky. "You sit up there on your royal butt and treat people any way you damn well please. You promise peace and justice and forgiveness and fairness, yet you deliver none of those things. I say you're a God-damn liar, you understand...a God-damn liar...and the truth is not in you..."

Finally, Roy and I were out of earshot of Virgil and his blasphemous exhortations.

Almost two years later, in late January of 1985, Roy called me and reported that Virgil Collier was dead. Virgil was drunk, Roy said, and had fallen asleep in a drainage ditch in a field behind the Paloosa County courthouse. Overnight, the temperature had dropped into the high teens and, during the early morning hours, a sudden storm had dumped almost seven inches of snow on the little town. The following morning, the post-man found the body. Virgil, drunk from drinking hair tonic, had fallen asleep in the snow and frozen to death.

ONE STUPID MISTAKE

Another Joe Namath?

8:06 a.m. Nov. 4, 1973:> Eighteen-year-old Robert James Worthington, high school football star, honor student and senior class president, turned over in bed and opened his eyes. For a moment, he stared straight up at the white tongue-and-groove ceiling of his bedroom and tried to wake up. The big game, he thought, the big game with Lanier is tonight. Got to get up and get started.

With that, he threw his feet over the side of the bed and sat up. As the fog of sleep slowly faded away, he reached for a small gray vial marked "High Energy Protein Supplements" on the bedside table. The team doctor had said they were good for building strong muscle fiber. Popping the cap, he shook four of the tablets into his hand, replaced the cap, then swallowed them down with one big, dry gulp. Moments later, he was in the bathroom shaving.

8:36 a.m.:> Shaved, showered and dressed for breakfast, Robert James Worthington—tall, handsome, muscular, a fine specimen of a young American male—strode down the stairs to the family dining room where he saw his father seated at the table, sipping coffee and reading a newspaper.

"Bobby," the father greeted him happily. "The paper says Lanier's star fullback may not play today. He's got a pulled hamstring."

"It's not a hamstring," the son replied. "It's a groin injury. Our team doctor knows their team doctor."

"If he plays, it could make a lot of difference."

"Maybe," the son answered, seating himself at the table. "He's never played against a defensive line as fast and as strong as ours."

The son looked over at his mother, who was standing in a bathrobe at the cookstove.

"Morning, Bobby," the mother said.

"Morning, Mom. What's for breakfast?"

"Steak and eggs with hash browns.

"I like my hash browns well done," he said.

"I know, dear," she said patiently, placing a cup of steaming hot coffee and fresh cream in front of him.

"Belinda called earlier," the mother continued. "She said that you should drop by sometime after ten a.m."

"I've got to be at the stadium at two p.m. for pre-game practice," he said, taking a sip of coffee.

"I promised her I'd tell you," the mother pressed.

"Thanks, Mom!" the son replied.

"Also," the mother added, "Jimmy called. He said to tell you to bring the lucky chin strap."

"Oh, yeah," the son remembered. "It's in the medicine chest in the downstairs bathroom. Will you get it for me?"

"Soon as I finish your breakfast," the mother replied.

The son turned to his father.

"I'll need the station wagon to go to practice," he said.

"That's fine, son," the father said. "Now that you're going to college, you're going to need your own car," he added, looking knowingly at this wife.

"Yeah," Robert James Worthington said absently, taking another gulp of coffee. "And soon…"

"How do you see the big game tonight?" the father asked.

"We can beat 'em if we can get it all together. Their big fullback is our main concern right now.

"You're gonna stomp 'em," the father said confidently.

"I hope so."

"Oh, you will," the father said again. "You're Bobby Worthington."

With that, eighteen-year-old Robert James Worthington's mother placed a huge platter, brimming with rib-eye steak, three scrambled eggs, well-cooked hash browns and a side order of protein-rich wheat toast in front of him. With no time to waste, Marshall County High's class president, top student and star quarterback dove right in.

10:06 a.m.:> Enjoying the crisp late November weather, Robert James Worthington swayed lazily in the front porch swing with beautiful Belinda Wilson, his fiancée, class valedictorian and head cheerleader at Marshall County High. A tall, statuesque brunette, she and Bobby had been going steady since they were juniors and had been engaged for seven months.

"After we graduate from Marshall," she said wistfully, "I want to get married, but I don't want to have any children until I get my degree."

"That's fine," the star quarterback said. "We can live in the married dorms on campus."

"After I get my degree and teach for a couple of years, then I want to have a child."

"I thought you wanted two," he injected.

"I do. A boy and a girl, but I want them to be spaced a few years apart."

"Your dreams are already laid out, aren't they?" he asked, almost making a statement.

"They sure are."

"All of that will happen," the star quarterback assured her. "Just the way you've planned it."

"I can always count on you," she said, looking at him lovingly.

He smiled.

"We'll be so happy together," Belinda said blissfully, "I love you so much."

"I love you too," he said, kissing her lightly on the lips, "but right now I got to get to practice."

"Tonight's going to be your big night," she said.

"Not unless I can throw some big passes to Jimmy," he said.

"You just wait," she said, smiling reassuringly. "You're Bobby Worthington."

2:04 p.m.:> Driving the family station wagon, Robert James Worthington pulled into the stadium parking lot at Marshall County High School. He was late. Jumping out, he pulled an equipment bag out of the back seat and hurried along the concrete corridor to the dressing room. As he walked in, the team was seated in front of the coach on gym benches.

"Bobby!" Coach Tom Walters said, looking up. "Let's go. We've got lots of work to do."

With that, Robert James Worthington took a place in the front row among the seated players.

"Tonight, we're going up against one of the best high school football teams I've ever seen," the coach began. "They can run the football, they have a highly effective passing and kicking game. If we're going to win tonight, we've got to be fast, we've got to be strong and we've got to be mean."

Robert James Worthington listened intently to his coach. Also listening and seated in the front row beside him was Jimmy Hagan, the star quarterback's best friend and the team's star receiver. Since the day the two had entered Marshall County High as freshmen four years earlier, Bobby and Jimmy had become the best of friends. They took the same classes, dated together, knew the intimate details of each other's personal lives and, when they were away from school, spent most of their time together.

As athletes, Bobby and Jimmy were perfect complements. During the 1973 Marshall High baseball season, Bobby had been the star pitcher and Jimmy the catcher and the team won second place in the state finals. On the school's basketball team, Jimmy, who was slightly taller, played center and Bobby played forward. Together, they had led Marshall High to the district basketball championships. But their greatest match-up was as a quarterback and pass receiver. In three years, Bobby and Jimmy had rewritten all the standing records for quarterbacks and receivers in the school's history. During the 1973 season alone, they had connected for a remarkable 34 touchdowns, which broke the old record of 32 set way back in 1946.

The coach was finishing his speech.

"Okay, men, meeting's over." the coach barked. "Let's get out there and start hitting."

As the meeting broke up, the coach turned to his star quarterback and receiver.

"Bobby! Jimmy!" he called.

Robert James Worthington and his best friend turned to their coach.

"You guys got your pass patterns down?"

"We're real close," Bobby said.

"Close ain't good enough," the coach said crisply. "We can't win unless you guys can pull off some big pass plays."

"We know, Coach," Bobby said.

The coach looked at his star players.

"Okay," he said. "Jimmy, you go on out and start warming up. Me and Bobby's got to look at some game film, then we'll be out."

2:38 p.m.:> Robert James Worthington and his coach, sitting in the film booth, watched the small movie screen as the flickering images of football players danced across it.

"Now you can see how that big guard is coming in from the left side of the line," the coach explained, pointing to the screen. "If you have to scramble, scramble right. That way, you'll be behind the strong side of our line."

Robert James Worthington nodded with understanding.

"It's the little things that win football games," the coach said.

They turned back to the screen and watched for several more minutes.

"Now you see right here," the coach said again, pointing to the screen, "Jimmy is running a post pattern and you were looking for a slant."

"Yeah," Bobby agreed.

"If the defender had been three yards closer, he could have intercepted the pass. That's why you and Jimmy have got to have the pass patterns down. I mean down perfectly with no margin for error. We can't afford any stupid mistakes."

The star quarterback nodded.

"One stupid mistake, just one...can cost us the whole game," the coach emphasized. "It's the same in life. A whole lifetime can be destroyed in one moment of stupidity."

4:38 p.m.:> Robert James Worthington, suited up at quarterback, was on the practice field scrimmaging with the Marshall High offensive team. Nearby, Coach Walters and a bevy of assistant coaches watched intently.

Over the past hour, Bobby had put the team through a series of the team's basic running plays. Now they were going through the pass plays.

"Give me a short slant pass over the middle," the coach barked.

The offensive and defensive teams went into a three-point stance.

"Hut! Hut!" Bobby barked to the center. At the snap, Bobby took the football and backed up into the pocket, then watched as Jimmy raced through the line of defending backs. At the precise moment, Bobby released the football with an almost playful flipping motion and the football plopped into Jimmy's outstretched hands like pure magic.

"Good work!" the coach, clapping his hands, shouted from the sidelines. "If you two can complete pass plays like that tonight, we'll kick their butts."

"Okay," the coach continued, stepping forward and motioning for the players to gather around him. As instructed, the players sidled up and formed a circle around their coach.

"I think we're ready," he said, glancing through the crowd. His eyes stopped on his star quarterback.

"What about the trick two-point play?"

"We've been working on it, Coach," Bobby said.

"Working on it ain't good enough," the coach said crisply. "I want you guys to spend the next hour running it over and over until you get it down. Okay?"

Bobby and Jimmy nodded obediently.

"We're going to win tonight," the coach continued. "That means we've got to put it all together."

He stopped again.

"Game time is 7 p.m. Anybody that's not in the dressing room and suited up at 6:00 will be in big trouble with me. Got that?!"

"Yes, sir!" the team shouted in unison.

"That's all!" the coach barked.

With that, Bobby, Jimmy and the other players watched as their coach, clipboard still in hand, turned and walked back to the dressing room.

"We got a job to do tonight," Bobby said, turning to Jimmy.

"I know" his best friend said.

"Let's work on the secret two-point play."

"Okay," Jimmy said. "Where's the lucky chin strap?"

The star quarterback reached in his hip pocket and withdrew the worn chin strap.

"Great!" Jimmy said happily, taking the piece of leather and rubbing it across his chin. "We're gonna kick their butts."

For the past two years, Bobby and Jimmy had had a superstition about the chin straps they had worn during the 1971 state championship game. In that game, nobody dreamed that Marshall High had a chance against a mighty Phillips High team from Birmingham. But Bobby, a sophomore who took over in the third quarter when the first-string quarterback was injured, had thrown a miracle pass to Jimmy in the closing seconds to win the game. Jimmy said the ball "hit my chin strap and just bounced into my hands." The now-famous pass play had made stars out of both players and they had saved the "lucky" chin straps. Since then, the two had made it a point to wear the "lucky" chin straps during all their big games.

7:08 p.m.:> Robert James Worthington, football helmet in hand, watched silently as the stars and stripes were raised and the assembled crowd of football fans sang the national anthem. Around him, the Marshall County High School stadium was filled to capacity. On one side, some 15,000 delirious Marshall High fans were clamoring to see their team give cross-state rival Lanier High a sound thrashing. On the opposite side, the stands were packed with screaming Lanier fans who carried signs and shouted victory chants in support of their team. Finally, with the words "land of the free and home of the brave," a massive yell erupted from the stands and the two teams took the field to do battle.

Lanier High won the coin toss and elected to receive. After two short gains and a failed pass attempt, however, they had to punt. Robert James Worthington and the Marshall high offensive team took the field. But the Lanier defense was tough. After two short passes and a busted running play, Marshall High had to punt. The big game was now underway.

8:42 p.m.:> At halftime, with Lanier High ahead 14-7, the Marshall coach said the team had done well to establish a running game, but the Bobby-Jimmy combination hadn't clicked yet.

"What's wrong?" he asked, turning to his star quarterback and receiver.

"I can't get open," Jimmy said. "Their guy on defense is really fast."

"I told you he's fast," the coach emphasized. "In their game with Jefferson, their quarterback only completed four passes. That same defender was with their receiver step-for-step on every play."

"We could send out other eligible receivers," the star quarterback suggested.

"No," the coach said thoughtfully. "He's got to have a weakness of some kind. Either that or we've got to find some way to throw him off his game."

"We haven't found it yet," Bobby said.

"Be watching!" the coach said.

9:55 p.m.:> With 2:12 left in the fourth quarter and Lanier ahead 21-14, Marshall High took over on downs on their own 37-yard line. Marshall was in a do-or-die situation. In the huddle on first down, Robert James Worthington called for a short slant pass.

"Jimmy, when you run the pattern, go straight out, then suddenly veer sideways, then go back in a straight line." the quarterback said.

"We've never run that pattern in practice," Jimmy replied."I know," the quarterback said. "Let's see what the defender does."

At the snap, Jimmy ran the pattern exactly as the quarterback had suggested. Immediately, when Jimmy went back to the straight route, he broke free and easily caught the pass for a 15-yard gain.

"That's his weakness," Jimmy said back in the huddle. "He does fine going from a straight line to a lateral motion, but he's all thumbs when it comes to moving from a lateral move back to a straight line."

"I know! I know!" Robert James Worthington said, smiling happily. "See the gold streamers hanging down on the goal posts?"

Jimmy Hagan looked away from the huddle toward the opposite end of the field.

"Yeah," he said.

"Line up directly in front on the streamers and imagine a straight line between you and them."

"Okay," Jimmy said, peering down the field.

"Off the line and about ten yards out, veer off to the right, then come back and run in the same straight line toward the streamers."

"Got it!" Jimmy said.

"I'll hit you about the ten," Bobby said, rubbing his lucky chin strap.

With that, the Marshall High team broke huddle. As Jimmy broke from the line of scrimmage, the Lanier defender was keeping stride with him. Even as he veered off, the defender stayed right at his side. But once Jimmy fell back into the straight line pattern, the confused defender lost several steps and Jimmy broke free and clear.

Robert James Worthington could see that his tight end was racing ahead of the defender. Standing confidently in the pocket, he cocked his arm and threw the football. More than 30,000 pairs of eyes followed the football as it arched high above the stadium. Spiraling through the crisp November night air, the football traveled to the exact spot it had been intended at the ten yard line. As Jimmy Hagan caught the football and raced into the end zone, the Marshall High fans went wild with delirious joy.

Raising his arms happily in a triumphant salute, Robert James Worthington trotted back to the sidelines.

"Great work!" the coach said happily. "Now," he said, "get back in there! Run the trick play!"

As the Marshall High team trotted back on the field for the extra point, the score was 21-20 in favor of Lanier.

As the Marshall team lined up for the extra point, it was obvious to the Lanier defenders that Marshall was going for two points and the win rather than one point and the tie. They knew something fishy was about to happen, but they didn't know just what. The obvious two-point play was for the quarterback to take the snap and pass the football, probably to Jimmy Hagan. They were 99 percent sure it would be some kind of pass.

At the snap, the ball was centered to Jimmy Hagan. As the Lanier defenders looked on in confused horror, Jimmy slipped into the pocket and Bobby went out for the pass. Five seconds later, Bobby Worthington hauled in the 14-yard pass and stepped into the end zone. This was the very last time the Lanier defenders had expected. All of them were convinced the ball would be centered to the quarterback who would then pass it, probably to Jimmy. It was a complete reversal of roles for the star quarterback and his favorite receiver and it took the Lanier defense totally by surprise. It was the old Alabama "Flea-Flicker" play and it worked to perfection. As the confused Lanier defenders threw up their hands in disgust, the game clock ticked off the last few seconds and the final scoreboard read Marshall High 22, Lanier High 21.

10:30 p.m.:> After the big game, pandemonium reigned supreme in the Marshall High dressing room and it was filled to capacity with celebrating fans, school alumni, well-wishers, the players' families and friends and, of course, the press.

"You're gonna be one of the greatest," sportswriter William Vernon Johnson said, hunkering down in front of star quarterback Robert James Worthington as he removed his shoulder pads. "You got the arm, the eye, the quick release, the timing...everything you need to be a great quarterback...You could be another Joe Namath."

Bobby Worthington inhaled thoughtfully.

"Nothing on earth would make me happier," he said. "I love the game of football."

"How does it feel to have a full scholarship to the University of Alabama," 32-year-old Billy Johnson asked.

"I always wanted to play for Bear Bryant," the quarterback said. "To play for the Bear and be a star quarterback at Alabama is the greatest dream I ever had…"

"And you got a 4.0 grade point average to go with it," Billy Johnson noted. "Is there anything you can't do?"

The star quarterback laughed self-consciously.

"I've been lucky," he said, reaching down and touching the chin strap on his helmet.

"What'll it be after college?"

"Either the pros or med school," the quarterback said. "If I play in the pros, I'd like to play for Dallas."

"One last question," sportswriter Johnson ventured.

"What's that?"

"How does it feel to have the world on a string?"

Robert James Worthington paused to consider the question.

"Pretty good!" he said, with a slow, confident smile. Then, almost as an afterthought, he added: "No, not just pretty good; it's great!"

11:03 p.m.:> Robert James Worthington, dressed in street clothes, was walking from the football dressing room to the stadium parking lot with his girlfriend Belinda and Jimmy Hagan when he saw place-kicker Wayne Thompson hurrying to his car.

"Wayne!" Bobby called.

"Hey!" the place-kicker answered.

"My folks are having a little victory celebration over at my house," Bobby said. "You're invited."

Wayne hesitated.

"No, I better not," he said apologetically. "My girlfriend's mother is in the hospital. I promised I'd be there after the game."

"Okay," Bobby said, "Maybe some other time."

"Thanks anyway," Wayne said. "See you later."

With that, Wayne Thompson, having made possibly one of the most important decisions of his life, waved goodbye to Robert James Worthington and continued walking to his car.

12:04 a.m.:> All the people who were important in Robert James Worthington's life—his parents, his girlfriend, Belinda, his best friend, Jimmy Hagan, and his head coach Bill Walters—were all present at his parents' celebration.

For the event, his father had bought four magnums of champagne and his mother had prepared cheese snacks, green onion chips and dip and finger sandwiches.

For Robert James Worthington's father, the night was a cause for true celebration so he wasted no time opening the champagne. After several toasts and a round of glorifying comments, Bobby had four or five glasses of champagne.

"Did Marshall High play a great game or what?" Bobby's father asked the crowd jubilantly. A whoop of joy and elation erupted from the crowd. Finally, after the celebratory mood had died down, the father asked for quiet.

"I got something I want to say," he said. "All of you know how proud I am of my son. He has been the greatest son I could ever have asked for."

There was a round of approving nods and proud smiles from the crowd.

"What I'm about to do is really just a little thing, but I wanted my son to know how proud I am of him," the father said.

With that, he motioned for the crowd to come out to the garage. Outside, he unlocked the garage door and opened it. The assembled crowd gave a collective gasp of envy as the door raised and revealed a brand spanking new 1974 Ford Custom Sports Sedan.

"Wow!" Robert James Worthington said, his eyes glistening with delight. "This is great. Just great!"

With that, he opened the door to his new car. "Wow! Leather seats. Cassette deck and factory air. Sports package. Oh, dad, this is too much!" he said joyfully.

"Nothing is too good for my son," the father said.

With that, the son hugged his father. The older man beamed with delight. Tears of joy formed in the father's eyes as he held his son tightly for a fleeting moment. Finally, the father broke the embrace and kissed his son on the cheek. Then, beaming proudly, the father reached into his pocket and pulled out the keys.

"Go ahead!" he said. "She's all yours."

"Jimmy!" Robert James Worthington said, taking the keys. "Come on, let's take her for a spin."

"Ready when you are!" Jimmy said.

"Are you okay to drive after that champagne?" the coach asked.

"Oh, sure," his star quarterback replied confidently.

With that, Robert James Worthington got inside the car and started the engine. For a moment, he listened as the mighty engine roared.

"That's music to my ears," the star quarterback beamed as his best friend got in and slammed the door on the passenger side.

"We'll be back," he said.

"Be careful!" Belinda cautioned, as the star quarterback backed the car out of the garage.

"We will," her husband-to-be replied with a confident smile.

12:38 a.m.:> Robert James Worthington pulled the shiny new sports car off the residential side street and on to the main highway.

"It's really a nice machine," Jimmy commented, opening the passenger side window to let in the crisp November night.

"Yeah," the star quarterback agreed happily. "It's a V-8. Let's see what this thing will do."

Jimmy looked at the speedometer.

"She'll do up to 140," he noted.

"And probably more," the star quarterback added. With that, he rammed the accelerator pedal to the floorboard and the speedometer began to climb.

"The straight-away over the lake is just around this curve," Robert James Worthington said. "I'll open her up then."

Within seconds, the sports car was whizzing along the rural highway at 95 miles an hour as both young men watched the speedometer climb.

At 100 miles an hour, Jimmy, a worried look on his face, was no longer enjoying the ride.

"Bobby," he said, "we're going too fast. You better slow this thing down."

"Nah," the star quarterback said confidently. "These things are made to go fast."

With that, he pushed the accelerator all the way to the floorboard and the speedometer shot up to 105 miles per hour. As the car rounded the curve and approached the bridge to the lake, Robert James Worthington suddenly saw two concrete blocks that had fallen off a truck in the middle of the highway. At 110 miles an hour, Robert James Worthington swerved very slightly and missed the first block, but the four glasses of champagne had dulled his reflexes just enough that it was too late to avoid the second one.

"Look out!!" Jimmy screamed, genuine fear in his voice.

For a brief instant, Robert James Worthington tried to brake, but it was too late. The car's right front tire hit the second concrete block dead-on and, since it was traveling at 110 miles an hour, the car flew up into the air and flipped over the bridge railing. As the car tumbled through the air, Robert James Worthington watched helplessly as his best friend was thrown out the open passenger window and he could feel himself being tossed around willy-nilly inside the vehicle. As the car slammed on to the surface of the water right side up, the star quarterback instantly regained his senses. Water was pouring through the open passenger's window and that side of the car was rapidly sinking.

Robert James Worthington knew he had to act quickly. Wasting no time, he tried to force open the driver's side door, but it was stuck. With all his might, he pushed against the door again and again but it was futile. The car was almost filled with water. Quickly, he jumped to the passenger side of the car and tried to pull himself through the open passenger window, but the onslaught of water pouring into the car was too much for him. Twice, three times, four times he tried, but with each new effort, the force of the water rushing into the car pushed him back. He had one last chance. Quickly, with his head underwater and holding his breath, he swung himself into the rear seat and, with desperate fists, he beat on the car's cracked rear window, but he was helpless to break the glass. He was trapped. The interior of car was totally filled with water now and he had no breath left. As his oxygen-starved body thrashed helplessly in the last throes of life, he thought to himself: "This can't be happening to me. I'm Bobby Worthington."

1:14 a.m. Nov. 5, 1973:> Once filled with water, the shiny new 1974 Ford Custom Sports Sedan sank slowly and quietly to the bottom of the lake. Inside, the star quarterback's bloated body—eyes still wide open, lungs and body cavities completely filled with water—floated aimlessly within the murky, liquid darkness. Eighteen-year-old Robert James Worthington, high school football star, honor student, class president, lover boy and a young man who had "the world by a string" was dead.

ELAINE

The Dream Girl

William Vernon Johnson could get women if he wanted them. He was a good-looking guy, sexy, charming, well-spoken, the kind of man that women would naturally perk up to when he was around. Not only could Billy attract women, but he knew what, when, why, where and how to say the right things to worm his way into their hearts. And once he had arrived, he was expert at discovering those secret places within a woman's body that would make them moan and scream and call his name. Even now, at age 45, Billy still got more than his share of invitations, subtle "come hither" looks as well as outright propositions. Attracting members of the opposite sex was not a problem for Billy Johnson.

His first marriage had been an ill-advised affair. In late 1966, Billy began dating a secretary who worked for a Hamilton auto dealership. Although neither Billy nor Charlotte wanted to get married, they loved to go to the drive-in together, listen to Herman and the Hermits and roll around in the front seat of his 1962 Chevrolet. This went on for over a year. Then in the spring of 1967, Charlotte woke up one morning and began vomiting. Three months later, when she began to show, the two decided they should be married. When their daughter Barbara was born in the spring of 1968, the child quickly became the light of both their lives. Although Billy and Charlotte's marital relationship began to wear thin shortly after the birth, they remained partners for the child's sake for almost five years. By then, the marriage had become little more than a business arrangement. Finally, in the spring of 1978, after both had been involved in extra-marital affairs, Billy and Charlotte decided to call it quits. Although Billy and the child's mother agreed that she receive primary custody of Barbara, Billy and his daughter maintained a close, personal relationship during the years following the divorce.

Now, in mid-September of 1986, eight years after the divorce, Barbara was 18, engaged to be married and a first year student at Birmingham-

Southern College. Although Billy's daughter had urged him to "get married and settle down again." he had sworn it would never happen. After all, he was basically married to his job at the Herald. As an assistant editor in the Herald's sports department, he spent at least 10 to 12 hours most days either talking to coaches and players in several different sports or actually covering sporting events in person. During football season, he was the paper's foremost authority on the University of Alabama football team and the state's coaching legend, Paul "Bear" Bryant. The job wasn't perfect, but it provided him an enormous sense of personal fulfillment and the money was pretty good. It wasn't a bad life.

***

When Billy could find time away from his job, his favorite pastime was playing golf with his best friend, Herald photographer Tommy Thompson, at the Roebuck Public Golf Course in East Birmingham. Tommy, a confirmed bachelor, considered himself an expert on the subject of women.

"All that women are good for is bonking and having fun with," Tommy said, as he maneuvered the golf cart up a steep hill, then jerked to a sudden stop behind another golf cart.

Ahead of them, on the par 5 sixth hole, a foursome was playing through.

"No, I don't agree," Billy said, shaking his head doubtfully. "There has got to be more to the male-female relationship that just sex and partying. God, in his infinite wisdom, didn't intend for human beings to just move from one sexual encounter to another."

"Why not?!" Tommy asked exuberantly. "Personally, I just LOVE sexual encounters."

"You know what I mean," Billy continued seriously. "There has got to be some kind of spiritual connection between a man and a woman…an exchange of ideas…some kind of intellectual bond…"

"So how come you didn't like Sylvia?"

"The one you lined me up with last week?" Billy asked.

"Yeah," Tommy continued, "She's good-looking, her father is rich and she's smart."

"You're right about the first two," Billy answered. "I'm not so sure about the 'smart' part. I asked her if she liked Tolstoy and she said she loved all of his symphonies, especially the 1812."

"So…?" Tommy asked.

"Tolstoy is a novelist!" Billy corrected. "Not a composer. She didn't know what the hell I was talking about."

"She's got a master's degree from Auburn."

"That doesn't mean anything," Billy said. "I can tell you that she's not what I would call 'smart.'"

Tommy shook his head in frustration.

"Look, Billy boy," he said. "That's the sixth woman I've lined you up with in the last three months and you haven't liked any of them. Every one of them was too stupid or too shallow or too this or too that. I don't think there's a woman in this world that's good enough for you."

Ahead of them, Tommy could see that the foursome had played through.

"Tee off!" he said.

With that, Billy stepped out of the cart and selected a driver from his golf bag. Then, taking practice swings, he turned back to his old friend.

"No, that's not true," Billy replied. "If I was to meet my dream girl, I'd marry her in a heartbeat."

"Dream girl?" the photographer asked.

"Yeah," Billy added. "The perfect woman."

His friend looked at him, then chuckled.

"Now just what kind of woman is this…dream girl?"

"The perfect woman," Billy said. "The woman of my dreams."

"I KNOW that," Tommy said, "but what would you like for her to be like?"

"Well," Billy replied thoughtfully, taking practice swings with the driver. "First of all, she'd have to be good-looking."

"A beauty queen?"

"No, not necessarily," Billy explained. "I don't expect a knockout, but I'm not looking for a dog either…Let's just say she would have to be attractive enough that I wouldn't be ashamed to be seen with her."

"Okay," Tommy said, obviously amused. "What else?"

"Good in bed," Billy said quickly. "I mean a woman who could sexually knock my socks off."

Tommy burst out laughing.

"You like 'em hot, don't you, Billy boy!" Tommy said, "Hot! Hot! Hot!"

"Yeah," Billy replied, "A woman that loves sex as much as I do."

Tommy was still chuckling.

"Okay," he said finally, "Good-looking and hot…What else?"

"Well…," Billy continued. "She'd have to be smart. Really smart. Especially about literature."

"You looking for an English teacher?"

"Not necessarily," Billy said, "but I'd like for her to know the difference between Dickens and Dostoyevsky. It would really be nice if she had read the Romantic poets, especially Keats and Shelley."

Tommy, who was enjoying their little game, giggled to himself.

"What if she was beautiful, but had no brains?" he asked.

"No way!" Billy added quickly. "I'd much rather she be smart and medium attractive than be a knockout and stupid as hell."

"Why is that?" Tommy asked.

"Who wants a woman you can't talk to?" Billy answered. "If she was stupid, what would I do with her after I'd taken her to bed?"

Tommy laughed out loud again.

"Anything else?"

"Yeah, Billy said, "One more thing…If I were to meet a woman who knew who Gerard Manley Hopkins was, I would know I had my dream woman.

"Who in the hell is Gerard Manley Hopkins?"

"He was this poet that lived in England a long time ago…"

Billy's friend feigned impatience.

"Okay. Is THAT all?" Tommy asked gain,

"Yeah," Billy said thoughtfully. "I think that covers it."

Tommy looked at his old friend.

"And you actually expect to meet this woman?"

"Well, let's just say I haven't met her yet," Billy said.

"I wouldn't get my expectations too high if I were you," the photographer commented.

"Yeah, you're probably right," Billy said wistfully, still swinging the driver, "but it doesn't hurt to dream."

✳✳✳

The following Saturday afternoon, Billy Johnson found himself in the press box at Birmingham's Legion Field covering the Alabama-Florida game. In the contest, Florida had kicked a field goal on its first possession then scored two touchdowns on long pass plays to take an early lead. But the Crimson Tide came back in the second quarter and scored one touchdown on a fumble recovery and another on a running play for a halftime scored of 17-14. After a scoreless third quarter, Alabama kicked a field goal early in the fourth quarter to tie the score. Now, late in the fourth quarter, Alabama's defense had held Florida for four straight downs on their three-yard line and, with less than six minutes left and the clock ticking away, Alabama was marching back up the field.

As Billy watched the closing minutes of the game, he intermittently glanced toward the opposite end of the press box for the food hostess. After he had gotten up late that morning, he hadn't had time to eat at his apartment. At the office, he had rushed in, grabbed his reporting materials and was quickly out again. Finally, just before the kickoff, Billy had wolfed down two jelly doughnuts and a container of milk in the stadium parking lot. At halftime, the press box food hostess—a red-haired woman wearing a blue apron—had passed out sandwiches to the sports writers, but Billy declined because he wasn't really hungry at the time. Now, almost two hours later, he was ravenous. Finally he caught the eye of the press box hostess and motioned her over.

"What can I get for you?" the redhead asked, wiping her hands on the blue apron.

"I want a roast beef sandwich on wheat bread," Billy asked, looking away from the game. "Is that possible?"

"Sure," the woman said. "What do you want on it?"

"Lots of mustard," Billy said.

"That's all? No lettuce, mayonnaise...?"

"No, just mustard," Billy said. "With a bag of chips and some pickles."

"I'll be right back," the woman said. With that, she returned to the food service area.

On the playing field below, the Crimson Tide had just ran a little off-tackle play that had given them a first and goal on the Florida three-yard line. Alabama was knocking on the door for the winning touchdown. As Billy watched, the food hostess returned with the sandwich and set it before him. Billy looked away from the game and lifted the top layer of bread.

"Is it okay?" the woman asked.

"I've got to have more mustard," Billy said.

"I'll be right back," the redhead said.

Billy nodded and turned back to the game. On the field below, the Alabama quarterback had tried a sneak play but had been stopped at the one-foot line. The Crimson Tide had no time-outs left and the final seconds were ticking away.

As Billy watched the action on the field, the food hostess returned with a squeeze bottle container of mustard. Billy, still watching the game, distractedly removed the top piece of bread and waited for the woman to apply more mustard. While Billy waited, the woman tried several times to squeeze mustard out of the container, but only a tiny bit oozed out.

"I think it's dried in the spout," the woman said, looking at the container with obvious irritation.

With that, she vigorously shook the container, then squeezed it with all her might. Again, only a tiny bit of mustard oozed out on the sandwich.

"This mustard just doesn't want to come out," she said, shaking the container vigorously again.

On the field below, only 12 seconds were left on the clock and Alabama was in a do-or-die situation. In desperation, the woman placed the squeeze bottle on the table and hit it sharply with the palm of her hand.

Suddenly, a giant stream of mustard shot across the sandwich, into Billy's face and on to his notes, his shirt, his pants and his sports jacket.

"Yaiiiiikeee!" Billy screamed, as he felt the mustard splatter across his face and his clothes.

But no one had heard his sudden cry. The stadium erupted in one mad howling scream as the Alabama quarterback flipped a short pass into the end zone for a touchdown and a resounding victory for the Crimson Tide.

"You idiot!" Billy shouted angrily. "You total idiot!"

"Oh, God, I'm so sorry," the woman said apologetically. "It just all came out at once."

"Look at this suit!" Billy said, shocked with disbelief.

In one fell swoop, Billy had not only missed the biggest play of the game, but he had huge splotches of thick yellow mustard on his face, the lapel of his coat and the leg and front of his pants.

"Oh, God, I'm so sorry," the woman said. "Here, let me help."

With that, eager to do anything to be helpful, the woman started trying to wipe the mustard off with a paper towel.

"Stop! Stop!" Billy shouted angrily. "You're making it worse."

The woman, horrified anew, yet helpless to correct her mistake, quickly stepped back from the exasperated sports writer.

"I'm so sorry," the woman said.

"This suit is ruined!" Billy shouted.

"Oh, I feel so terrible," the woman said.

"How do you think I feel?" Billy asked, glaring at the woman.

"Isn't there anything I can do?" she asked.

"NO!" Billy said angrily. "Just get away from me. That's all I want from you. Okay?"

"There must be something I can do," the woman pleaded.

"I can't deal with this right now," Billy said. "I've got to go to the office and write my story."

"At least let me pay to have the suit cleaned," the woman offered.

Angrily, Billy shook his head in frustration. At that point, all he really wanted was just to get away from this woman. Quickly, he began gathering his notes and stuffing them into his briefcase.

"Please," she asked, as she watched him. "I feel so terrible. The least you can do is let me pay to have the suit cleaned."

Billy took a deep breath.

"Okay! Okay!" he said finally. Calmer now, he reached into his pocket and handed her his business card.

"Call me next week," he said. "I've got to go back to the office right now."

"I'm so sorry," the woman said again. "I should have known better."

With that, the woman watched helplessly as Billy slammed his briefcase shut and strode angrily out of the press box.

The following Monday afternoon, William Vernon Johnson, the stained suit in hand, was waiting in front of the Magic City Cleaners in Homewood at 12:30 p.m. Promptly, at the appointed time, the redheaded woman drove into the cleaners parking lot. She got out, greeted Billy and examined the suit.

"Oh, that's pretty bad," she said.

"I got some of it out," Billy said, all the anger gone now, "but it really could use a good dry cleaning."

"That's the least I can do," she said.

With that, the two went inside the cleaners.

"No problem," the man behind the counter said, upon examining the stains. "It will be ready on Wednesday. That will be twelve dollars."

The redhead produced the money from her purse and handed it to the clerk.

"Thanks," Billy said.

"You're welcome," she said. "Thanks for allowing me to do that for you. I feel better now."

Once they were back on the street, the woman turned to say good-bye.

"That was very fair of you," Billy said.

"Thanks," the woman replied. "I'm so sorry for the inconvenience."

"I accept," Billy nodded.

"Thanks again," the woman said. "I've got to go now. Take care."

With that, the woman waved goodbye, turned and started walking back to the parking lot. Billy waved goodbye then watched as she walked back to her car.

"Hey," he called suddenly.

The woman stopped.

"Yes...?," she asked, turning to Billy again.

"Maybe I was a little too harsh with you in the press box," he said apologetically.

"No, it's okay," she said. "I understand."

"No, I want to do something...," Billy said, "just to show you I'm really a nice guy. Can I buy you a cup of coffee?"

"You don't have to do that," she said.

"But I want to," Billy pressed.

"Really I need to go," she explained.

"Please," Billy insisted. "Give me just fifteen minutes."

She looked at her watch. Then she looked back at Billy.

"Okay," she said. "Fifteen minutes, then I have to go."

Over coffee at a small restaurant across the street from the cleaners, Billy Johnson learned that the woman's name was Elaine Murphy Malone O'Brien. She was 38, recently divorced and worked as a paralegal for a law firm in downtown Birmingham. At the end of 15 minutes, she got up to leave.

"I really have to go," she said urgently.

"I understand," Billy said. "Can I have YOUR card this time?"

"Sure," she said.

With that, she fished through her purse and handed him a business card.

"Thanks for the coffee," she said. Then she waved goodbye and strode off up the street.

As Billy Johnson watched the woman walk away, he had a strange feeling. There was something very special about this woman, but he couldn't quite put his finger on it. The red hair, the quiet gentleness, the disarming honesty had a special effect on Billy. He sensed that there was more to this woman than met the eye. Billy had never had a red-haired girlfriend before.

The following morning, which was Tuesday, Billy Johnson was at Phillips High in West Birmingham to interview the school's baseball coach about prospects for spring training. Once the interview was completed, he started back across the school grounds to his car. As he walked down the high school corridor, he saw a red-haired woman, some sort of school employee, hurry past him carrying a sheaf of papers. After the woman passed, Billy instinctively turned and glanced back at her. Instantly, his thoughts flashed on Elaine Murphy Malone O'Brien. Back at the newspaper office, he fished through his wallet until he found her card, then he called the law offices where she worked.

"Elaine Murphy Malone O'Brien?" Billy asked.

"Oh, Hi!" she said, recognizing his voice. "I didn't think I'd ever hear from you again."

"Why not?" he asked.

"After what I did, I figured you never wanted to see me again."

"All that's history," Billy said. "I called to tell you that I enjoyed our little chit-chat yesterday."

"So did I," she said. "So what can I do for you?"

There was a long pause.

"I was wondering if you'd like to have dinner with me one night this week," Billy asked.

She didn't answer at first.

"You mean...like a date?" she asked finally.

"Yeah," he replied. "I know a little Italian restaurant downtown that serves great pasta," he continued. "The fettuccine Alfredo is the best in the world."

"That's quite a recommendation," she commented. "Aren't you afraid I might spill a bowl of lemon sauce all over you?"

"I'll take my chances," Billy said, with a chuckle.

Another long pause.

"When?" she asked finally.

"You name it."

"What about Thursday night?" she explained. "I have to clean my apartment tonight and, on Wednesday night, I'm going to a dance recital."

"Perfect," Billy said.

When Billy met Elaine at the door of her Woodlawn apartment the following Thursday night, he didn't recognize her at first. In the press box, she had been wearing a blue apron over a black skirt and a loose-fitting top that made her look matronly. At the cleaners, she was dressed in jeans and a tank top and had a certain preppie look. Now, Billy saw her dressed up for the first time in a flowery, full-length dress and high heels. Billy found her very attractive.

As they walked into the Italian restaurant, all eyes turned to look at her. Billy Johnson was proud. Then, over a dinner of veal scaloppini and fettuccini Alfredo, she told Billy her life's story. A 1972 graduate of the University of Alabama, she had a bachelor's degree in elementary education and had taught grammar school after graduation. After two years of teaching, however, she decided to pursue something that paid a living wage. Finally, her sister, who was married to an attorney, suggested that she become a paralegal, citing the high salaries and good working conditions. After completing a two-year course and becoming a registered paralegal, she quickly landed a good job. Now, she said, she was making more money, but she didn't enjoy it as much as teaching school.

Following dinner, Billy and the redhead left the Italian restaurant and drove eastward along First Avenue North to East Lake. There, in the early evening, Billy always enjoyed the lake with all the white ducks, the quietness and the trees. So he invited his new friend for a stroll.

"Since my divorce," she said, as they strolled, "I've dated several men, but I haven't met anyone I really liked. I dated one man for over a year, but he was a sworn bachelor and vowed that he would never get married again.

"It's so hard to find a man I trust," she continued. "My former husband was incapable of being faithful. He always felt that he should get whatever he wanted then give nothing in return. I lived with him for five years before I discovered he had a mistress."

As they strolled around the lake, Billy was listening. Finally, they stopped on a small viewing platform overlooking the water. On one of the rocks below, some wag, in bold, black letters, had written "The mass of men lead lives of quiet desperation."

Billy pointed out the rock to her.

"That's from Thoreau," she said. "Walden Pond."

Then she pointed to a blank rock nearby.

"See the rock over there," she said. "If you had a brush and paint, what would you inscribe?"

Billy looked at the unpainted rock.

"And the lone and level sands stretch far away..."

She smiled.

"That from Shelley's 'Ozymandias,'" she said. "That would be a good choice."

Then he turned to her.

"What would you write if you had the brush?" he asked.

She pondered for a moment.

"Sheer plod makes plough down sillion shine..."

Instantly, Billy recognized the line from Gerard Manley Hopkins's "The Windhover." It was Billy's favorite poem.

"Are you a fan of Gerard Manley Hopkins?" he asked.

"Oh, yes," she said. "I've read all of his work."

For a moment, Billy Johnson stared at the woman, but said nothing.

After they had finished their walk around the lake and returned to the car, she said she needed to get home because she had to get up early the next morning. Once they had returned to her apartment, Billy asked if she had had fun and if he could call her the following day.

"Yes. And Yes," she replied.

With that, he kissed her goodnight.

Two nights later, on the second date, William Vernon Johnson and Elaine Murphy Malone O'Brien went for sweet and sour pork at a Chinese restaurant in Green Springs, then to see a foreign film called "El Generalissimo," a story about the influence a Spanish army general had on the life of one of his soldiers. The actions and teachings of the general had influenced every part of the soldier's life. He had taught the soldier how to win the woman of his dreams and how to think for himself.

As they walked out of the movie, Billy turned to her.

"I don't understand why the movie didn't end after the soldier married the woman of his dreams," Billy said.

"Because the marriage and the love affair were just the first part of the general's teachings," she explained. "The story after the wedding was the second part of the general's teachings." Billy looked at her.

"You're right," he said.

"It was also the most important part of the general's teachings," she continued. "It was after the second part of the teachings that the soldier's true personal growth took place."

"Why didn't I think of that?" Billy asked.

"The story comes from the book of the same title by Ernesto Rodriguez," she explained. "I read the book several years ago."

"You have quite a knowledge of literature," he said.

"Yeah, especially poetry," she said. "I wrote several books of poems when I was in college. When I was a child, my fantasy was to be a great American poet like Emily Dickinson or Sara Teasdale. I dreamed of writing great poems about love and death and lost dreams. When I was in college, I wrote a book of poems, but I never did anything with them. Being a poet is a nice dream but you'll starve to death real fast."

Billy looked at her.

"Can I read your poems?" he asked.

She laughed.

"I've never let anybody see them," she said.

"Can I be the first?"

She laughed again.

"Maybe..." she said vaguely, trying to dismiss the subject. "Let's see how it goes..."

Over the next five days, Billy and Elaine were together every night. They went to a classical music concert, a dinner theater to see "Tobacco Road," an investment seminar on mutual funds, a high school basketball game and finally a Renaissance Faire. During those five days, the two learned a great deal about one another; they began to feel comfortable together; the relationship was blooming.

At the end of the second week, when Billy arrived at her apartment for the eighth date, she greeted him at the door with a long kiss.

"I really like you," she said lovingly. "I feel like I've been knowing you for a long, long time."

"Does that mean I can read your poems now?" he asked.

She looked at him.

"Why not?" she answered. "You're the first man I've met who could appreciate them."

With that, she went to a closet and hefted down a stack of aging spiral books. Over the next three hours, the two were spread out on the living room floor, reading the poems, commenting, analyzing and interpreting.

"You really do like my poems, don't you?" she asked.

"They're good," he said.

"You're just saying that," she said.

"No," he said. "I really do like them."

Afterward, they sat on the couch and she showed him photos of her family.

"My family in Ireland were the O'Briens," she explained. "Most of the women in the family have red hair. My father, who was Scottish, had dark hair, but me and all my sisters have red hair."

Billy touched her hair and began stroking the tiny carrot-colored strands.

"I love your red hair," he said.

"Thanks," she replied. "My grandmother always said you should never make a redhead mad because all of the red in their hair turns into fire."

"I'll remember that," Billy said.

"My grandmother was a very wise woman."

Suddenly, she glanced at her watch.

"My God, it's one-thirty," she said, looking at her watch. "Time flies when you're having fun."

Billy continued stroking her red hair.

"When are you going to sleep with me," he asked.

She looked at him, not answering at first.

"You think we're ready for that?"

"I'm very attracted to you," he said.

"Same here," she added.

On the ninth date, which was on a Monday, both knew that sex was what the date was all about that night. After they had dinner, they decided to skip the movie and go to a little bar in Roebuck called the Filling Station. There they got silly-drunk together and bared their souls. They told dirty jokes, laughed a lot at nothing, and, at closing time, left the bar pretty drunk. Back at her apartment, they said nothing, undressed quickly in the darkness and started attacking one another. That first night, they were just two drugged, sex-starved animals trying to fulfill their basic physical needs.

But the second night was different.

The following afternoon, she called him at work and said she wanted to prepare dinner for him. When Billy arrived at her apartment, she had laid out a spread of steak, Brussels sprouts, mashed potatoes, French rolls and a tart red wine. After dinner, they sat on the couch and discussed Aristotle's early scientific dabbling. Finally, after they started snuggling on the couch, she led him into the bedroom and undressed him.

"I'll be right back," she said.

Moments later, she appeared in a flaming red negligee with multi-colored flowers across the breasts. Once he had slipped her out of the negligee and she lay on the bed, he could closely examine her entire body for the first time. She had small, firm breasts with big nipples that pointed skyward. Her legs were long, lean and clean-shaven and she had a scar on her left knee that she got in a bicycle accident as a young girl. She had a firm, shapely rear and the curve of her waist from her shoulders down to her hips was quite nice. In the center of her body, located exactly between the tip of her toes and the top of her head, was the crown jewel of her anatomy, an innocent-looking little tuft of pale-orange hair which grew straight up from her pubic bone. The hair on her head was a dark carotenized color, the color of light iron rust, but the hair perched atop her pubis—where the harsh rays of the sun never penetrated—was a light-orange color and those little vermilion strands seemed to have a life all their own.

That night, as she sat naked on the bed reading Coleridge's poems by candlelight, Billy Johnson gazed at her. Before him, he could see the book of poems and her face reading the lines, but the central focus of his vision was the little tuft of pale-orange hair. As she read the lines from "Xanadu": "A savage place, as holy and enchanted as e'er beneath a waning moon was haunted by woman wailing for her demon lover…," the little strands appeared to be quietly weeping. As Billy watched, the pubes seemed to lean their tiny orange heads over on their stems ever so sadly. Then, when she reached a dramatic peak in the poem, they would suddenly become fully erect again and stick out their tiny chests with pride, affection and outrageous courage. Billy Johnson found this absolutely amazing.

For their third night together, she bought a collection of Dylan Thomas's poems which included "Fern Hill," "The White Giant's Thigh" and "Do Not Go Gentle Into That Good Night." As she sat cross-legged on the edge of the bed and read the lines: "Though wise men at their end know dark is right..." Billy Johnson watched in awe as the tiny strands of pale-orange hair peeped at him over the tops of her folded legs. She had showered before she came to the bed and some of the smaller pubic hairs still had tiny droplets of moisture nestled among them. The droplets glistened in the soft candlelight. As she began reading the third stanza... "Good men, the last wave by, crying how bright..., Billy started at her lips and began moving slowly downward. Finally, by the time she was reading "Rage, rage against the dying of the light..." she was so overcome she had to lay aside the book. Finally, when they had finished pouring their passions into one another, they stopped and slept peacefully in one another's arms. Then, two hours later, they awoke and began to stroke and grope and love one another all over again.

Over the next two weeks, they were together every night. During that time, Billy learned every inch of her pale, lithe body, especially the little triangular-shaped tuft of pale-orange hair. There seemed to be no end to the fascination those little strands of orange-colored natural fibers held for him. For hours on end, he would sit on the bed and stroke the forest of little pale-orange hairs. He liked to imagine that the tiny silken strands were like fans at a football game and each little strand tried to crane its neck as high as possible to see over the heads of its fellow pubes. Sometimes, as he stroked them, he could hear them cheering for the Crimson Tide.

And she had a mind. After they had made love and she lay naked in his arms, the full force of her intellectuality would burst forth. Every night, there was a new topic to discuss. Oriental religion. The meaning of Plato's shadows on the cave walls. The geology of Australia. The influence of Judaism on human history. Dostoyevsky's mental instability. Freud's concept of the id. And, of course, the Romantic poets. They both agreed that the English and American poets of the mid-19th century, Poe, William Cullen Bryant, Lord Byron, Keats, Shelley and Coleridge, represented the English language's golden age for poetry.

"Many of the world's greatest literary scholars consider Thomas Gray's 'Elegy Written in a Country Churchyard' the greatest poem ever written in the English language," she said one night as she lay in his arms.

"After the Battle of Quebec in 1759," she continued, "the British, under the command of General Wolfe, had won the battle, but the great general had been mortally wounded and lay dying. As the general's death drew near, his secretary asked him what he considered his greatest accomplishment and he named some great battle he had won as a young military officer. As the secretary jotted down the quote, the great general added, 'But I would give up all of my military accomplishments to have written and be allowed to put my name on "Elegy Written in a Country Churchyard"'."

"I've read that story," Billy commented, "but the British general was Montcalm, not Wolfe."

"No," she said, "the British general was Wolfe. Montcalm is a French name."

"Are you sure?" he asked.

"I'm sure," she said.

The next day, Billy went to the library and checked. She was right.

***

The following Saturday afternoon, Billy was back on the golf links with his friend Tommy. Billy, after surveying his shot on the par 3 eighth hole, pulled a nine iron from his bag. Then, after several practice swings, he whacked the tiny spheroid high into the air. Both men watched as the white ball sailed high above the trees and plopped down on the green.

"Good shot!" Tommy said.

With that, Billy returned the nine iron to his bag and hopped into the golf cart. Tommy gunned the engine then maneuvered it bumpily over some thick grass to a nearby cart path.

"So what's happening on the romantic front, Billy boy?" Tommy asked as they cruised to the green.

At first, Billy didn't answer.

"So...?" Tommy pressed.

"I think I've found the dream girl," Billy said.

"Aw, get out of here!" Tommy laughed.

"No, I think I have," Billy said. "I've met a hell of a woman."

"It's only been three weeks," Tommy protested. "She must have popped up out of nowhere."

With that, Billy explained how he had met Elaine and their history.

"So this crazy redhead spills mustard on you, you start dating her and, now three short weeks later, you've met the woman of your dreams?"

Billy didn't say anything at first.

"I know it sounds crazy," he said finally, "but she is close...Really close."

"She's a redhead," Billy said.

"Redhead, brunette, blonde...whatever," Tommy said, not interested in details. "What's that got to do with it?"

"Nothing...," Billy said.

Tommy waited for the information to register.

"You telling me this redhead is all the things you said you were looking for?"

Billy nodded.

"Smart, good-looking, good in bed, knows how to be a good pal...all of that?"

"All that and more," Billy said.

"HOW good in bed?"

Billy looked at his old pal.

"Great!" Billy said.

Tommy chuckled knowingly.

"You're in lust, Billy boy," Tommy said. "Not love."

They rode is silence for a few moments.

"Does she know who this 'Gerald Hopkins' is?"

"Yeah," Billy replied. "She read all of his poems.

Tommy looked at his old friend disbelievingly.

Suddenly, ahead of them, Tommy could see that part of the cart path had been washed out.

"Hang on!" he shouted.

Billy quickly grabbed the side of the cart to support himself as Tommy swerved the cart around the washout, then gunned it up a small hill. Finally, the cart jerked to a sudden stop beside the green.

"You gonna get me killed in this thing," Billy said.

"You're too young to die," Billy boy," Tommy said. "You gotta live for this...this dream girl."

Billy gave his friend a miffed expression, then got out of the cart. On the green, Billy handily rolled in a beautiful four foot putt for a par. Tommy, complaining that the grass on the green was too high, two-putted for a bogey.

"So where do you stand with this redhead?" Tommy asked, as the two walked back to the golf cart. "You ain't getting married or anything like that, are you?"

"Oh, no," Billy said. "Nothing like that, but we are moving in together."

"That's nice," Tommy said with mild sarcasm. "Now all you got to do is get along with her."

"Oh, that'll be the easy part," Billy said.

"Good luck," Tommy answered. "The more you like 'em, the harder they are to get along with."

***

The following weekend, William Vernon Johnson began the task of moving his belongings out of his Roebuck apartment into Elaine Malone Murphy O'Brien's two-bedroom apartment in Woodlawn. As usual, whenever he moved, he was reminded of all the non-essentials he had been hauling around for all those years. The books, the camping equipment, the old battery charger, old clothes, personal memorabilia, collectibles and an assortment of other items he somehow could never find the courage to throw away. Finally, after surveying his belongings and deciding he didn't want to commit too much too fast, Billy put the bulk of his furniture and personal belongings in storage. Then, armed only with four suitcases, a stand-up shaving mirror and some personal towels, Billy set up housekeeping with Elaine Malone Murphy O'Brien.

For two months, Billy and Elaine, whom he called his partner in love, lived happily together in her Woodlawn apartment. Each paid half of the household bills; they shared housekeeping chores; each knew when and how to respect the other's "quiet" time. As before, he went to his newspaper job each day and notified her each night as to his comings and goings. Meanwhile, Elaine spent her days working at the law firm and her nights with Billy at the apartment. At least twice a week, they ate out at a restaurant and, on weekends, they spent all of their time together. They were quite happy together.

Then one night, after dinner at their favorite Chinese restaurant in Green Springs, they were driving along First Avenue North back to the apartment.

"You know I expect to get married at some point," she said.

Billy didn't answer at first.

"Did you hear what I said?"

"I heard," he said.

"Well, what do you think about it?"

"I'm not sure I can get married again."

There was a long pause.

"Do you think I'm just going to continue living with you without being married to you?"

"It's been fun so far," he said.

"Have you even thought about marrying me?" she asked.

"Not really."

"Well, you should," she said, "Because I want to be married at some point."

"Why?"

"Because I feel better in a relationship that way..." she said.

He didn't answer at first.

"Like I told you," he finally, "I'm not sure I'm capable of that again."

"Why not?"

"I'm just not ready."

"Just because you aren't ready isn't a good enough excuse," she said. "If I'm going to live with you and give myself to you, I expect you to marry me."

He didn't answer.

During the rest of that week, they returned to their jobs and nightly routines and she didn't mention the subject again. On the following Saturday, Billy played golf with Tommy again while Elaine went to a volunteer service function for the Daughters of the Confederacy. On Sunday, the following day, the couple went to visit her parents in Homewood where her mother had prepared fried chicken, candied yams, fresh string beans and chocolate cake. After goodbyes, Billy and Elaine started back to their apartment in Woodlawn.

"Have you thought about getting married?" Elaine asked, as Billy drove.

"I told you, I'm not sure I'm capable of it," Billy said. "Marriage limits you in such incredible ways."

She looked at him.

"That sounds SO familiar," she said.

"Why do you say that?"

"The last man I dated couldn't make a commitment either."

"It's not a matter of commitment," Billy said. "It's the idea that you've got to tie yourself down to the same person for the rest of your life."

"That's commitment!" she said emphatically. "The act of marriage seals the sense of mutual trust between a man and a woman."

"Well," he said, it's pretty scary to me."

"It's not scary to me," she said firmly, "And, like I told you before, I'm not going to continue like this and not be married to you."

During the rest of the trip to Woodlawn, Billy and Elaine didn't speak. Finally, when they arrived back at the apartment, she immediately got out of the car.

"I expect to be married at some point," she said curtly. Then, arms akimbo, she turned from him and strode quickly into the apartment. That night, Billy slept in the spare bedroom.

The following day, which was a Monday, Billy was up at 7 a.m., packed and ready to go to Auburn where he was due to cover a basketball game between Auburn's War Eagles and Mississippi State. Before he left the apartment, he dutifully kissed Elaine goodbye and tried to forget the incident.

Over the next four hours, Billy drove from Birmingham to the Auburn campus in southeast Alabama. It was a long, dusty trek past cotton fields, dairy farms, pecan orchards and the flat, rolling farmlands of southeast Alabama. Finally, around 4:30, Billy arrived in Opelika and checked into a hotel room. Afterward, for dinner, he met Jerry Bridges, the Herald photographer for the game. With Jerry was his wife, "Crazy Wanda." All the guys in the office called her "Crazy Wanda" because she was a little nutty. Especially after she had had a few drinks.

After dinner, Billy, Jerry and Wanda drove to Eaves Memorial Coliseum on the Auburn campus for the game. From the opening tip-off until the final buzzer, the contest was a donnybrook. For more than three quarters of the game, Mississippi State maintained a slim lead. Finally, after what seemed like a miracle, Auburn took the lead in the closing minutes and, on a miraculous three-point play at the final buzzer, won by 84-83. Pandemonium reigned supreme in Eaves Coliseum as the home crowd went wild with the joy of victory. After the game, Auburn's coaches declared a celebration and, during the press conference, Billy, Jerry and Wanda took part in the festivities.

Finally, Billy, anxious to get back to the hotel and write his story, said goodbye to Jerry and his wife and left. As he stepped outside into the November night, Billy was hit with a sudden blast of cold air. Over the past three hours, temperatures had suddenly dropped to near-freezing and, wearing only a thin cotton shirt, Billy was shivering with cold when he finally made it to his car.

No sooner had arrived back at the hotel and started writing than he heard a knock on the door. It was Jerry and Wanda.

"Billy!" Jerry said, standing at the door and trying to support his unsteady wife.

"What's wrong?" Billy asked.

"I can't get my car started," he said. "The photo lab is expecting me back in Birmingham tonight so they can develop the game film."

Billy looked at Wanda.

"What's wrong with her?" Billy said.

"Oh, she had too much champagne," Jerry said. "She'll be okay."

"Okay, let's go take a look at your car," Billy said. "We've got to hurry. I haven't written my story yet."

"Now, Wanda," Jerry instructed his woozy wife. "You've got to stay here. It's cold out there."

"But, dahling...," Wanda said drowsily, leaning on her husband.

"Now this is no time for Zsa Zsa," Jerry said. "I've got to go with Billy to try and start the car."

Jerry, looking very apologetically at Billy, guided his wife over to a nearby chair and carefully helped her into it.

"Now stay here until we get back," he said.

"But dahling...," she said, flipping her wrist limply. "You know how I just hate being alone..."

With that, she closed her eyes, curled up in the chair and dozed off.

"Will she be okay there?" Jerry asked.

"Yeah," Billy said.

With that, Billy and Jerry left the hotel room. For some ten minutes,

Wanda slept soundly in the chair. Then, the phone rang. Drowsily, Wanda woke up.

"Hello, dahling," Wanda answered.

It was Elaine.

"Hello..." Elaine said.

There was a long pause.

"Is this room 316?" Elaine asked.

"It certainly is, dahling," Wanda answered lustily. "How may I be of service to you...dahling?"

Another long pause.

"Can I speak to Billy Johnson?" Elaine asked.

"He's quite indisposed at the moment, dahling," Wanda replied lustily.

"Who is this?" Elaine asked.

"This is Zsa Zsa, dahling," Wanda said, "I'm Billy's lover for tonight."

"What?" Elaine asked. "Where is Billy?"

"Dahling, he can't be disturbed," Wanda said. "He's chilling champagne and putting on some music for us to make love by."

"Put him on the phone," Elaine demanded.

"Dahling," Wanda replied lustily, "I simply CAHN'T do that."

"Who is this?" Elaine asked again.

"Dahling, I told you...it's Zsa Zsa..."

Suddenly the phone line went dead. For a moment, Wanda listened to the dial tone, then hung up the phone and went back to sleep.

Five minutes later, Billy and Jerry burst back into the room, shivering from the bitter cold. Jerry went straight over to his wife.

"Wanda, let's go," he said. "We've got to get a tow truck."

With that, Jerry pulled his drowsy wife unsteadily into a standing position.

"Come on," he said. Finally, supporting his wife with an arm around her waist, Jerry managed to guide her out of the room and out the door.

An hour later, after seeing Jerry and Wanda safely on their way back to Birmingham, Billy returned to the hotel room and wrote his story. After he had filed it, he decided he should call the apartment and say good-night to Elaine.

"This is the home of Billy and Elaine," the message machine reported,

"We can't come to the phone right now, but if you'll leave a message, we'll return your call as soon as possible." Then he heard the beep.

"Elaine, are you there?" Billy asked.

He waited for her to pick up.

"You must be in bed and fast asleep," Billy said to the message machine. "I'm finished here for tonight. I'll see you tomorrow. I hope everything is okay."

The following morning, Billy was out of bed early. By 9 a.m., he had shaved, showered and packed and was ready to return to Birmingham. First, he felt he should call Elaine and check in.

"Who was the woman in your room last night?" she asked.

"What?" Billy answered. "There wasn't woman in my room last night."

"At 10:45, I called room 316 and some woman answered," she said.

Billy thought for a moment.

"Oh, my God," he said, "It must have been Wanda."

"Wanda who...?"

"She's Jerry's wife," Billy said.

"Who is Jerry?"

"He's a photographer."

There was a long pause.

"So what's the story on the woman?" she asked again.

"I told you," Billy said. "It was Wanda Bridges, Jerry's wife."

"Am I supposed to believe that?"

"It's the truth."

"How do I know that?"

"You just have to trust me."

"I don't have a reason to trust you," she said firmly. "I'm not married to you."

"You mean you can't trust me unless I'm married to you?"

"Not completely..." she said. "Until I'm married to you, you're still fair game for Barbara or Betty or Wanda or whoever..."

Billy didn't answer.

"Is this the old marriage speech again?"

"Do you think I'm just talking when I tell you I want to be married to you?"

"No."

"Yes, you do," she said accusingly. "It goes in one ear and out the other. As long as I will allow you to be with me and not commit yourself, you will continue to do so."

There was a long pause.

"You're jealous," Billy said.

"Yes," she answered angrily. "One part of me IS jealous. I care a great deal for you and, if I suspect there is another woman in your life, then I get jealous."

She stopped.

Billy didn't reply.

"On the other hand," she continued angrily. "Another part of me has no intention of letting another man drag my heart around..."

Billy could hear her fuming.

"I've told you," Billy said finally. "I'm just not capable of getting married again."

Another long pause.

"There is just no way to reason with you...," she said. "Is there no way to make you understand that I want to be married to you?"

"I'm afraid not," he said, "Not on that one."

There was a long, very pregnant pause.

"Then, I fear we've reached the end of the line..." she said with finality. "When will you be back in Birmingham?"

"Late this afternoon."

"Then, can you do me a little favor?" she asked.

"What's that?"

"Could you please drop by my place and get your bags," she said. "They will be packed and sitting on the front porch."

"What!?" he replied disbelievingly.

"You heard what I said."

"You can't do that!"

"Just watch me," she said.

Billy was fuming.

"Is this one of those red-haired fits you've been warning me about?"

"YES!" she screamed into the telephone.

Suddenly, Billy heard the phone slam down, then a dial tone.

Around 3:30 that afternoon, Billy arrived back in Birmingham. When he saw the tall buildings of the Birmingham skyline rise into view, he took the first exit off I-59 to First Avenue North, then drove eastward to Woodlawn. There on the front porch, exactly as she had promised, Billy saw the same scene he had witnessed when he had moved into the apartment two months earlier. The same four suitcases, the stand-up shaving mirror and the stack of personal towels were waiting.

God-damn women! Billy thought to himself angrily, as he grasped the nearest two suitcases and started back to the car. You can't live with them and you can't live without them. At the car, he unlocked the trunk and threw in the first two suitcases. No damn woman in this world is going to treat me like this, he thought. Moments later, he was back at the front porch and hefted down the other two suitcases. At the car, only one more suitcase would fit into the trunk, so he opened the rear door and threw the fourth suitcase into the back seat. Finally, after everything was loaded, Billy slammed the trunk lid and got into the car. Billy's car tires squealed in anger as he pulled out of the driveway and headed back to Birmingham and the Herald offices.

Later that afternoon, after work, Billy rented a room at the Holiday Inn in downtown Birmingham. That night, Billy had to go back to the office to lay out the inside pages for the early edition. Finally, around 7:30, he returned to his room at the Holiday Inn and decided to call a truce.

"Hello...?" she answered.

"Elaine...?" he said cautiously, trying to find some softness.

"What do you want?" she asked harshly.

There was a long pause.

"Can we talk...?"

"Don't you think we have already talked enough?" she said. "It's time for some action."

There was no reply at first.

"Look," Billy said finally. "What can I do to make things right?"

"You know exactly what's required," she said firmly.

"I've told you...," Billy started. "I'm not capable of getting married again."

"And I told you that I want a man that's capable of saying he's mine, mine alone and totally mine to the exclusion of all other women."

Billy didn't answer.

"There is no need for you to settle down with one woman when you can have just about any of them you want," she continued. "You're a good-looking guy. That's the REAL reason you have stayed single for so long."

"So what do you want?"

"A commitment," she said sarcastically. "You know…, like a marriage ceremony. That traditional ceremony where the male gives the female his sacred word that he will be hers and hers exclusively forever…"

There was a long pause.

"If that were to happen, could you make the same kind of commitment, in both quantity and quality, to me?" he asked.

Absolutely," she said. "I can commit all of my heart and soul and mind to you. In many ways, I've already done that."

Another long, long pause.

"I'm sorry," Billy said finally, inhaling resignedly. "I can't do it. It's just not in me…"

That was the last straw.

"Okay," she said, "Until you can, don't call me again."

With that, she slammed down the phone. Instantly, Billy, angry beyond words, dialed her number again, but the answering machine was on. All that night and the following day, he tried to reach her, but all he got was the answering machine.

***

The following Saturday, Billy was back on the golf course cruising the links with his friend Tommy. As usual, on the par 5 sixth hole, they had to wait for a foursome to play through.

"So what's happening with you and the redhead?" Tommy asked, propping his feet up on the golf cart.

"It's over."

"Over?" Tommy reacted.

"Yeah, she wants to get married."

"Married? I'd be very careful," Tommy said. "It's a lot easier to get into marriage than it is to get out."

"Oh, I know," Billy said.

"What about the living arrangements?"

"Oh, she threw me out. I'm staying at a hotel downtown."

"My! My!" Tommy said, chuckling to himself. "The fortunes of love do change rapidly, don't they? Only last week, she was the greatest thing since sliced bread and you and her were living in la-la land."

"Not any more," Billy said, shaking his head. "No woman on this earth is going to push me around like that."

"Like I been telling you, Billy boy," Tommy said, "You gotta be careful. A woman can have you eating out of the palm of her hand and you won't even realize it."

Billy nodded.

"But I'll say one thing, Billy boy," Tommy added, "You sure did play fast and furious with this one."

"Well, I might have been a little too fast and a little too furious."

Tommy looked consolingly at his old friend.

"But, it'll be okay," he added. "You'll live to fight another day."

"I hope so," Billy said glumly.

"Just be glad it's over," Tommy added, "All she wanted to do was to get her claws into you. Now, you're a free man again. You better enjoy it."

***

On the following day, which was a Sunday, Billy had to cover a men's softball tournament in southwest Birmingham, so he got there early, covered the games and was back in the office by 5:30 p.m. After writing his story, Billy spent almost an hour chatting with the deputy sports editor, then around 7 p.m. he left the office. All that day, Billy's mind had been occupied with work and the trappings of work and he hadn't had a chance to think about Elaine. En route back to the hotel room, Billy decided to stop by the supermarket and pick up some drinks and snacks for the evening.

As he stood in line to pay, he saw a red-haired woman at the cashier's stand. Instantly, his mind flashed on Elaine. The very sight of the red hair sent a charge of electric energy throughout his very being. Suddenly, he was overwhelmed with an urge to be near her, to smell her smells, to hear her voice and feel her presence. At first, Billy couldn't believe it. Quickly, he looked away from the red-haired woman, thinking the reaction would subside. But it didn't. For several moments more, Billy stood in the check-out line trying to fight off his feelings. Then, finally, unable to help himself, he suddenly bolted from the supermarket, leaving his snacks and drinks behind.

Back at the Holiday Inn, the first thing Billy wanted to do was call her, but he knew he couldn't. His pride wouldn't allow it. She had injured his ego and he couldn't permit that. After all, he told himself, he was a man and she was a woman. Despite this, another part of Billy yearned to be near her, to hear her voice, to smell her body and have access to that little tuft of pale-orange hair. His blood raced at the very thought. Although it was only 9 p.m., Billy decided to try to get some sleep. Maybe sleep will help, he thought. For over three hours, Billy tossed and turned sleeplessly, trying to make sense out of what was happening to him. Finally, after a glass of warm milk and some chocolate cookies from room service, Billy managed to fall asleep at 1 a.m.

The next morning, Billy was in the office bright and early at 8:30 a.m. After he had rewritten some wire copy for the daily edition, he had to take an expense report for his Auburn trip up to the accounting department. Then, he suddenly realized he shouldn't. The secretary to the company accountant was a flaming redhead. He knew if he went up to the fourth floor and saw the accountant's secretary, he would go crazy again with thoughts of Elaine. Finally, after lunch, Billy told the deputy editor he wanted to take off early. When the editor asked why, Billy cited personal reasons. After leaving the office shortly after 3 p.m., Billy drove out to East Lake. There, he retraced the steps he and Elaine had made around the lake two months earlier. At the rock with the painted Thoreau quote, Billy paused and remembered how he had been blown away by the fact that she read Gerard Manley Hopkins. For more than two hours, Billy lingered at the lake. Finally, long after darkness fell, he drove back to the Holiday Inn.

That night, for over five hours, Billy Johnson lay in bed again, tossing, turning and trying to make sense of it all. Over the past two months, you've been happier with Elaine than any other, he told himself. You have never in all your days met another woman who is as compatible with you as this one, he told himself. And in every conceivable way..., he thought. Intellectually. Socially. Sexually. Culturally. You name it and she is your spiritual and intellectual complement, he told himself. There isn't anything about her that you don't like. That little boy inside you thinks it will be a mistake if you DO marry her. The REAL mistake will be if you DON'T marry her, Billy thought to himself.

All that night Billy tossed and turned, longing for the smell of her body, the sound of her voice and her quiet, gentle touch. Over and over, his mind was filled with visions of that little tuft of pale-orange hair. Nothing on this earth smoothed out his rough edges quite as completely as those little strands of carotene. They alone were his sole source of peace and security and calmness and togetherness in this world. He remembered how he loved to run his fingers through the little forest of pale-orange trees and feel them lean back to his touch, then spring forward to their original position as his hand passed over them. They were his little friends and he had given them names. There was George and Hilda and Gladys and Frank and Harriet and James and Doyle...Oh, but he missed them so!

Finally, around 3 a.m., Billy, weary and tired from all the soul-searching, managed to drift off to sleep. Once he was sleeping, he had a dream. In the dream, Billy was standing under a clear, blue sky in a grassy mountain meadow dotted with wild daisies, pink poppies and sweet williams. From far across the field, Billy could see a beautiful, naked woman—laughing to the sky and throwing rose petals—dancing toward him. As Billy watched, the woman danced closer and closer and closer, all the while laughing and throwing rose petals. Mesmerized, Billy watched as the laughing woman danced right past him, leaving a glistening path of rose petals for him to follow. Without even questioning why, Billy turned and ran after the laughing woman. For hours on end, in the dream, Billy chased the laughing, dancing woman across the grassy, flower-dotted, mountain meadow. Every time Billy would catch up to her, she would laugh hysterically, wildly throw more rose petals, then quickly dance away again. Finally, at the precise moment Billy thought he had the woman in his grasp, there was a loud scream. As Billy watched, the laughing woman plunged helplessly off the edge of the grassy mountain meadow and disappeared. Eager to help, Billy raced to the meadow's edge and peered off into a void of endless space. As Billy looked down into the emptiness, the laughing woman was nowhere to be seen. Inside himself, Billy knew she was gone forever. At that moment, he woke up.

Drowsily, Billy raised himself in bed, rubbed his eyes then looked at the clock. It was 7:30 a.m. Although he had only slept four hours, Billy felt remarkably well-rested. With no time to waste, he got out of bed, took a shower and drove directly to the Western Union office in downtown Birmingham. On the counter he found the message form and scribbled four words: "Will you marry me?" With that, he instructed the clerk to send it to Elaine's office address. Then he went to his own office and waited. Around 11:30, she called.

"I got a telegraph here today that says you want to marry me," she said in a very businesslike tone. "Is that true?"

"It's the truth."

"You want to exchange vows with me and be faithful to me for the rest of your life. You want to commit to me as the only woman in your life for the remainder of your life. Is that what you're saying?"

"That's what I'm saying."

"You're sure that's what you want?"

"I'm sure."

"How do you know for sure?"

"I'm sure," he said again. "As sure as I'm capable of being."

There was a long pause.

"What kind of wedding do you want?" she asked.

"Something small and sincere," he said. "Not too many people…And not too expensive."

There was another long pause.

"You ARE serious, aren't you?" she asked.

"I told you I was," he said.

Another long pause.

"Want to meet at my place tonight to discuss it?" she asked finally.

"Name the time," he said.

At 6:30 that night, William Vernon Johnson drove out to her apartment at Woodlawn. It was the first time he had been there in four days. After dinner at their Chinese Restaurant in Green Springs, they went to a bookstore downtown and bought the collected poems of Edgar Allen Poe. Upon returning to her apartment, he requested that she read "Annabel Lee." She said the pleasure would be all hers. That night, in her bed at precisely 2:13 a.m., William Vernon Johnson pledged himself to Elaine Malone Murphy O'Brien for all eternity.

"I might live another lifetime—two lifetimes—and not meet another woman like you," he said. "You're the woman I've been looking for all my life and, now that I've found you, I'm not going to let you get away."

She seemed amused at his words.

"Why didn't you say all that a month ago?"

"I wasn't ready."

She looked into his eyes. She knew he was telling the truth.

***

The following Saturday, Billy and his friend Tommy were back on the golf links at Roebuck. As usual, at the par 5 sixth hole, they had to wait for a foursome.

"So, Billy boy, you back to looking for little Miss Perfect?"

"I'm going to get married," Billy said.

"Yeah...Right," Tommy said sarcastically.

"No. Really, I am."

"To who?" Tommy asked.

"Elaine."

"The redhead?"

"Yeah."

"Just last week you said it was over."

"That was last week," Billy said.

"As I recall," Tommy said, "The exact quote was, 'No woman in this world is going to push me around like that.'"

"Well...," Billy said reflectively. "I changed my mind."

"That's what you said a month ago," Tommy said. "First, you go one way, then suddenly you go another. Look, Billy Boy, I told you, you're in lust, you're not in love."

Tommy searched his old friend's face for a reaction.

Billy wasn't laughing.

"My God, you're serious, aren't you."

"I sure am," Billy said.

"You're telling me that you and this redhead are really going to get hitched up...You're going to buy the ring, rent the tux and say all that stuff in front of the preacher...?"

"That's right," Billy said, "And I want you to be my best man."

For a moment, Tommy stared at his friend in shocked disbelief.

"I think you got a screw loose," Tommy said, shaking his head slowly. "I mean...I think you need some help."

***

The following Saturday afternoon, 45-year-old William Vernon Johnson, clean-shaven and dressed in a tuxedo, along with 37-year-old Elaine Malone Murphy O'Brien, her red hair coifed to perfection, were joined in the holy bonds of matrimony in the rose garden of her parents' home in Homewood.

"And do you, William Vernon Johnson, take this woman to be your lawfully wedded wife?" the minister asked.

"I do," Billy said.

"And do you, Elaine Malone Murphy O'Brien, take this man to be your lawfully wedded husband, to love, to honor, to obey in sickness and in health...?"

"I do," she said.

"Then, I now pronounce you man and wife," the minister announced. "The groom may now kiss the bride."

With that, the newlyweds touched lips and the onlookers—Elaine's family, Billy's daughter and her husband and a few close Herald friends—applauded with delight. It had all been too easy.

Later at the reception, after the crowd had thinned out, the best man, a bit tipsy from too much champagne, pulled the groom aside.

"You were the guy that said you'd never get married again," Tommy chided.

"A man's got to do what he's got to do," Billy said.

Tommy shook his head.

"You been whipped," he said. "Whipped! Whipped! Whipped! She has beaten you over the head with that thing and now you can't live without it."

Billy laughed.

"Well, if this is being whipped," he said confidently, "I'll take ALL I can get."

With that, Tommy shook his head in futility and headed back to the champagne table.

So, the impossible had happened; William Vernon Johnson was married a second time. Never say never, he told himself, because you never know in which direction the winds of life may blow you. But, in his heart of hearts, Billy knew he had made the right decision. He knew he loved Elaine and that she loved him. He also knew that, if he stayed faithful and tried to get along with her, she would be with him for all eternity. He liked the thought of that. He LOVED the thought of that. And during all those nights ahead, he would stroke her small breasts in the moonlight, feel her slowly moisten to his touch, hear her giggle at his silly jokes and listen quietly as she discoursed in the darkness on the animal imagery in Shakespeare, the hidden meanings in Freud, the reign of Louis XIV, and the astrological significance of the Chinese calendar.

Finally, and best of all, he would have constant access to that little triangular tuft of pale-orange hair. Those little carotenized strings of protein sitting atop her pubic bone that lifted his spirits and soothed his nerves and provided a sense of comfort and peace and security like nothing he had ever known. Now, he would have those little pale-orange strands all to himself forever and ever. They were his little friends and there was no end to the fascination they provided. There was George and Hilda and Gladys and Frank and Harriet and James and Doyle and all the others. Oh, how he loved them so!

REUNION

Remembrance of Things Past

When William Vernon Johnson glanced through his mail that afternoon in late May of 1989 and saw a letter with a Hamilton, Alabama, postmark, he wondered what it was. Must be a letter from an old friend or relative, he thought. After he went inside his Miami apartment, Billy opened all the other mail first. There was a telephone bill, statements from credit card companies and an advertising flyer from a carpet store. Finally at the bottom of the stack, he found the home town letter. Inside, there was a neatly folded form letter signed by Gloria Rakestraw, one of the long-time classmates at his alma mater, Hamilton High School. In the letter, Gloria explained that she was organizing the thirtieth-year reunion of their class. As a result, she was contacting each of the 63 members of the 1959 graduating class and inviting them to a get-together so that all the former classmates could see "what happened to everybody." There was a telephone number to confirm his attendance.

Looking up from the letter, Billy remembered his days at Hamilton High as not exactly the happiest of times. As a high schooler, he was a shy, often socially awkward student and, most of the time, felt like an outsider. As for high school itself, he found it very boring and tiresome. Many times, he would skip class to go to the pool hall or the movies. Many days, he would sit in class and daydream. Oh, he made the grades all right and, outside of a couple of instances in which he was disciplined for skipping class, he had no problems. But there were still certain things he would rather forget about his high school days. There was the girlfriend who dumped him for no apparent reason. Also, he remembered the school bully had pushed him around more than once. Without a further thought, William Vernon Johnson wadded up the invitation and threw it into the kitchen garbage can.

"They're holding my high school reunion on June twenty-third," Billy said to Gwen Anne, his female friend, over dinner that night.

"June twenty-third?" Gwen Anne answered. "That's the weekend Fran and I are going to Nashville for Sandra's wedding shower."

"Oh, that's right," Billy said, remembering.

"And you'll be alone here at the apartment all weekend," she added.

"Anyway, it's not important," Billy said, trying to dismiss the subject. "You can't go home again."

"Why do you say that?"

"I wouldn't know those people after thirty years," he said. "I've changed too much."

"They've changed too."

"Yeah, I guess so, but I wouldn't fit in with them," Billy said.

"You don't know that," she said. "You can learn some very special truths in a situation like that."

Billy looked at his significant other.

"Also, you could look up your old pal Jimmy," she added.

"Oh, yeah," Billy said, smiling at the thought. "I'd love to see Jimmy Stevens."

"You should go," she urged. "You won't be spending the weekend alone in this apartment."

Billy looked at her. He had great respect for her opinions.

"I'll think about it," he said.

The following morning, while shaving for work, Billy's thoughts drifted back to his high school days again. He wondered what had happened to Dianne Watson, the high school sweetheart who had dumped him. Who did she end up marrying? And he wondered what had happened to Donald Brown, the all-everything athlete in high school whom he had looked up to with such reverence. And Wayne Ferguson, the class's bad boy, who was always in trouble…Did he just fall off the face of the earth? His thoughts were interrupted by Gwen's voice through the bathroom door.

"Honey…"

With half his face still covered with shaving cream, Billy poked his head out the door.

"Yes," he answered.

"I'm off," she said.

With that, Billy offered his clean-shaven right cheek and she gave it a peck.

"I'll call you around noon," she said.

"Bye."

"Bye," she said and turned to go. Suddenly, she turned back to him. "Billy..."

"Yes."

"I do wish you would go to your reunion," she said urgently. "I'll be gone two whole days and I'd feel better knowing you had something to do with yourself."

"I'm still thinking," he said.

Some thirty minutes later, stuck in traffic on I-95 in downtown Miami, Billy's mind was still sifting through high school memories. And Linda Blevins, the prettiest girl in the class, what did she look like now at age 48? Was there any beauty left? And David Dickson...Billy slowly took a deep breath at the thought of the name. David Dickson was the high school bully who had made his life miserable at Hamilton High. David, who was almost 20 years old when he graduated, was always bigger and stronger than the other students and pushed some of the younger boys around unmercifully. One of those was Billy Johnson. More than once, David Dickson had picked a fight with Billy just to prove his physical dominance. Although Billy was smaller, he had fought with David the first time, but had come away with a black eye, a bloody nose and sorely aching ribs.

Inside, Billy's blood boiled as he relived the memories. He wondered what would happen if David Dickson wanted to square off with him these days. After taking up martial arts as a hobby several years earlier, Billy now owned a green belt in karate and today, at age 48, he could damn well do what he couldn't do in high school. In his mind, he loved the thought of delivering quick justice to David Dickson after all these years. Three good kicks to the face, a hard neck chop and a rousing body slam would render his old enemy semi-conscious. For Billy Johnson, that single act would make up for all the pain and humiliation David Dickson had brought him in high school. Suddenly, Billy slammed on the brakes and took the next exit off the expressway. Back at the apartment, he ran inside, dug through the kitchen trash and found the wadded-up invitation. There were coffee grounds on it, but he wiped them off with a napkin.

Later that day, from the offices of Acme Publishing, the Miami publishing company Billy owned, he phoned Gloria Rakestraw.

"Oh, we'll have a great time," Gloria said. "All of our friends from high school will be there. Kay Hutchins, Walter Hughes, Nell Jenkins, Paul Smothers, Harold Greene, Bobby Whisenant, Wayne Mathis...all the people we knew in high school."

"What about Dianne Watson?"

"Oh, yes, I talked to Dianne," Gloria said. "She's living up in Virginia now. She promised to be there."

"And Jimmy Stevens?"

"I talked to Jimmy too, but he hasn't confirmed. He owns a paint store in Hamilton now."

"What about David Dickson?"

"I didn't talk to David, but I talked to his wife," Gloria explained. "She said she and David would be there."

There was a long pause.

"Everybody I've talked to so far said they would attend," Gloria continued. "You've GOT to attend, Billy."

There was a long pause.

"What's the name of Jimmy's business?" Billy asked finally.

"Stevens Paint Supply. It's in the phone book."

Another long pause.

"So can I count on you?" Gloria pressed.

"Let me talk to Jimmy first," he said. "We'll let you know."

Later that afternoon, Billy called directory assistance in Hamilton, Alabama and got a number for Stevens Paint Supply. He dialed the number.

"Stevens Building Supply," the voice answered.

"Jimmy Stevens?"

"That's me," the voice said.

"Jimmy, this is Billy Johnson."

"My God!" Jimmy said happily. "Billy Johnson! It's been a long time."

"It sure has," Billy said. "Remember the time we skipped English class to go see '20,000,000 Miles from Earth' at the Rialto?"

"Oh, yeah," his old friend answered. "I also remember the time Miss Sewell got us expelled for skipping school and going to the Stag."

They laughed at their mischief.

"Have you heard about the big reunion," Billy asked.

"Yeah, but I'm not sure I'm going," Jimmy said. "What about you?"

"Well, I haven't decided either," Billy added. "My girlfriend is out of town that weekend and I hate to go alone."

"Then let's go together," Jimmy said. "Glenda and I are divorced and I don't have a date either."

"Sounds good," Billy said. "It would be great to see you again."

"Same here," Jimmy said. "We got lots of catching up to do."

Three weeks later, on the morning of June 23, 1989, which was on a Saturday, Billy carried his wife's luggage out to her friend's car.

"Now have a good time at the reunion," she said.

"I will," he answered, "and tell Carl that I'll be up to visit him sometime this fall."

"Okay," she said. "I'll see you Sunday afternoon."

With that, Billy kissed her goodbye, then watched as she got into the car with her friend and the shiny sedan pulled out on the main highway and vanished out of sight.

An hour later, Billy was cruising northward along I-95 from Miami toward the hills of North Alabama. This was Billy's first trip back to Hamilton in five years. The last time was when he went to visit his Aunt Gail in the Hamilton hospital. Every time he went back to his old stomping grounds, he always did so with a certain trepidation. On one hand, Billy was always glad to see it again, but, once it was over, he was always glad to be leaving.

By late afternoon, after an eight-hour journey, Billy arrived in downtown Hamilton and checked into a hotel. After unpacking and settling in, he drove to the south side of town to find Jimmy's house. The part of town where Jimmy lived now was the older section of Hamilton where, during his high school days, the original steel mill owners and wealthy farmers had lived. When Billy pulled up in front of the house at 752 Walnut Street, he saw a quaint, well-kept two-story Southern home from the late thirties that had a huge front porch with green, ornate lattice banisters, a steeply sloping clapboard roof and gables with little green shutters. Billy could see that Jimmy had done well for himself.

Moments later, Billy was standing on the porch ringing the doorbell. Coming down the hallway, through the glass door panels, he could see Jimmy.

"Billy Johnson!" Jimmy said happily, opening the door.

"Jimmy Stevens!" Billy said.

The two old friends shook hands and hugged one another.

"It's good to see you," Jimmy said.

"Same here," Billy said. "You ready?"

"Yeah," Jimmy answered, "But the reunion doesn't start for another two hours."

"That's okay," Billy said. "Let's go down to Schwartz's Drug Store and have a cherry coke."

"It's not Schwartz's any more," Jimmy said. "It's not even a drug store now; it's a delicatessen."

"I guess nothing stays the same," Billy said. "Okay, let's do it."

"Wait a second," Jimmy said, "there's something I want you to do."

"What?"

"My father wants to see you."

"Your father?" Billy asked, remembering.

"Yeah. Come on."

With that, Billy followed his old friend into the house where he saw Walter Stevens for the first time in 34 years. Sitting in a rocking chair and looking very wizened, the old man raised a withered hand and Billy shook it warmly.

"You used to shoot a good stick of pool," the old man said.

"So did you," Billy added. "You could get more bottom english on a cue ball than anybody I ever saw."

Billy knew the old man would love that.

"Remember the time when I snuck you and Jimmy into the Smoke-house to see Johnny Daytona?"

"I'll never forget it," Billy said.

"…And you and Jimmy was only fourteen years old," the old man said with a snicker.

"That's right," Billy said.

"That house man knew better than to mess with me," the old man said confidently. "We had some good times."

"We sure did," Billy said.

The three giggled at their mischief.

"Well, Daddy," Jimmy said, "Billy and me are going to the reunion. We'll be back about nine."

"I'll be asleep," the old man said. "Good to see you again, Billy."

"Good to see you, Mr. Stevens."

With that, Billy waved goodbye and he and Jimmy left the house. Outside, Billy turned to Jimmy.

"I want to take my car," Billy said. "I'll meet you in the parking lot behind the football stadium."

Some twenty minutes later, Billy and Jimmy were walking across the Hamilton high campus to the corner of Oak and 11th Street, directly across from the school. Thirty years earlier, this was the corner where Al's Market and Schwartz's Drug Store had stood. It was also the place where Billy and Jimmy would meet in the mornings to watch girls, match quarters and make their plans for the day.

For a long moment, the two lingered at the corner in front of the old building, trying to relive the past.

"Remember when we used to hide in those bushes," Jimmy asked, indicating the thick shrubs surrounding the rear of the building.

"Oh, yeah," Billy said. "We would hide in there until the tardy bell rang, then we would run down to 12th Street to catch the bus into town."

The two looked at each other, then laughed.

"Come on," Jimmy said, opening the door to the delicatessen. Inside, the two old friends were seated for coffee. They had a million questions for each other.

"Well, after Glenda and I got married, I went to work for Mr. Penn at the paint store," Jimmy said. "For six years, I did everything. Stocked the shelves, set up displays, worked the counter, and finally started buying the paint. Then, after Mr. Penn got sick, he made me manager and I started running the whole business."

"By then," Jimmy continued, "Glenda and I had three kids and she was working part-time at a beauty shop. When Mr. Penn died in '81, I bought the store from his family."

Billy was listening.

"Then last year, me and Glenda decided to call it quits," Jimmy continued. "The kids were grown and gone, we didn't have to worry about money any more and we weren't spending any time together. After twenty-six years, there wasn't much left."

"Think you'll get married again?" Billy asked.

"Nope, once is enough for me," Jimmy said. "What happened to you and Charlotte?"

"Oh, we divorced in 1973," Billy said. "I got married again in '75 to a woman I met in Birmingham. That was Elaine. It lasted eight years. I was divorced again in '83."

The two grew quiet for a moment and sipped their coffee.

"I used to see your name on write-ups in the sports pages of the Herald," Jimmy said. "Now I don't see them any more."

"No, I left the Herald in 1975," Billy said. "After I was divorced a second time I decided to change my life all around. I moved to Miami and started two sports magazines.

"What kind of sports magazines?" Jimmy asked.

"Well, I started with a college football magazine," Billy said. "It's still my bread and butter. Now I've started a new one on baseball cards."

"Baseball cards?"

"Yeah, it's been a great little moneymaker," Billy said. "You'd be surprised at how much interest there is in baseball cards."

"I never really thought about that," Jimmy said. The two old friends smiled at each other.

"What about your daughter?" Jimmy asked.

"Oh, Barbara is married and still living in Birmingham," Billy continued. "She graduates from Birmingham Southern next spring. She's twenty-one now."

"We aren't getting any younger," Jimmy said.

"That's for sure," Billy added.

"Ready?" Jimmy said, reaching for the check.

"I'm ready," Billy said.

As William Vernon Johnson and his old friend Jimmy strode across the front lawn of their old high school, they could see a huge blue and gold banner hanging over the entrance archway which proclaimed "Welcome, Class of '59." Five minutes later, Billy and Jimmy walked through the archway and into the school's main reception area.

"Billy! Jimmy!" they heard someone call.

Billy and Jimmy turned and saw Gloria Rakestraw, a clipboard in her hand, standing at the entrance to the school auditorium. Gloria had grown heavy in her older years.

"How are you two doing?" Gloria gushed, hugging each of them warmly. "I'm so glad you two could come."

For several minutes, the three old classmates made small talk about told times at Hamilton High. As he looked around, Billy could see that the auditorium had been prepared for the reunion. At the front, a stage had been improvised and, along either side of the auditorium walls, a food buffet had been set up and servers were waiting. The tables, all set with white linens, shiny silverware and drinking glasses, were numbered.

"Okay," Gloria said finally, looking at her clipboard, "You two will be seated at table number eight. That's our bachelor table."

With that, she pointed to a table directly in front of the stage. Billy and Jimmy glanced over at the indicated table.

"I'm not a bachelor," Billy protested.

"I know," Gloria said. "But if you don't have a date, that's where you have to sit."

"Who else is sitting there?" Billy asked.

Gloria turned back to her list.

"Well, already I have Gene Watkins, Henry Wilkerson, and you two. If I run short of space, I might have to put Linda Blevins and her husband over there. You remember Linda?"

"Oh, yeah," Billy said.

Jimmy looked at Billy.

"Is that okay with you?" Jimmy asked.

"That's fine," Billy said.

Ten minutes later, Billy Johnson, his old pal Jimmy Stevens and 58 of the 63 souls that graduated from Hamilton high in 1959 were all seated. As the celebrants waited for the program to begin, Billy Johnson's eyes briefly searched through the crowd for David Dickson. Suddenly, his attention was diverted by the ringing of a small bell and he turned to the podium where Gloria was beginning the program.

"I'm happy to see the 1959 Class of Hamilton High all gathered here again," Gloria said. "As I look across this audience tonight, I can't tell you how many memories—memories that last a lifetime—come back to me.

"Tonight's program will consist of four parts," she continued. "First, I will award door prizes. Then, after we eat, we'll have open microphone and anybody can talk about anything they like. After open mike, we'll all mix and mingle and find out what's happened to each other over the last thirty years. Is everybody ready?"

"Yeah!" the group yelled in unison.

"Okay," Gloria said, shuffling some papers. "Let's get started. The first door prize is for the former student with the most kids."

With that, the assemblage cheered with delight.

"That prize," Gloria announced, "Goes to Terry Griffin, who has nine children."

"Wooooooooooooo…," the crowd responded.

"Terry, come on up and get your prize," Gloria commanded.

With that, all eyes turned to Terry Griffin, who fancied himself a lover boy in high school, as he strode across the stage. Once he reached Gloria, she pinned a small blue pin on his lapel which read "Most Kids." Everybody applauded as Terry, looking very sheepish, started back down the podium steps.

Gene Watkins, the loud, obnoxious class clown at Jimmy and Billy's table, shouted, "He couldn't keep it in his pants when he was in high school either."

This brought a big roar from the crowd.

"Next, I'd like to present the door prize for the person who traveled the furthest for this reunion," Gloria continued. "That prize goes to Edward Narramore, who came all the way from Stuttgart, Germany where he is a member of the U.S. Armed Forces."

With that, Edward Narramore, a tall lanky kid in high school who was now a tall, lanky 48-year-old, strode up the steps and onto the stage. In high school, Edward's family had been so poor that the county had to pay for his school lunches.

"Yea Edward!" several students shouted as the former student received his blue pin, then strode back off the stage.

"Next, I want to present the door prize for the man with the most hair," Gloria continued. "That goes to Tommy Lee Haines."

In high school, Tommy Lee Haines had had shoulder-length blonde hair before it became fashionable for men in the early sixties. Even now, as Tommy Lee strode across the stage at age 48, he still a beautiful mane of hair. After Tommy accepted the award and strode back across the stage, he ran his hand through his long hair proudly and flipped it playfully toward the crowd. Several women in the crowd shrieked with delight.

"We had a little problem awarding the prize for the most marriages because we had a tie," Gloria continued. "Both Susan Hawkins and Judy Stancill have been married six times. Since Susan couldn't attend, I guess our winner will have to be Judy Stancill."

With that, all eyes turned to table number six and Judy Stancill, the class's bleached-blonde, foul-mouthed wild child, got up and started for the podium. Several males in the crowd emitted gorilla mating calls as Judy, twisting her hips sexily, strutted across the stage. In high school, Judy never wore a brassiere and swore she would never get married because she said she could never be satisfied with just one man. Once she had had a few beers, Judy wasted no time in letting the males around her know what she wanted. Both Billy and Jimmy, like most of the other guys in the class, had had a taste of Judy Stancill at least once.

"Okay," Gloria said, as Judy Stancill started off the stage. "That's all the prizes..."

"Let's eat," Gene Watkins interrupted.

This brought a big laugh from the crowd. Gene hadn't changed much since high school.

"Okay," Gloria said, with a big smile, "it looks like Gene is hungry, so I guess the rest of us will have to join him for dinner. Let's eat."

With that, a chorus of chairs scraping across the wooden floor filled the small auditorium as the celebrants left their seats and began lining up for the food buffet. As Billy Johnson stood in the serving line, his eyes searched through the crowd again. Slowly and carefully he scanned both serving lines. David Dickson was nowhere to be seen.

During the meal, Billy and Jimmy ate quietly. Seated directly to Billy's left was Linda Blevins and her husband Doug. In high school, Linda had been the class beauty. And she knew it. Tall, lithe and statuesque with soft, flowing black hair, long legs and high, firm breasts, Linda was the fantasy of all the guys in the class. After high school, she had married Doug Whitman, a 1957 graduate whose father owned a farm implement company in the town. Today, after four children and 28 years as a housewife, the beauty had faded.

Also seated at table number eight was Wade Ferguson, the class's troublemaker and the most unlikely to succeed. Throughout high school, Wade couldn't stay out of trouble. Numerous times, he had been expelled for smoking and shooting dice in the boy's gym. Once he was accused of flushing a lighted cherry bomb down the commode and flooding the boy's rest room. Another time, he had had been caught spray-painting the windshield of the principal's car and the cops were called to arrest him. Now Wade owned a chain of supermarkets in north Alabama and he wore a big diamond ring, an expensive silk suit and smoked cigars. Accompanying

Wade was a shapely, young blonde-at least 20 years younger—who wore a flashy, black sequined dress, chewed gum and said "Ya know!" a lot. Although Wade said he was married, neither he nor the young blonde were wearing a wedding ring.

Also, at table eight and seated at Billy's right was Henry Wilkerson, the rowdy cut-up who had been Wade's best friend in high school and was now a heavy equipment operator for a local construction company. During PE classes, Henry would keep an eye out for the coaches while Wade and his cronies hid behind the football stadium and smoked cigarettes.

After a round of polite conversation and a hearty meal of fried chicken, English peas and mashed potatoes, the celebrants turned to the podium again at the sound of Gloria's ringing bell.

"Well, I hope everybody enjoyed their fried chicken," Gloria said. "Gene Watkins said the English peas were a little greasy, but he ate them anyway."

This brought several ripples of polite laughter.

"Now we're going to have open mike," Gloria continued. "Anybody that's got anything to say is invited to come up and say it. If you want to recall any memories, tell stories, make confessions, or whatever, then come on up.

Please try to keep it in good taste."

That brought a big laugh from the assemblage.

With that, Gloria waited. For several moments, nobody approached. As the crowd waited, Billy Johnson's eyes were scanning the audience again. This time, Billy had a full view of all the tables. David Dickson was nowhere to be seen. Meanwhile, no one approached the microphone.

"After all these years," Gloria said, "surely, some of you have got something to say."

Finally, Sylvia Waddell, the class's goody-goody two shoes, got up and went to the microphone. The daughter of a wealthy furniture dealer, Sylvia had been a cheerleader, a member of the Future Homemakers Club and quite popular on the social scene.

"I just wanted to tell everyone how much I loved high school," Sylvia gushed. "I had so much fun at Hamilton and I'm so glad that I had all you nice people to be my friends. I just loved all the teachers and I just loved being in the Future Homemakers of America and the National Honor Society and the Glee Club and all those other great organizations. One of the happiest moments of my life was when I won first prize for the best cake at the Future Homemakers of America convention. Now I'm married to a doctor in Birmingham and we have three beautiful children and a lovely home in Vestavia. I thank God for all the good things I've been blessed with, but I really don't think I would be where I am today if I hadn't had so many good friends at Hamilton High. Well, that's all I wanted to say," Glenda said. "I just wanted everybody to know how much I loved going to Hamilton High."

Sylvia curtsied, then stepped away from the microphone. The crowd applauded mildly. With that, Timmy Cox, a bespectacled, nerdy little guy who was president of the Chess Club, quick to kowtow to authority and always brown-nosing the teachers, stepped to the mike.

"I just wanted to thank all the kind and wonderful people I knew at Hamilton High," Timmy said. "There was Mr. Davis who taught me quadratic equations; Cecil Coleman, the academic counselor who prepared me for college; Inez Wimpee, the head of the lunchroom; Miss Suzie Herman, who let me be monitor during sixth period study hall; Mr. Robert Townsend, the Spanish teacher who taught me..."

After talking for more than 20 minutes and thanking virtually every person in authority at the old high school, Timmy finally, to the delight of the weary crowd, returned to his seat.

With that, tall, lanky Edward Narramore walked to the mike and the crowd grew quiet. In high school, Edward never said much.

"I just wanted to say that I couldn't have asked for a nicer bunch of people to go through high school with than you folks," Edward said quietly. "As you all know, my family was poorer than Job's turkey and I had it pretty rough during high school. Now I just want to say thanks to all of you for not making fun of me for being poor."

Then, just as suddenly as he had appeared, Edward sat down again. For a moment, the assembled crowd didn't know how to respond. This was a subject that everyone was aware of, but no one would have ever mentioned. As Edward retook his seat, several members of the class applauded politely.

With that, Odessa Smith, a plain, homely girl who throughout high school always seemed to be on the outside looking in, stepped up to the microphone.

"I just wanted everybody to know that the father of the baby I had out of wedlock in high school was not Bobby Jenkins," Odessa began. "The child's real father was Darryl Hollingsworth and he said he would marry me if I got pregnant, but when I missed my period, he dropped me like a hot potato..."

"Odessa, hold on!" Gloria interrupted, standing up, "Nobody wants to hear that kind of stuff. I told you to keep it nice."

"But it's the truth," Odessa protested.

"It may be," Gloria said, "but nobody wants to hear about now. If that's all you got to say, sit down."

Odessa started off the podium, then suddenly turned.

"You said we could make confessions...," Odessa countered.

"I know I did," Gloria said, "but you can't say things like that. Take your seat."

Odessa, miffed at the rejection, haughtily strode off the podium.

"Okay, who else wants to say something?" Gloria asked, scanning the audience. Nobody moved.

"Surely, somebody else has got something to say."

Again, nobody moved. The episode with Odessa Smith had put a quietus on the open mike event. Still nobody stepped forward.

"Okay, Gloria said, "this is last call. Still no takers."

Again, no one stepped forward.

"Okay," Gloria said, "then let's start the visiting. That's the part everybody has been waiting for anyway."

With that, Gloria stepped away from the microphone. As she started down the steps to the auditorium floor, Billy was waiting.

"Gloria!" Billy called.

"Yes, Billy."

"Have you see David Dickson?" Billy asked.

"No, I haven't," Gloria said, looking through the crowd. "His wife said she and David would be here, but I haven't seen either of them."

"He didn't call or anything?"

"No," Gloria said, "He's probably not coming. If he was, surely he would have been here by now."

With that, Billy turned and, together with Jimmy, he started moving through the crowd, meeting and greeting old classmates. There was Harold Bowling, who now owned a farm in south Alabama; Hoyt Hill, who married Lisa Manning and now owned a service station in Hamilton;

Terry Matthews, his best friend in biology class who was now a state senator; and many, many other old friends.

At table number three, Billy got one of the biggest shocks of his life. As he approached the table, he saw an attractive young woman and a familiar-looking man in a wheelchair. For a moment, Billy hesitated, then he recognized Donald Brown, his old high school hero, seated in the wheelchair.

"Hi!" the woman said when she saw Billy's hesitation. "My name is Carol. I'm Donald's wife."

Billy shook the woman's hand, then tried to not act shocked at what he was seeing. His old hero was seated askew in the wheelchair and Billy could see that the right side of his body and face was paralyzed and Donald could raise his head only slightly off his chest. Billy reached down and touched Donald's paralyzed hand.

"Good to see you, Donald," Billy said.

His old hero managed a weak smile.

In high school, Donald Brown had represented everything Billy Johnson wanted to be. Tall, handsome and intelligent, Donald was the high school's sports hero, a top-notch student and very popular with the girls. Donald's dream was to become a doctor and do research to find a cure for multiple sclerosis. After several minutes of small talk with Donald's wife, Billy said goodbye.

As Billy started back to table eight, he glanced absently over at table number two. There, he saw Dianne Watson, his former girlfriend, sitting alone. As Billy approached, Dianne looked up.

"Billy!" she said.

"Dianne! How are you?" he asked.

"Fine," she said, "Sit down. It's been a long time."

With that, Billy took a seat and briefly narrated his marital and personal history. Finally, he asked about her.

"Oh, I've had a travel agency down in Fort Lauderdale for almost eight years," she said. "I book cruises throughout the Caribbean."

As she talked, Billy could see that Dianne was still a very attractive woman. The long slim legs, the same classy high cheek bones and the naturally curly, jet-black hair were all still noticeably present.

"Did you ever get married?" he asked.

"Oh, no," she said vaguely. "I stay too much busy in my business."

As Billy listened, a tall, striking brunette in her early forties and dressed in black leather pants, a black, sleeveless top and lots of jewelry, took a seat beside Dianne. Once she was seated, Billy noticed a tattoo of a spider web and a giant spider on the woman's forearm.

"This is Natalie," Dianne said, introducing the tattooed woman.

"Pleased to meet you," Billy said, reaching across the table to shake the woman's hand. As Billy's old high school girlfriend continued talking about herself, Billy noticed that Natalie was playfully running her fingertips along the top of Dianne's leg. Finally, Billy said goodbye to the two women and started back across the auditorium floor to table number eight.

Back at his own table, Jimmy was waiting.

"Jesus!" Billy said. "What happened to Donald Brown?"

"He's got multiple sclerosis," Jimmy said. "You haven't heard that story?"

Billy shook his head.

"Oh, it was terrible," Jimmy said. "Donald was about to graduate from the University of Alabama Medical School when it happened. He was working in a chemistry lab one day when he suddenly collapsed. They carried him to the hospital, but they couldn't find anything wrong. Then two days later, his roommate found him in the shower all folded over, unable to move. Three days later, he was diagnosed with multiple sclerosis."

"My God, what a shame," Billy said. "He could shoot the sweetest jump shot I ever seen."

"I know," Jimmy said sadly. "Sometimes, we don't know how lucky we are."

Suddenly, Jimmy glanced over at a nearby table.

"Oh, there's Frank Hodges," Jimmy said. "I'll be right back."

As Jimmy got up and left the table, Billy turned to Henry Wilkerson. Although Billy and Henry had been good friends during high school, they hadn't had a chance to talk during the reunion. Throughout all four years of high school, Henry and Billy had been in Coach Lamon's PE class together.

"You remember all those wind sprints we used to have to run in the May heat?" Billy asked.

"Oh, yeah," Henry said. "If we hadn't, Coach Lamon would have failed our butts in PE."

They laughed.

"Remember all those guys in our class?" Billy asked. "Tommy Barrett, Walter Silvey, Jerome Marshall..."

"Oh, yeah," Henry said. "I remember them all...Bob Jones, Ted Taylor, the Swindall twins, David Dickson..."

The last name rang a loud bell in Billy Johnson's mind. He had forgotten that David Dickson had been in their PE class when they were juniors.

"Whatever happened to David Dickson?" Billy asked.

"Oh, I see David from time to time," Henry said. "He's married and lives over in Eatonville," referring to a small town some eight miles north of Hamilton.

"What's he doing these days?"

"Oh, he works for McClain Dairy," Henry said. "He's been driving a milk truck since high school."

"Oh, really?" Billy said. "Know where he lives?"

"Not exactly," Henry explained, "But most nights you can find him at a little bar in Eatonville. A little place called Al's. Everybody knows where it is."

"Think I might catch him there tonight?"

"Probably," Henry said. "He's there most nights."

Moments later, Jimmy returned to table number eight. Billy was waiting.

"Let's go out into the hallway for a second," Billy said, motioning with his hand.

"What's wrong?"

"Come on!" Billy said again. With that, he strode out of the auditorium into the hallway. Jimmy was right behind him.

"I want to say goodbye," Billy said, turning to his old friend.

"What?!" Jimmy asked. "The reunion is not over yet."

"Yeah, I know," Billy said. "But I need to be going. I've got something to do before I leave town."

"Is it more important than the rest of the program?"

"Yeah," Billy said.

Jimmy could see there was no need to argue.

"Okay," Jimmy said, "It was good seeing you."

"Same here," Billy said. "You've got my telephone number. You'll have to come down to Miami and visit me sometime."

"Okay," Jimmy said. "And you can come back to Hamilton and visit me."

"I will," Billy promised. "And tell your father it was good to see him."

"I will," Jimmy said, "He'll never forget the time he got us into the Smokehouse to see Johnny Daytona."

"Neither will I," Billy said.

With that, Billy shook his old friend's hand and waved goodbye. Then, as Gloria Rakestraw was ringing her bell to begin the closing portion of the reunion, Billy walked back to his car behind the football stadium.

Some twenty minutes later, Billy Johnson arrived in the little town of Eatonville, Alabama. The tiny rural hamlet had changed very little over the past 30 years. There was still the old city hall, the hardware store, the barber shop and the little shopping mall with the supermarket and the auto parts store. As Billy stopped at the red light at Fourth and Main Streets, he saw a neon sign which read "Al's Place." The letter 'l' in the owner's neon name was burned out. Billy parked his car and got out. After he had walked up the street to the bar, he stopped in front of a large plate glass window and peered inside.

Surveying the row of patrons along the bar, Billy immediately spotted David Dickson, aged 50, sitting on the third stool from the end. For several moments, Billy stared at his old enemy. David, looking very old and very tired, was smoking a Camel, had a fresh beer in front of him and was watching a boxing match on television.

Before he went in, Billy tried to decide just how he wanted to handle the confrontation. Perhaps he should just go right in, ask David if he remembered him, then insult him into a fight. On the other hand, he could go in, present himself to David, then, without saying anything, deliver a hard karate chop across David's face. In high school, the two years age difference had given David a definite height and strength advantage. Now the tables would be turned, Billy thought. After all the cigarettes and booze, David would be slow and weak. One sharp chop across the throat and a swift kick to the ribs would put his old enemy on the floor, heaving for breath.

Wasting no time, Billy Johnson turned from the window and walked into the bar. Inside, the room was noisy and smelled of stale smoke, sour beer and bathroom deodorizer. Casually, Billy walked to the end of the bar. The bartender and the patrons, their eyes glued to the televised boxing match, hadn't noticed his entrance.

"Hit him!" one bar patron shouted through the thick smoke.

"Come on! Give him a hard right!" another patron yelled.

"Kill the son of a bitch!" David Dickson shouted, striking the air with imaginary blows.

For several minutes, William Vernon Johnson watched from the opposite end of the bar as his old enemy dragged on a Camel, swigged his draft beer and flailed the air in mock violence. The past 30 years had not been kind to David. He was grossly overweight and almost bald. His faded tee-shirt, which proclaimed "McClain Dairies," hung over a massive beer gut and the dark circles underneath his eyes testified to many weary, sleepless nights. For some five minutes, Billy watched his old enemy from the opposite end of the bar.

Then, suddenly Billy began chuckling to himself. After a few moments, the chuckle became a quiet laugh and finally, unable to control himself, Billy laughed out loud. His laughter caught the attention of the bartender.

"Can I get you something?" the bartender, a balding, sad-looking, little man with a big scar under his right eye, asked.

Billy Johnson was suddenly jolted back to reality. He didn't know what to say at first.

"Uh...no, thanks," Billy said politely.

With that, William Vernon Johnson got up from the bar stool and walked out. Back at his car, he couldn't control his joyful laughter. The sense of justice he found within himself knew no bounds. Finally, he got into the car and started the engine.

The following morning, which was on a Sunday, Billy checked out of the hotel. Once he was in his car, however, he had an unquenchable thirst to revisit his old haunts. At the corner of Sixth and Main where the Stag had stood, there was a Baptist church now. The Stag had burned down several years before. At Maple and Fourth Streets, Billy slowed down in front of the old Hamilton Courier building. As he did, his mind was filled with memories of Charley Ryan. En route back to I-20, Billy decided to drive through the rural area south of town where he had grown up. The old house where he and his father had tended crops, raised cattle and lived all those years was no longer in existence. Instead, a propane gas company had bought the property and now the site served as a storage area for several giant propane tanks. Nearby, at the site of the "Little House" where he and Roy had "spied" on Annie Atkinson, there was a tool and die company. The spot where his grandmother's old house had stood now served as the parking lot for the tool and die company. All the physical remnants of his childhood had vanished. Finally, having seen enough, Billy picked up I-20 to Birmingham and headed back to Miami.

As he cruised eastward along the expressway, Billy was glad he had attended the reunion. He chuckled to himself at Edward Narramore's speech. It warmed his heart to know that Dianne Watson's reason for dumping him during his senior year was not because he was unattractive or had bad breath or didn't have a nice enough car, but because she was a lesbian. And Donald Brown, who had everything as a high schooler, had nothing now. It all seemed so ironic.

Gwen Anne had been right; Billy had learned some very special truths. Of those, the truth of David Dickson took the prize. Life itself had delivered a revenge upon David Dickson more powerful and terrible than anything William Vernon Johnson could ever have hoped to administer. For the past thirty years and probably for the rest of his days, Billy's old enemy was destined to remain forever in the tiny town of Eatonville, live on the wrong side of the tracks and drive a milk truck. At the age of 19 or 20, David had peaked. From there, it was all downhill. If David was lucky, he would finally retire when he was 65, a broken shell of a man destroyed by the toll of alcohol, cigarettes and workaday drudgery. This truth, like all the others, would have remained forever unknown had he not attended the reunion. As he drove, Billy knew these truths had no meaning for the lives of Dianne Watson or Edward Narramore or Donald Brown or Wade Ferguson or Judy Stancill or David Dickson. These truths were for Billy Johnson, and for Billy Johnson alone.

TRAPPING RABBITS

Parental Love

During his boyhood years, William Vernon Johnson always spent his summers with his father and the black hired hands working the flatland fields of North Alabama growing cotton, corn and alfalfa hay. By mid-April of each year, when the land had lain fallow after the spring plowing, Billy's father and the hired hands would lay off the rows and plant the cotton and corn seeds that would soon cover the brown fields with a rich carpet of green for as far as the eye could see. By late June, when school was out, the young corn and cotton plants would be almost knee-high and Billy, his father and the black hired hands would then "cultivate" the plants by turning fresh earth over the weeds around the plants which, if left alone, would smother out the young corn plants. On one particular day in late June of 1951, ten-year-old Billy, his father and the two black hired hands were cultivating the corn plants when something happened that he would never forget.

Billy's father always referred to the 15-acre field near the river as the "big cornfield" because, while he had two other fields, the 15-acre field contained most of his corn crop. On the days they would work the "big cornfield," the black hired hands would take the mules and the plows to the field while Billy and his father would take their lunches and the pickup truck and meet them at the haybarn near the river.

On that particular day, the quartet had started working just after sunrise and, by 9 a.m., had "cultivated" almost five acres of lush, green corn plants. When work started, the sun had presented itself high and hot in the eastern heavens and, from all indications, it promised to be a hot, sweltering summer day. By late morning, however, the temperatures had cooled quickly and huge, black thunderheads began forming in the northern skies.

"We're going to get some rain," Robert Johnson told his son as he stopped at the end of the field to get a drink of water. "Might as well take your plow to the haybarn," he added, "and go tell Rufus and Calvin to stop until we see what the weather's gonna do. I'm gonna make another round."

Obediently, ten-year-old Billy turned his mule and plow away from the field and guided it along a hedgerow to the haybarn. There he un-hitched the mule and tied the animal to a sheltered feed trough. Some 50 yards away, Billy could see Rufus, the older of the two black hired hands, guiding his mule and plow to the end of the row.

"Rufus!" Billy called.

The black man turned at the sound of his name.

"Daddy said to stop plowing 'cause it's gonna rain."

The black man looked up at the sky. Then, wiping the sweat from his brown forehead, he nodded.

"We'll be at the shed at the big oak tree," the black man replied.

By the time Billy had returned from the barn to the feed trough with hay, the sky overhead was blanketed with black, rain-laden thunderclouds and huge drops were beginning to fall. As Billy looked up, he knew that rain would be coming down in bucketfuls any minute. With no time to waste, Billy threw the half-bundle of hay into the feed trough, then dashed back to the haybarn.

Finally, standing under the eave of the haybarn, Billy watched as his father hurriedly guided his mule from the field to the feed trough. By the time his father had tied his mule at the feed trough and started for the haybarn, rain was beating down.

"Damn!" his father said, taking his hat off and slinging the water off the brim. "What a rain!"

Some ten minutes later, Billy and his father were sitting in the door-way of the haybarn eating their lunches and watching the rain fall. In his lunch bag, Billy had his favorite food, a tomato and mayonnaise sandwich with lots of black pepper and lettuce. From the other lunch bag, his father pulled out a bulging cold chicken sandwich and wasted no time taking a bite.

As they ate, the father and son watched as the wild rabbits, who lived in the bushes and thick undergrowth along the river banks, scampered to and fro among the low weeds. By day, the rabbits would hide in the thick undergrowth along the river's edge. By night, they would come to the barn and feed off the oats that fell through the cracks in the barn floor and walls. Usually, if someone was at the haybarn, the rabbits would scamper off and hide in the undergrowth. Then, when the barn was unattended again, they would return to eat their fill of grain. On that particular day, for some reason, several extraordinarily bold rabbits had ventured to the edge of the undergrowth and were feeding on the sweet green grasses that had sprung up along the river's edge.

After his father had finished lunch, he reached into his lunch sack again and pulled out his favorite snack, a large red apple. Examining the apple, the father polished it on the sleeve of his blue workshirt.

"An apple a day keeps the doctor away," he said. Then he bit a huge chunk out of the apple and began chewing. After a few moments of silence, the father turned to his son.

"Remember the old apple crate we put tools in last spring?" the father asked.

"Yeah," Billy replied.

"Go get it."

The son hesitated.

"What are you going to do?"

"I want to show you something," the father replied. "Go get the apple crate."

Billy quickly gobbled down the rest of his tomato sandwich, got up from the doorway and went inside the haybarn. There he found the old apple crate with the tools inside. Quickly, he set the tools aside on the barn floor and picked up the empty apple crate. Back at the barn door, he watched as his father began whittling three small sticks of wood. Within minutes, the father had expertly cut several well-placed notches in the sticks and together they formed a triangle. With that, Billy's father ordered him to get the empty apple crate and follow him to the edge of the river.

"What are you going to do, daddy?" the son asked.

"We gonna trap a rabbit," the father answered.

At the river's edge, the father stopped and Billy watched as his father fitted the sticks together and used them to hold up one end of the upturned apple crate. As Billy watched, he could see that the carved sticks, when fitted together, formed a collapsible support for the upturned end of the apple crate. Next, his father sliced off a piece of the apple he had been eating and placed it on the pointed end of a stick which served as a triggering device. If a rabbit so much as touched the apple, the support apparatus would collapse and the apple crate would fall, trapping the rabbit under it.

"Now, let's go back to the barn," the father said.

As they walked, ten-year-old Billy could see that, high overhead, the sky had cleared and the sun had reappeared. Billy knew his father would want to return to the fields soon.

"It's cleared off, daddy," the son noted.

His father looked up at the sky.

"Yeah," the father replied absently. "We'll go back in a little while."

Billy looked curiously at his father, not quite understanding. He had never seen his father not want to plow before. Despite this, the son obediently followed his father back to the haybarn and took a seat beside him in the doorway to watch their trap.

The first rabbit, longs ears upright and nose wiggling curiously, scampered up to the apple crate and sniffed briefly inside. Apparently suspecting some sort of trouble however, the animal didn't venture any farther. Moments later, another rabbit which had also smelled the sweet apple fruit, ventured up to investigate. Suspecting nothing, the second rabbit wasted no time in scooting under the upturned apple crate and nibbling at the apple. Immediately, the flimsy scaffolding collapsed and the apple crate fell over the helpless rabbit.

"We got one!" Billy yelled gleefully as he ran to the captured prize. Through the cracks in the apple crate, Billy could see the trapped rabbit, a furry ball of fear and panic, lunging helplessly against the sides of the apple crate. With that, Billy's father, with a burlap feed sack in hand, went to the apple crate. Carefully, the father slid the feed sack over the apple crate and the frantic rabbit lunged into the sack. With that, the father gathered the top of the sack and held it upright with the helpless rabbit inside.

"Now," Billy's father said triumphantly, "we got a trapped rabbit in a feed sack."

As his father held the bag, Billy could see the frightened rabbit jostling around frantically inside. Suddenly, their attention was diverted by a call from across the field.

"Mr. Johnson!"

Rufus, the older black hired hand, was calling.

The father, still holding the feed sack with the flouncing rabbit, turned.

"It's stopped rainin'," the black man said. "We goin' back to the field."

Billy's father looked up at the sky.

"Yall go on," Billy's father said. "I'll be on in a while."

Billy couldn't believe what he was seeing and hearing. His father had never let a hired hand plow unless he was in the fields with him.

"Now there are several ways to kill a rabbit," Billy's father continued, holding the bag for his son to see. "The best way is to break its neck."

With that, the father gathered up the space in the feed sack and trapped the rabbit in one corner. Then, grasping the rabbit inside the sack, the father placed one hand around the animal's body and the other around its head.

"If you can get him like this," the father said, demonstrating, "it's pretty easy to break his neck."

Billy was watching.

"Now if it's a big rabbit," the father continued, "and he's strong, you may not be able to grab him through the sack to break its neck."

Billy glanced back toward the field. He could see Rufus and Calvin following their plows along the rows of corn.

"If that's the case, then you tie up the top of the bag and sling the rabbit against a tree," the father said. "Like this."

Billy then watched as his father showed him how to gather the sack at the top so it could be slung against a hard surface.

"It's pretty easy to kill a rabbit this way," the father continued, "but, when you do, you break some bones and it's harder to clean."

Billy—still not understanding the reason behind this demonstration—was listening.

"If nothing else," the father continued, "You can always tie up the top of the sack and beat the rabbit to death with a stick. If you have to do that, always try to hit it in the head so you won't break the bones."

The father, still stood holding the bag, was looking down at his son. Inside the burlap bag, the rabbit was still flouncing frantically.

"You got all that?" the father asked.

"I think so," Billy said thoughtfully.

Billy's father smiled. Then he untied the top of the burlap bag and dumped the frightened rabbit out on the ground. In a mad dash for freedom, the rabbit quickly darted across the grass and into the thick undergrowth along the river banks to join his brethren.

Billy's father looked up at the sky. The sun was shining brightly and the skies were clear again. The father turned back to his son.

"Think you could catch a rabbit and kill it?" he asked.

Billy nodded.

The father smiled, then he turned away from his son and peered across the cornfield where he could see Rufus and Calvin following their mules along the rows.

"Let's go," the father said. "I want to get this field done today."

With that, Billy and his father retrieved their mules from the feed trough and returned to the fields.

Billy never questioned his father's impromptu lesson in rabbit trapping. He was well aware that his father had a great love for the outdoors and enjoyed all types of hunting, fishing and trapping. In later years, when Billy thought back on the incident, he dismissed the lesson as nothing more than a devoted outdoorsman teaching his son the art of trapping a wild animal.

✵✵✵

In June of 1975, 34-year-old William Vernon Johnson was working as a sports writer for the Herald in Birmingham. Although he was a well-respected writer, the sports editor had said during a recent staff meeting that he wanted more in-depth features from Billy.

"Hard-hitting, colorful pieces," the editor had said. "I want good solid human interest stories with a strong sports angle, particularly baseball and football."

"How about an interview with the stepmother of a major league baseball player?," Billy asked.

"Who?" the editor asked.

"Pig Thomas," Billy replied.

"Howard 'Pig' Thomas? The one that played catcher with the Detroit Tigers?"

"Yeah," Billy said.

"Good possibilities," the editor said, "But I want drama, good quotes and lots of color."

Many years before, Billy had heard his father talk about Howard "Pig" Thomas Jr., a Birmingham native who had played minor league ball with the old Birmingham Barons and later played seven years with the

Detroit Tigers. He was nicknamed Pig because once, during a game in Birmingham, he had chased a farmer's pig off the playing field. His father, Howard Thomas Sr., had played in the minors and had had major league aspirations, but had never made it in the big leagues. After drifting around the old Southern League for several years, the father finally gave up his baseball aspirations, got a job at a local car dealership and married Nellie Hardy, Billy's father's sister. That meant that Billy's aunt was Pig Thomas's stepmother.

The following morning, Billy called his Aunt Nellie.

"Billy!" the aunt said when she heard his voice. "My goodness, I haven't seen you since Robert's funeral."

Billy explained that he was working as a sports writer in Birmingham and wanted to come visit her and do an interview about Pig Thomas.

"Why, sure..." she said, "I'd love to see you, Billy."

Late that afternoon, Billy drove from Birmingham down to his Aunt's house in Bessemer. As always, she hugged him and seemed so happy and surprised to see him. Although he was a grown man now, she still made over him as if he were still a little child. Finally, after the greetings and small talk were finished, the aunt and nephew sat down to do the interview.

Of course, she remembered Pig, she said, and how he had made lots of money as a professional baseball player, but could just never seem to hold on to it.

"If Pig had money, everybody had money," his Aunt Nellie said, "and he would give just it away to his friends. He was too good for his own good."

With that, she told several stories about Pig's relationship with his father, how his heart had been broken when the Tigers dropped his contract and how finally, broke and deep in despair, he shot himself to death in a car one night in Tarrant, Alabama.

Finally, after the interview, their talk turned to a discussion of his father's childhood. When Billy was growing up, he remembered that his father talked very little about his own childhood. Somehow, Billy sensed that his father didn't want to remember those years because there were hidden pains and bad memories he didn't care to relive. Despite this, Billy had always wondered about the details of his father's childhood, so he plied his aunt for answers.

"When our mother died in 1909, she left behind five children ranging in ages from six to thirteen," the aunt recalled. "Our father couldn't work and take care of all us kids too, so he married a woman who had six children of her own. This meant there was a houseful of eleven kids and we had it pretty rough."

"How do you mean 'rough'?" Billy asked.

There was a pause.

"Didn't Robert ever tell you about our stepmother?" the aunt asked hesitantly.

"Not really," Billy answered.

"Well, our father would go off to work in the coal fields," the aunt continued, "and he would be gone two and three weeks at a time. Lots of times, there wouldn't be enough food in the house to feed eleven kids, so our stepmother would lock us kids out of the house and feed what food there was to her own kids. One time, when things were really hard, she locked us out of the house for three weeks."

"What did you do?"

"Well, the oldest ones could do some kind of work and take care of themselves, but the three youngest, me and your daddy and Aunt Evie, were left at the mercies of the world."

"Daddy never talked about that," Billy said.

"Your father didn't talk about it because we had some really hard times," the aunt continued. "We borrowed quilts and slept under trees and in old houses."

"How did you eat?" Billy asked.

"Your father would trap rabbits," the old woman said. "He was the best rabbit trapper God ever made. If there was a rabbit anywheres around, your father could catch it and cook it."

"You mean all you had to eat was wild rabbits?"

His Aunt Nellie nodded sadly.

"We young kids would have starved if your daddy hadn't known how to trap rabbits."

With that, a bright light suddenly glowed inside 34-year-old Billy Johnson and his mind trailed off to early June of 1951.

GRANDFATHERS

From a Barlow® to a Pentium®

Everybody in the McKinney family knew that William Vernon Johnson, the first-born of the McKinney's oldest daughter Virginia, was grandfather McKinney's favorite grandchild. When he was born in early April of 1941, the child's grandfather had made a special trip to the hospital to see the day-old infant. Although there was another grandson, that was the one and only time the grandfather had made such a trip. And while the parents of the other grandson were aware that their offspring was playing second fiddle to "little Billy," as the grandfather called him, they never mentioned it. They just looked the other way and accepted it. So, in late July of 1946 while grandmother McKinney was in south Alabama visiting a sick sister, no one was surprised when the grandfather asked that "little Billy," who was five years old, come spend a few days with him at the McKinney homestead.

On a warm Saturday morning, oldest daughter Virginia Johnson delivered the child, along with a bagful of toys, clothes and coloring books to the McKinney's non-electric home deep in the backwoods of North Alabama. Once the daughter's car had stopped, the five-year-old jumped out and ran up to the front porch to greet his grandfather.

"How's little Billy doing?" the grandfather asked.

"Oh, he's doing fine, granddaddy," the child's mother said. "He can count to a hundred, he knows all of his ABCs and he is a big fan of Roy Rogers and the Lone Ranger."

"And Tonto," the child said, correcting his mother.

"Oh, yes," the child's mother said. "I forgot about Tonto."

Virginia smiled at her father, then turned to the child again.

"I'll be back Monday morning," the mother said. "Now, you be a good boy and mind your granddaddy."

"I will, Mommy," the child promised. With that, Billy kissed his mother goodbye, then the grandfather and grandson watched as she returned to the family car and drove back down the dirt road that led to the main highway. Once the car was out of sight, the grandfather turned to his grandson.

"Let's go, little Billy," the grandfather said. "We got things to do."

Some ten minutes later, the two were in a small greenhouse behind the barn where the grandfather grew tomato seedlings for later transplanting into the garden.

"First, we've got to cut some strings," the grandfather said.

"What are strings, granddaddy?"

With that, the grandfather took down a roll of cotton twine from a shelf and held it before the child.

"We get strings from this," the grandfather said. "First, we pull off a little bit at a time, then we cut it."

The grandfather showed the child how to pull a length of string off the roll, then hold it steady while he clipped it with a pocket knife. After working for some twenty minutes, the two had cut more than twenty lengths of string which would be used to hang earth-filled styrofoam cups from the greenhouse ceiling.

"What are those?" the child asked, curiously examining the small round objects the grandfather had shaken out of a small envelope.

"Those are tomato seeds," the grandfather explained. "When we put these in the dirt in the cups, a little tomato plant will grow. Just like those," he said, pointing to several cups already hanging from the ceiling. With that, the grandfather reached down one of the cups so the five-year-old could examine it. Inside the cup, several small tomato plants had sprouted.

"All life begins with little seeds," the grandfather explained. "All living things...plants, animals, insects, humans...everything begins life with a little seed."

With that, the grandfather proceeded to show the child how to push the tiny seeds into the fertile soil in the cups. Once the seeds were planted, he gave the child a small container of water and showed him how to water each and every plant. Finally, as the grandson watched, the grandfather tied the strings around each of the cups and hung them from the greenhouse ceiling.

"Now," the grandfather said, "after a few days, the seeds will sprout into young tomato plants and each and every one will have a new life all their own."

"Yeah," the grandson agreed thoughtfully, still holding the small empty water container.

Once the seedlings were planted, the grandson and grandfather returned to the back yard of the farmhouse where the grandfather took a seat in a rocking chair, withdrew his pocket knife again and began whittling. Nearby, the grandson, on his knees in front of a chair, began coloring pictures in a Roy Rogers coloring book.

"What was it like when you were a little boy, granddaddy?" the child asked, using a black crayon to color the bridle of Roy Rogers's horse, Trigger.

"Well, that was a long, long time ago," the grandfather said, "And the world back then wasn't like it is today. When I was growing up, there was thirteen of us kids and we all lived on a big farm and everybody had to work. We had to pick cotton and milk the cows and bale the hay and tend the crops. There was always lots of work to do on the farm."

"What kind of car did your daddy have?" the child asked, coloring Trigger's long mane with a white crayon.

"Oh, we didn't have a car," the grandfather answered, "but we had a good rubber tire buggy."

The grandson looked up from the coloring book.

"What's a buggy?" the child asked.

"A buggy is like a wagon," the grandfather continued. "A horse pulls it and you can ride in it."

The child was still coloring Trigger's mane.

"Would the horse doo-doo on the street when it pulled the buggy?" the child asked seriously.

"Sometimes," the grandfather laughed.

"I saw a zebra doo-doo one time when I was at the zoo," the grandson noted thoughtfully. "All the zebras were running and running and running. Then, one stopped and started doo-dooing right in front of everybody at the zoo."

The grandfather chuckled to himself.

"That's the way those zebras are," the grandfather noted.

Some ten minutes later, the child grew bored with the coloring book and went to the rocking chair to inspect his grandfather's activity. For several minutes, the child watched as his grandfather, in sure even strokes, sliced small, curled strips of wood shavings from a small wooden block.

The grandson knew that his grandfather's prize possession was his pocket knife.

"That's my Barlow," the grandfather said, looking longingly at the pocket knife. "A Barlow is the best friend a man ever had. You can cut a limb with it, clean your fingernails, skin an animal, turn a screw...even kill a man with it if you had to."

The child looked curiously at his grandfather.

"Have you ever killed anybody, granddaddy?"

"Oh, no," he said.

The child continued to watch his grandfather's whittling.

"I got my first Barlow when I was sixteen years old," the grandfather continued. "It was a knife my father had given to Paul, my oldest brother. I had to give Paul two dollars and a pair of good work boots for that knife. You wouldn't believe how happy I was when I put it in my pocket the first time."

"Can I touch the blade?" the child asked.

"Okay, but be careful, the grandfather cautioned. "It's sharp. Give me your hand."

The large older hand grasped the young smaller hand and moved it toward the sharp blade. The child knew exactly what to do and expertly ran his index finger across the sharp edge of the knife blade.

"It's sharp, isn't it," the grandfather commented.

"Yeah, real sharp," the child said.

"When you're twelve years old, I'll buy you a Barlow," the grandfather said. Then, almost as an afterthought, he added, "No, when you're ten, I'll buy you a Barlow."

Later that evening, after the child had followed his grandfather around the farm to feed the cattle, the pigs and the chickens, they returned to the farmhouse for supper. Once seated at the table, the grandfather had prepared two bowls of shredded wheat with fresh milk and peach slices. They ate quietly by the flickering light of a kerosene lamp.

"Look, granddaddy," the child said, eating the last few bites of shredded wheat and looking at the box. "It's the Lone Ranger and Tonto."

The grandfather glanced at the cereal box and saw three cartoon drawings of the famous cowboy hero and his faithful Indian companion on the back of the box.

"Let's make us a little comic book," the grandfather suggested.

"Oh, boy!" the child said anxiously.

With that, the grandfather removed the remaining shredded wheat biscuits from the box and placed the waxed paper foil packet in the cupboard. Next, he ripped apart the cereal box with strong hands and placed the cartoon panels flat on the table. Finally, using his trusty Barlow again, he carefully cut the cartoon panels out of the cardboard. Once removed, the grandfather folded the panels and set up them up on their edges to display them.

"What does this one say, granddaddy," the child asked, anxiously peering at the first panel.

"In this one," the grandfather noted, "the bad guys are stealing the rancher's cattle."

The young child peered at the indicated panel and examined an evil-looking man in a dark hat who was ordering his minions to drive the cattle away off the ranch.

"And in this one," the grandfather said, moving to the second panel, "the Lone Ranger and Tonto are chasing the bad guys and trying to get the cattle back."

The child, with infinite interest, peered at the second panel and wondered if his heroes would get the bad guys.

"And here," the grandfather said, indicating the third panel, "the Lone Ranger and Tonto have captured the bad guys and turned them in to the sheriff."

"Hooray!" said the child, examining the third panel. "We don't like people that steal and hurt other people, do we, granddaddy?"

"Oh, no," the grandfather said, "We like people that are honest and good and do the right thing."

"People like the Lone Ranger and Tonto," the child said. "They're our friends, aren't they."

"That's right," the grandfather said.

"And Roy Rogers and Gene Autry?"

"Oh, they're our friends too," the grandfather added.

The child smiled at the thought that good, honest people would always win out over bad, dishonest people.

"Did you have the Lone Ranger and Tonto when you were a little boy?"

"No," the grandfather answered thoughtfully. "At least not on cereal boxes. We had dime novels about Jesse James and Wild Bill Hickock, but we didn't have pictures on cereal boxes."

Some twenty minutes later, the grandfather, using a kerosene lamp for light, led the child up the stairs to his bedroom, then helped him into bed.

"Good night," the grandson said.

"Good night," the grandfather answered, getting up to leave the room.

"Granddaddy," the child called.

"Yes," the grandfather answered, turning back to the child, the kerosene lamp illuminating his weathered face.

"When we put water on the tomato plants today, you said we did it so they would have a good life."

"That's right," the grandfather said.

"What is life?" the child asked.

The grandfather, still holding the kerosene lamp, took a seat on the side of the bed.

"Well," the grandfather said thoughtfully, "Life is like a big wheel. It's always turning and turning and turning. When anything is born, a big wheel starts going round and round."

The child looked at his grandfather.

"When the tomatoes are born, does a wheel start turning?"

"That's right," the grandfather said.

The child, still thoughtful, peered at the adult.

"Is there a wheel in me, granddaddy?"

"Of course," the grandfather answered. "There is a big wheel in every life, but your wheel has just started to turn. In my life, the wheel had been turning for a long, long time."

The child pondered the thought.

"And when somebody dies, does the wheel stop turning?" the child asked.

"That's right," the grandfather said.

The five-year-old looked away from his grandfather. His questions had been answered and he was lost in thought.

"I'll see you tomorrow," the grandfather said, the kerosene lamp still illuminating his face.

"Good night, granddaddy" the child answered. Alone in the darkness, he listened as his grandfather's footsteps echoed back down the stairs. Five minutes later, Billy Johnson was sound asleep.

Early the following morning, the grandfather was back at the child's bedside at the break of day.

"You ready?" the grandfather asked.

The five-year-old sat up in bed and rubbed his eyes.

"I'm ready, granddaddy."

With that, the grandfather helped the child get dressed then fed him another bowl of shredded wheat and fresh peaches. Then he packed warm, buttered biscuits in a wooden bucket and led the child to a motor scooter that was parked at the side of the house.

Next to his Barlow knife, the grandson knew that his grandfather's prize possession was his Cushman motor scooter. After he had retired, the grandfather said he was finished with cars and he had bought the scooter because it was cheaper on gas.

"Can I push it, granddaddy?" the child asked.

The grandfather knew that nothing delighted the child more than pushing down the motor scooter's kick starter to start the engine.

"Let me get it ready," the grandfather said. After adjusting the throttle and lifting the crank, he picked up the child and sat him on the motor scooter.

"Now," the grandfather instructed, putting the child's foot on the crank. "Push!"

With that, the child pushed downward with his foot. The engine turned over, but failed to start.

Again, the grandfather checked the throttle and lifted the crank.

"Okay," he said, "now push real hard!"

Again the child pushed down on the crank, but again the engine failed to start. With that, the grandfather manually used the crank to turn the engine over so that the next slightest movement would start the engine.

"Okay," the grandfather said, holding the child's body so he could grasp the seat for support and use his full body weight in the effort. "We're going to do it this time."

With that, the child pushed down on the crank a third time. Instantly, the small two-cycle engine roared to life.

"I did it! I did it!" the five-year-old screamed delightedly, beaming with personal pride at his accomplishment. "I did it! I did it!"

"You sure did," the grandfather said. "Come on."

The grandfather placed the wooden bucket between his legs on the floorboard of the motor scooter. Then he swung the child up behind him and instructed him to put his arms around him.

"Now hold on tight," the grandfather instructed. "Real tight!"

The grandfather turned the throttle and the motor scooter with the grandfather, the grandson and the wooden bucket safely in tow, chugged across the farm's front yard to the driveway, then down a small hill to the main road.

Over the next hour, the grandfather guided the motor scooter over several miles of bumpy, unpaved country roads deep into the North Alabama backwoods. Finally, the motor scooter turned off on a narrow, muddy side road and, after some ten minutes, came to a stop under the shade of several oak trees.

"Come on," the grandfather said.

With that, the grandfather, carrying the wooden bucket, led the child across a small field, then into a patch of shady undergrowth thick with pines, oaks and water reeds.

"Listen," the grandfather said.

The grandson listened with all his might. Somewhere nearby, he could hear a high buzzing sound. He looked at his grandfather.

"I hear it, granddaddy."

The grandfather peered through the undergrowth into a stand of black oaks some 50 feet away. Finally, his eyes stopped and he motioned to the child to come closer. As the child stepped up, the grandfather parted the leaves and lifted up his grandson so he could see.

"Look!" the grandfather said, indicating a black oak tree which was growing out of a large mound of earth. "See the bee hive?"

The child peered into the dense undergrowth. In the forks of the black oak, not more than 6–7 feet off the ground, the child could see thousands upon thousands of wild black bees swarming around a hive.

"I see it," the child said.

The bees had built the hive into a huge gaping hole in the forks of the black oak. The hive hadn't been disturbed in several years and there was so much honey that parts of the combs had spilled out of the hive into the forks of the tree.

"The bees are quiet now," the grandfather said expertly, studying the hive. "Bees are like people. They can be quiet for a while, but any kind of excitement will cause them to jump up and run off."

For several minutes, the grandfather studied the beehive. Then, when he was ready to make his move, the grandfather took a pair of gloves, a long woman's woolen stocking and a small toy bell out of his pocket. Next, he removed his hat, placed the stocking over his head and tied it to his shirt collar to protect against the bee stings. Then he slipped on the gloves and, toy bell in hand, turned to the child.

"Now you wait right here," the grandfather instructed. "I'll be back in few minutes."

The child watched as his grandfather skirted the beehive through the undergrowth of oaks and pines and took up a position in a small clearing some 30 feet from the bee tree.

Then very faintly, the child could hear the gentle tinkling of the toy bell. At the sound, the mood of the bees changed instantly. The swarm became instantly agitated and the buzzing grew louder as most of the bees left the hive and began flying around the hive in an ever-widening circle.

Then the bell rang again. Suddenly, more bees left the hive and began circling. Then, when the bell rang again—this time a long, almost singing sound—the vast majority of the bees flew away from the hive toward the sound of the bell. Then child watched as his grandfather moved even farther away from the hive and rang the toy bell a fourth time. Suddenly, a full 95 percent of the bees gathered in a huge swarm and flew toward the direction of the bell.

Now that the hive was basically unguarded, the child watched as his grandfather darted back through the undergrowth to the bee tree. Standing on a small log under the tree, the grandfather, using his trusty Barlow and protected by the woolen stocking and the gloves, reached into the interior of the bee hive and began slicing off huge chunks of fresh honey combs and placing them in the wooden bucket. As he worked furiously, the remaining bees lunged at him angrily to protect their life's work.

Then, almost as quickly as he had appeared at the hive, the grandfather disappeared. An expert, he had needed only a few minutes to fill the wooden bucket with fresh honey. Mission accomplished, the grandfather darted back out of the wooded area back into the undergrowth. Then together, the grandfather and grandson made their way out of the undergrowth.

Back at the motor scooter, the two took a seat under the oak trees and examined their prize. The grandson peered into the wooden bucket and saw the dark brown and black natural combs of honey. As he looked at the honey, Billy Johnson was extremely proud of his grandfather for having outsmarted the bees and taking their life's work so easily. The grandfather said he had been stung only once.

"When you rob a wild bee tree," he instructed, "you have to work fast and have lots of protection. Always remember that."

With that, the grandfather unpacked the container of buttered biscuits and spread a cloth on the ground. Then, again, using his trusty Barlow, he cut a large piece of honeycomb filled with fresh honey and placed it on a buttered biscuit.

"Taste this," the grandfather said, handing the honeyed biscuit to the child.

The child examined the morsel, then took a bite. As he began to chew, he looked at his grandfather and smiled delightedly.

"It's so sweet, granddaddy."

"It's supposed to be. It's honey."

In almost no time, the child, who was feeling very grown-up, had wolfed down the honeyed biscuit and was ready for another.

"Damn! That's good," the child said, using a word he had heard his father use when he wanted to emphasize something.

The grandfather looked sternly at his grandson.

"What did you say?"

"I said it was damn good honey," the child said again, thinking that, after he and his grandfather had gallantly joined forces to steal the honey, the use of that word would be acceptable.

Saying nothing, the grandfather rapped the child in the middle of the forehead with the blunt handle of the pocket knife.

"Don't talk like that around me," he said sternly. "Little boys aren't supposed to talk like that."

Although the rap on the child's forehead didn't hurt all that much, it had done enormous damage to the child's pride. While his grandfather had opened his heart and his life to the child by taking him to the secret bee tree, the child didn't understand why the word had been so offensive. After all, his grandfather had been treating him like an adult all day then suddenly he started treating him like a child. The child was confused.

Inside, a secret part of him wanted to cry, but he knew he couldn't and he mustn't. Although tears formed in his eyes, he knew he must not cry. If his mother had been present, he could not have stopped himself from crying, but under these circumstances, the very facts of the situation prevented him from crying. Quietly and strongly, the five-year-old gallantly held back the tears, said nothing and continued eating the fresh honey.

Finally, after the two had eaten their fill of buttered biscuits and honey, the grandfather covered the wooden bucket with a cloth, then tied the top and placed it securely in the floorboard of the motor scooter.

"Are we ready?" the grandfather asked.

"Yeah," the child answered, feeling much better now.

The grandfather hesitated.

"Let's go over here first," the grandfather said.

The child followed his grandfather who had stopped under an oak tree. When he saw his grandfather unzipping his pants, he knew he was going to urinate at the base of the oak tree. The child, who had tried to bond with his grandfather is every other way, wasted no time unzipping his pants and joining in this exclusively male ritual.

With that, the adult and the child looked down at the respective streams of urine forming the puddle. The child's hormoneless urine was a stream of light-brown liquid the same color of day-old tea. The adult's urine was a pale yellowish color and caused huge bubbles to form on top of the puddle.

"Look," the child said, peering at the puddle of urine, "Your pee has got white bubbles in it."

The grandfather looked then he turned to the child.

"When you get big like me," the grandfather explained, "Your pee will have white bubbles like that."

The child looked at his grandfather, but said nothing. Both had finished urinating. His grandfather buttoned his fly. The five-year-old did the same.

Back at the motor scooter, the grandfather swung the child up behind him on the seat.

"Now hold on tight," the grandfather said.

With his short arms, Billy Johnson reached around his grandfather's waist and clasped one hand inside the other and held tight. The grandfather started the motor scooter engine and, minutes later, the two were chugging back along the narrow, muddy path back to the main road.

Three years later, the big wheel in Billy Johnson's grandfather's life ceased to turn.

On a Thursday afternoon in early May, the County sheriff, a long-time friend of Billy's grandfather, came by the homestead and asked him if he could go into town the following day to serve on a jury. He said the judge had had the trial scheduled for over a week, but they could only find eleven jurors. The sheriff said he would see that Billy's grandfather was paid 50 cents a day for as long as the trial lasted and he would get a free, hot lunch every day in the courthouse cafeteria. The old man hadn't been into town for a while, so he accepted the invitation.

The following morning, after he had put on his brogans and dressed in his khaki pants and shirt with the top button fastened, he went outside and started the motor scooter. His wife came out on the back porch to say goodbye.

"I'll be back about dark," he said.

"Alright…," she said.

He revved the engine and the motor scooter started off.

"John!" the wife called.

He slammed on the brakes and the motor scooter jerked to a sudden halt.

"What?!"

"Now don't you go around Ross," she said, shaking her finger and referring to his younger brother who worked for the Alabama Power Company down the street from the County Courthouse. The wife knew that Ross was trouble. Big trouble. Ross had always managed to get her husband in trouble each and every time they got together. Ross liked to drink whiskey.

"Okay," he said, "I won't."

With that, the wife waved goodbye and then watched as the motor scooter disappeared up the dirt road in a cloud of red dust.

Well, as fate would have it, John Davis McKinney did go into town and did serve on the jury on Friday. That night, however, he did meet his younger brother Ross and they drank a pint of whiskey each. Billy's grandfather didn't get home until about 9:30 that night.

The next morning, John Davis McKinney woke up and threw his legs over the side of the bed. Suddenly, his body lurched forward. Instinctively, he grabbed his chest and grimaced in pain as the heart muscles inside his chest cavity failed to perform. After several seconds of clutching his chest, his body went limp and he fell back dead on the bed.

At the funeral, eight-year-old Billy Johnson cried his heart out. After the services, he watched as the workmen lowered the casket containing his grandfather's body onto a bed of crushed rock in the bottom of the grave. Then, he watched as they placed two-inch pine strips over the casket until there was a little wooden floor built over the top of the casket. Billy knew his grandfather would like that. He always felt comfortable around wood. As the workmen began filling the grave, Billy Johnson cried and cried and cried.

For all the years afterward, he would remember the sharp rap on the forehead his grandfather had given him with the butt handle of the Barlow. When he was 12 or 13 years old and young boys would test their "dirty" words on one another, he would invariably hesitate before he used the word "damn." Even after he was a grown man, he found himself using words like "durn" and "dang" and "darn" as substitutes for the word "damn." The rap on his forehead had made a lasting impression.

***

By the early summer of 1996, the big wheel was still turning in William Vernon Johnson's life. At age fifty-five, he had been married twice, had a grown daughter and a five-year-old grandson of his own. Although he loved the grandson dearly, it seemed that he could never find time to go to Alabama and visit with the child. His Atlanta publishing company—which now printed four magazines—had become very successful and his job required 10–16 hours six days a week in the office. Recently, his wife Elaine had said that now was the time Billy should be doing things with Christopher. In another four to five years, she explained, the child would be in his own world and would have his own individual set of interests.

So, in mid-July of that year, during the summer lull, Billy decided to take some time off work, drive over to Birmingham and spend a few days with his grandson. Billy had a close friend who had a weekend cabin in the mountains north of Birmingham and it would be a perfect place for the grandfather and the child to spend some time together. For the trip, Billy had packed a small computer, several children's books and some nature videos.

Upon arrival at his daughter's house in Birmingham, the grandson was the first to greet him at the door.

"Granddaddy!" the child yelped happily as he leaped into his grandfather's arms.

"Mistopher Christopher!" the grandfather said, hugging his grandson. "How are you?!"

With that, Billy greeted his daughter Barbara.

"So how's this little boy doing?" the grandfather asked.

"Oh, he's doing fine," the daughter said. "He can count to a hundred, he knows all of his ABCs and he is a big fan of the Teenage Mutant Ninja Turtles® and the Power Rangers®."

"And Biker Mice from Mars," the child added firmly.

The child's mother smiled knowingly at her father.

"Now I've packed toys, clothes and coloring books in here," the mother continued, referring to a canvas bag she was holding. "Also, there is an extra pair of tennis shoes and clean pajamas in the side pocket."

The mother turned to her son.

"Now, you mind granddaddy," the child's mother instructed. "And have a good time."

"We will, mommy," the child promised as the grandfather hefted the canvas bag over his shoulder and started out the door.

"And be sure to call me when you and granddaddy get ready to leave the mountain house."

"I will, mommy," the child promised again.

Some ten minutes later, the grandfather and grandson were headed north on I-59 out of Birmingham.

"I want to go to Toys 'R Us," the grandson said.

"You don't have enough toys?" the grandfather asked. "I've got Pac-Man and Duke Nukem on the computer."

"Yeah, I know," the child said, "but I want to get a set of Super Blocks to make a fire truck and a fire station," referring to a popular child's toy which consisted of numerous pieces of molded plastic used for building.

Some twenty minutes later, the grandfather and grandson were walking hand-in-hand down the aisles of a Toys 'R Us® store in North Birmingham.

"There it is," the child said, pointing to a big red box.

The grandfather took down the box and examined it. The box said the enclosed kit—a complete fire station with two fully equipped trucks—represented the company's biggest project. There were 1,154 pieces and a total of six hours was required for complete assembly.

"You'll never finish this in two days," the grandfather said.

"Yes, I will."

"To finish it you'll have to spend at least three hours each day."

"I can do it!"

"Yeah, but WILL you do it?"

"Yeah."

"Promise?"

"Promise."

The grandfather looked at the grandson.

"I'm going to hold you to it," the adult said.

"Okay."

With that, the grandfather and grandson took a place in the check-out line to pay for the toy. As they approached the cash register, the grandfather looked up at a display rack with a big sign that read "Name Bracelets! Make your own name bracelets with our kit!" Billy Johnson peered at one of the packages. Inside, he could see several pieces of stiff cotton string and an assortment of 500 colored beads which bore inscriptions of the ABCs and numbers 1 to 100. The child watched as his grandfather removed one of the packages from the display and placed it beside the Super Blocks.

"What is that, granddaddy?" he asked curiously.

"It's a surprise."

"I want to see."

"No. If you see it, it won't be a surprise," the grandfather explained. "Like I told you, I'll show it to you later."

"But I want to see it now."

"I told you it's a surprise," the grandfather said. "I'll show it to you when we get to the mountain house."

An hour later, the two were cruising along I-59 high in the mountains of North Alabama. As the grandfather pulled the car off the expressway into a gas station, a brisk wind was whipping through the mountains, bending the trees and picking up giant swirls of loose debris.

"Now stay in the car," the grandfather said as he opened the door. "It's very windy out here."

Billy Johnson gave instructions to the attendant, then went inside the service station. Moments later, when he started back to the car, he had to shield his face from the powerful wind which was whipping about stronger than ever. Quickly, he opened the car door and got inside.

"Look, granddaddy! Look!" the child shouted suddenly.

In the gas stall in front of the car, the strong wind was about to blow over a motorcycle. As the two watched, the motorcycle leaned slowly with the force of the wind, then suddenly toppled over on its side with a loud crash.

"Damn!" the child said anxiously, standing up in the seat as high as possible and pressing his nose against the windshield to peer over at the fallen motorcycle. At the sound of the word, the electronic grandfather immediately looked at the child but said nothing.

"The man that owns that motorcycle is going to be mad. Really mad," the grandson continued, still pressing his nose against the windshield.

Five minutes later, back on the expressway again, the grandfather withdrew a bag of candy he had bought at the service station. As the grandson watched, the grandfather unwrapped one of the candies.

"Taste this," the grandfather said.

"What is it?" the child asked.

"Just taste it."

The child examined the object, then plopped it into his mouth. For a moment he chewed, then looked at his grandfather and smiled happily.

"It's so sweet, granddaddy."

"It's supposed to be," the grandfather said. "It's a chocolate-covered cherry."

For the next ten minutes, the child and the adult rode quietly, sharing the bag of chocolate-covered cherries.

"Where did you hear that word you said back there," the grandfather asked.

"Which word?" the child asked innocently.

"The word you used when the motorcycle fell over."

The child looked at the electronic grandfather, trying to read the adult's intentions. He could sense no anger or sternness in the face.

"I heard it from Tyler," the child said.

"Oh," the grandfather said, remembering that Tyler was a member of his grandson's kindergarten class.

"He's older and he knows about grown-up things."

"How old is Tyler?"

"Oh, he's seven," the child said, with a certain air of respect.

Around 3:30 in the afternoon, Billy Johnson turned his car off the expressway on to a two-lane, farm-to-market road which led deep into the mountains. Finally, after guiding the car through several miles of winding, mountain roads, Billy maneuvered the vehicle up a steep hill and brought the car to a stop.

"We're here!" the grandfather said.

Once the car had been unloaded, the grandfather and grandson worked together connecting appliances, putting food away and unpacking toys, books and clothes. Finally, after their arduous journey, the grandfather and grandson plopped down on the couch with two fruit punch soft drinks.

"Now I want to see my surprise," the child said. "You promised."

"Okay," the grandfather said. With that, he withdrew the Name bracelet kit and opened it.

"Now we're going to make some little strings," Billy said, as he withdrew several pieces of stiff cotton string from the package.

"What are strings, granddaddy?"

"Strings are the building blocks of information," the grandfather explained. "A word is a string of letters. A sentence is a string of words. A paragraph is a string of sentences."

The child listened, pretending to understand.

"Okay," the grandfather said, "First, let's make a string that spells your name."

With that, Billy Johnson gave the child a piece of string, then handed him each of the letters in his name in sequence. Next, he watched as the child carefully placed each bead on the string.

"Now," the grandfather said, "What does that say?"

"C-H-R-I-S-T-O-P-H-E-R," the child said, spelling out the letters. "That's my name."

"It's a little string of letters," the grandfather said.

"That's neat, granddaddy," the child said happily, examining the string. "Let's do another one."

"Okay," Billy said, "Let's do mommy's telephone number."

With that, Billy handed the child another piece of string, then withdrew each of the individual digits for I-205-369-II87, his daughter's Birmingham telephone number, and handed them to the child. Quickly the child threaded the beads on the string.

"What does that say?"

"1-205-369-1187."

"Now, as long as you have that," the grandfather explained, "You'll always know mommy's telephone number."

The child studied the stringed beads.

"Now, if this is a string of letters," the grandfather said, indicating the beads with the child's name, "what is this a string of?" the grandfather asked, indicating the telephone number.

"A string of numbers," the child said.

"Very good!" the grandfather said. "And how many numbers are in the string?"

The child counted.

"Eleven." the child said. "The same as the number of letters in my name."

"Very, very good," the grandfather said.

That night, after a dinner of frozen pepperoni pizzas and soft drinks, the grandfather and grandson began the Super Blocks project. Once the package was opened and spread on the floor, there were a total of 1,154 pieces. After working together for more than two hours, the two had completed one fire truck and assembled a small portion of the fire station. Finally, around 10:30, the child turned to his grandfather.

"I'm tired, granddaddy," the child said.

"I know. It's late," Billy said. "We've had a big day, We'll stop now."

With that, the grandson crawled up into his grandfather's arms. Five minutes later, the child was sound asleep.

Early the following morning, the grandfather was up at the break of day, setting up the computer. Once the child was out of bed and dressed, the grandfather fed him scrambled eggs, canned biscuits and orange juice. As the child gulped down his last sip of juice, he saw that the computer had been set up.

"Come on, granddaddy," he said, "Let's play on the computer."

The grandfather took a seat in front of the computer and the grandson plopped into his lap.

"This is my new Pentium®," the grandfather said proudly, flipping the switch to boot the computer.

Instantly, the image of a cartoon-like, mischievous-looking black cat wearing an oversized red bow-tie and a red hat with white circles around the crown, flashed on the computer screen.

"What does that say?" the grandfather asked, indicating the caption.

"The Cat in the Hat®," the child answered eagerly.

"How many words is that?"

"Five," the child said.

"What are the two words that are the same?"

The child studied for a moment, then pointed to both instances of the word "The."

"Very good," the grandfather said.

"And which two words are similar, but not exactly the same?"

Again the child studied for another moment. Then he pointed to the words "Cat" and "Hat."

"And what's the one word that's different from all the others?"

The child pointed to the word "in."

"Very good," the grandfather said.

"A word is a little string of letters," the grandfather explained.

"Like Christopher," the child commented.

"That's right," the grandfather added, "And a sentence is a string of. . .?"

". . .Words," the child answered.

The grandfather studied for a moment, trying to come up with a new and different question.

"Very good. Now can you give me an example of a sentence?"

The child pondered for a moment, then looked at his grandfather.

The child shrugged.

"What. . .?" he asked.

"The Cat in the Hat," the grandfather said finally. "There are five separate words, but when they are all strung together, they form a sentence. 'The Cat in the Hat.'"

"The Cat in the Hat," the child said out loud. "The Cat in the Hat," he said again.

Then he turned to his grandfather.

"It's fun learning on the computer."

"A computer is the best friend a man can have in the world today," the grandfather said. "There is no end to the ways that computers can handle information."

"What's information, granddaddy?"

"Information is little pieces of new knowledge that everybody needs to make their lives better."

The child was listening.

"I got my first computer in 1984," the grandfather explained, "It was a little Apple IIE. I saved for over a month to buy it. You won't believe how proud I was when I set it up for the first time."

"Someday I'll have my own computer," the child said.

"I'll buy you a computer when you're twelve," the grandfather said. "No, ten," Billy added. "I'll buy you a computer when you're ten."

"I want to color," the child said, jumping down from his grandfather's lap and going to the canvas bag filled with toys.

"You don't want to play Pac-Man®?" the grandfather asked.

"No," the child said, withdrawing a box of crayons and a Teenage Mutant Ninja Turtle® coloring book from the bag, then plopping down on the floor.

Billy Johnson watched as the child occupied himself with the coloring book, while he played Pac-Man on the computer. For some ten minutes, the two entertained themselves independently.

"Granddaddy, did you read 'The Cat in the Hat®' on a computer when you were a little boy?" the child asked as he colored Leonardo's mask a dark green color.

"No," Billy said. "The first words I learned were 'See Dick run! See Jane run.' I learned to read from a book, not a computer."

With that, the grandfather, bored with the Pac-Man game, got up from the computer and turned on the television. As he flipped through the channels, there was a news show, a golf match, a rock and roll show and two talk tabloid shows. Absently, the child looked up from the coloring book at the precise moment the grandfather flipped the channel to the opening credits of the Mighty Morphin Power Rangers® show.

"Right there! Right there!" the child said frantically, upon seeing the images of his masked heroes. "I want to see the Power Rangers."

Instantly, Billy Johnson changed the channel back and the child wasted no time abandoning the coloring book and plopping down in front of the television. On the screen, the show's title read "Power Rangers Vs. Rebel Aliens from Zor."

With that, the grandfather and grandson took a seat in front of the television and watched as the Mighty Morphin Power Rangers, regular high school students in real life, donned their ranger suits and did battle with the evil renegade rebels from the planet Zor. Once the Power Rangers get wind of the renegade's evil plans to take over earth, they use a combination of expert karate moves and some gymnastic expertise to drive the Zorians from earth and save all mankind.

"Hooray!" Christopher said happily as he watched the rebels' spaceship escape the earth's atmosphere en route back to its own planet. "The Power Rangers won again!"

The grandfather turned to the child.

"Don't you think it's time we finished the fire station and fire trucks?" the grandfather asked.

"No, I want to watch TV," the child said.

"Come on, let's finish the fire station and the trucks."

"Granddaddy, I'm tired," the child pleaded.

"Remember the promise."

"I know," the child said.

"Then let's go," the grandfather said, getting up and going to the corner where the Super Blocks project was laid out on the floor. Billy sat down and started connecting the plastic pieces. After working for some five minutes as the grandson watched, Billy turned back to the child.

"Come on now, we said we would do it."

The child looked away from the grandfather.

"Let's do 200 more pieces and then we'll go to see 'The Lion King.' Okay?"

"Oh, boy!" the child said. Instantly, he was in the corner to help with the Super Blocks.

Just after sundown that evening, Billy Johnson and his grandson drove into the nearby town of Blue Ridge, Alabama. After a stop at McDonald's®, they drove to a small movie house which was featuring "The Lion King." It was an animated movie about a young lion cub named Simba, who, after his father was deposed as king of the lions by his wicked uncle, spent his days being happy-go-lucky in the jungle with his devil-may-care friends. After a childhood friend discovers Simba leading a free and irresponsible life, she convinces the young lion prince that he must go back to the pride and take his rightful place as Lion King from the wicked uncle. Finally, Simba accomplishes that feat. The title song to the movie was a catchy little tune called "The Circle of Life." Throughout the trip from town back to the mountain house, the child was singing "The Circle of Life."

Finally, once back at the mountain house, the child made a bee line for the Teenage Mutant Ninja Turtle coloring book.

"I'm going to color," the child said.

"We still haven't finished the fire station and the fire trucks."

The child frowned.

"I don't want to play with the building blocks," the child said, looking away from the adult and back at the coloring book.

"You remember the promise?" the grandfather said. "You said we'd finish it before we went back home. We're leaving in the morning."

"I know, granddaddy," the child said, "but I don't feel like it."

The child continued coloring. The grandfather could see he was getting nowhere.

"Okay," the grandfather said finally. "Somebody's got to do it."

With that, he got up, took a seat on the floor and began assembling the plastic pieces. For several minutes, the two worked independently.

"Now, let's see here," the grandfather said, speaking to himself, "I need to find the right headlight for this fire truck."

With that, he started sorting through the plastic pieces. Suddenly, the child looked over at the grandfather.

"I can find it, granddaddy," the child said.

Instantly, the child was on to the floor beside the grandfather. An hour later, the project—including both of the fire trucks and the fire station complete with a flag on top—was near completion. As the child snapped the last few pieces into place, he knew he had lived up to his commitment.

"All done," the child said happily. "I did it just like I said."

"You sure did," the grandfather said proudly. "You did what you said you would do. That's very important."

"I'm glad we finished it, granddaddy," the child said happily.

"So am I," the adult said. "Now we've got to call mommy and tell her when we'll be home."

"Can I dial?" the child asked.

"Do you have the number?"

"Right here," the child said, indicating the string of beads attached to his wrist.

"And what's that called?"

"A string," the child answered. "A string of numbers."

"Very good, little boy," the grandfather said. "Very good! Now let's go call mommy."

With that, the child and the grandfather sat down at the table in the living room where the house's only phone was located. Then, as the grandfather watched, the child, using the string of numbers as a guide, started to dial.

"1-2-0-5-3-6-8...," the child said, stopping to look back at the number.

"No," the grandfather said. "Not an eight, a nine comes after the three..."

"Darn," the child said. "I'll have to start all over."

The child tried again.

"1-2-0-5-3-6-9-1-1-8-8," the child said, saying each number as he dialed it.

Although the grandfather saw that the child had dialed the last digit wrong, he said nothing.

The child and the grandfather listened. Then they both heard an operator saying, "If you'd like to make a call...."

"I can't do it, granddaddy," the child said, frustration in his voice.

"Oh, yes you can," the grandfather said. "Let me call out the numbers and you dial. Okay?"

"Okay," the child said, calmer now.

With that, the child dialed each of the numbers as the grandfather called them out. Then they waited. Moments later, the child eyes lighted up when he heard his mother's voice on the answering machine.

"Mommy, this is Christopher." the child said. "Granddaddy and I will be back at home about three o'clock tomorrow. Okay...I love you. Bye."

The child hung up the phone.

"I did it! I did it!" the child yelled joyfully. "I knew I could do it! I did it! I did it!"

"You sure did," the grandfather said with a big smile. "Now don't you think it's about time for bed?"

"Yeah, I am pretty tired," the child said.

With that, the grandfather led the child into the kitchen where he fed him warm milk and fresh chocolate drop cookies. Then, once the child had a bath and was dressed in his night clothes, the grandfather tucked him into bed.

"Good night," the grandfather said, turning off the electric light.

"Granddaddy...?" the child called out in the darkness.

The grandfather flipped the switch and the room was instantly filled with electric light again.

"What is it?" he asked.

"When you were a little boy, did you have the Teenage Mutant Ninja Turtles® and the Power Rangers®?"

"No," Billy said thoughtfully, "But we had Roy Rogers and the Lone Ranger and Tonto."

"Did they save the world from the bad guys?"

"Oh, of course," the grandfather answered. "That's the reason we liked them so much."

"I'm glad," the child said.

The grandfather started to reach for the light switch again.

"Granddaddy...," the child called again.

"Yes..."

"At the Lion King tonight, the main song was about the circle of life. What's the circle of life?"

The grandfather returned inside the room and took a seat on the side of the bed.

"Well," the grandfather said thoughtfully, "Life is a like a big wheel. It's always turning and turning and turning. When anything is born, a big wheel starts going round and round. That wheel is the circle of life."

The child, still thoughtful, peered at the adult.

"Is there a wheel in me, granddaddy."

"Of course," the grandfather answered. "There is a big wheel in all lives, but your wheel has just started to turn. In my life, the wheel has been turning for a long, long time."

The child paused for a moment so that the enormity of the thought could register.

"And when something dies," the child asked finally, "The wheel stops turning...?"

"That's right," the grandfather answered.

With that, the child looked away from his grandfather. He was lost in thought.

"Good night, granddaddy," the child said, plumping his pillow.

"Good night, Christopher," the grandfather said as he flipped off the electric light.

The following morning, the grandson was out of bed at 8 a.m. While his grandfather was still asleep, Christopher was busy playing with the Name Bracelet kit. Finally, around 8:30, the child went into his sleeping grandfather's room.

"Granddaddy!" the child called.

Billy was sound asleep.

"Granddaddy!" the child called again.

Billy Johnson rolled over, raised himself on one elbow and rubbed his eyes.

"Good morning, little boy."

"I have a surprise," the child said playfully, holding his right hand behind his back.

"What is it?"

"I can't show it to you now," the child said playfully. "If I do, it won't be a surprise."

"Then when can I see it?" Billy asked, playing along.

"When you get up," the child said.

With that, the grandfather sat up, stretched his arms then threw his feet over the side of the bed.

"Now," he said, "What's my surprise?"

"Okay...," the child relented, not wanting to delay the suspense any longer.

"Look!" the child said, suddenly holding up his latest Name Bracelet creation.

The grandfather looked at the string. It read "The Cat in the Hat."

The grandfather beamed at his grandson.

"And what's that called...?" the grandfather asked delightedly.

"A string of words...," the child answered. "A sentence."

Billy Johnson's innermost heart glowed with delight. Instantly, he fell on his knees and took the child into his arms.

"You're the finest little grandson I could ever have asked for," Billy said, hugging the child. "I love you so much."

"I love you too, granddaddy," the child said.

The grandfather dressed and once again prepared canned biscuits, scrambled eggs and orange juice for himself and the child. After eating, the two started making preparations to leave the mountain house. Together, they cleaned the kitchen, packed up the computer, the toys, the videotapes and recorder, their clothes and the books, then loaded everything into the car.

Some thirty minutes later, as they cruised back south along I-59 toward Birmingham, the child fell asleep in the front seat. Finally, over an hour later, the child awoke, sat up in the seat and rubbed his eyes.

"Granddaddy," he said, "I've got to use the bathroom."

"Can you wait until we get to a service station?"

"I've got to go now," the child said.

With that, the grandfather pulled off the expressway on to a narrow, farm-to-market road, then drove a short ways and pulled into a small turn-out. Some ten minutes later, the two were out of the car and the grandfather was leading the child up a muddy, weed-choked path into an area thick with scrub pine and oak trees.

"Okay," the grandfather said, realizing now that he had to urinate himself.

The adult and the child began urinating into the same puddle at the base of an old oak tree.

"Look, granddaddy," the child said curiously, staring into the puddle of urine forming at their feet. "Your pee has got white bubbles in it."

"Someday, when you're big like me," the grandfather said, "Your pee with have white bubbles like that."

The child looked at his grandfather, but said nothing. With that, the child finished urinating then tried to zip his pants closed again.

"Granddaddy, will you help me?"

The grandfather could see that the zipper was stuck.

"Hold still," the grandfather said, bending down to inspect the problem. With a quick jerk, the grandfather untangled the zipper from the material and zipped up the child's pants.

"There," the grandfather said.

The five-year-old looked at the fixed zipper, then at his grandfather. He smiled.

"Thanks, granddaddy."

Fifty-five-year-old William Vernon Johnson took his grandson's hand and together they started walking back down the muddy, weed-choked path to the car.

Later that afternoon, they arrived back in Birmingham at Billy's daughter's house. Billy unloaded the child's belongings and reported the events of the past two days to his mother. Finally, it was time for Billy drive back to Atlanta.

"Okay, Billy's daughter said. "Say goodbye to your grandfather."

The child smiled and perfunctorily went to his grandfather and gave him a hug. The child released his grandparent then went back to his mother.

"Bye, granddaddy," the child said, slightly waving his hand.

"Bye, little boy," the grandfather replied.

Billy turned and started to walk to the car.

"Granddaddy!!" the child called suddenly.

Billy turned back to the child.

"I like talking to you, granddaddy," the child said.

"I like talking to you too, little boy," the grandfather said.

Suddenly, the child burst into tears and ran to his grandparent.

"Oh, granddaddy," the child sobbed, leaping into his grandfather's arms. "I love you! I love you!"

For a full ten seconds, the child clung to the grandfather's neck with all his might, shedding huge tears.

As the grandfather and grandson held one another in a tight embrace, it was if the future was trying to hold on to the past. In his heart, the child knew that some day the big wheel would stop turning in his grandfather's life. The grandfather also knew that. He knew this child would someday stand over his grave and weep for him even as he had for his own grandfather. That was what made it so terribly sad. Both knew instinctively that nothing could stop the eternal transition from the old to the new. The forward movement of the big wheel was an undeniable certainty. Nothing, absolutely nothing, could stop its forward progress.

Finally, the grandfather broke the embrace.

"I've got to go now, little boy," Billy Johnson said.

The child, huge tears still streaming down his face, slowly released the grip on his grandfather's neck. Then, without looking at the grandparent, he ran to his mother's side. Then he turned back to the grandfather.

"Bye, granddaddy," the child said.

"Bye, little boy," Billy Johnson replied.

The mother and child watched as Billy strode to the car, got inside and the vehicle started backing slowly out of the driveway. Before starting the car forward, Billy looked back and waved one last time to his grandson.

The child waved and blew his grandfather a kiss. Billy blew back the kiss, then gunned the car's engine and the automobile pulled out on the main highway.

As Billy drove back to Atlanta, he felt an overwhelming sense of completeness within himself. Over the past three days, he had shared himself with his grandson as honestly and as completely as he knew how. Like his own grandfather 50 years earlier, Billy Johnson had tried to prepare his grandson for the future that he foresaw. The time they had spent together making word strings, going to the movies and playing on the computer had been little more than an updated version of the time he had spent with his own grandfather in the spring of 1946. In their own special way, Billy Johnson and his grandson had planted tomato seedlings, examined the blade of a pocket knife, cut out cereal box cartoon panels and robbed a wild bee tree. Human technology had moved from the Barlow® to the Pentium®. What an incredible leap in 50 short years! From a hard-bitten, agricultural-yeoman society to a kinder, gentler, electronic culture in which information was king. In the process, something had been gained, but something had been lost.

For William Vernon Johnson, the big wheel was still turning.

ABOUT THE AUTHOR

John Isaac Jones is a freelance writer/computer consultant who is currently living in suburban Atlanta. Like the main character, Jones grew up in Alabama, but later lived in several other states including California, Florida, Montana and Washington, D.C. "John I.," as he prefers to be called, settled in Georgia seven years ago. For 27 years, Jones was a reporter/writer/editor for newspapers and magazines throughout the world. Like the main character, Jones worked for two major dailies in Alabama before moving to national publications. After leaving Alabama, Jones worked for The National Enquirer, News of the World in London, the Sydney (Australia) Morning Herald and NBC television.

Today, Jones spends most of his time troubleshooting software conflicts on satellite computers. When he's away from digital stuff, he likes to read, especially poetry. His favorite poem is "The Windhover" by Gerard Manley Hopkins. He is also a fan of Robert W. Service, Carl Sandburg, Matthew Arnold and Bob Dylan.

His favorite book is *Tales of Power* by Carlos Castaneda.

His favorite rock CD is "Blondie's Greatest Hits."

The greatest gift life has to offer, Jones says, is "peace of mind."

Comments/critiques regarding these stories are welcome at author@alabamastories.com

Made in the USA
Columbia, SC
20 November 2018